IBM 1620 Programming

FOR SCIENCE AND MATHEMATICS

Hayden Series in Applied Mathematics

IBM 1620 Programming

FOR SCIENCE AND MATHEMATICS

IRVING ALLEN DODES, Ph. D.

Chairman, Department of Mathematics
Bronx High School of Science
Consultant, University Training Program
IBM Corporation

HAYDEN BOOK COMPANY, INC., NEW YORK
a division of HAYDEN PUBLISHING COMPANY, INC.

Dedication to Thomas J. Watson

Can machines replace men? No, they can not. Machines complement and supplement man, making it possible for him to rise effortlessly to heights once considered impractical or impossible. What does a man have that a machine does not have? A man has *intuition,* that flash of genius which enables him to bridge the vast gap between formlessness and form. A machine has only perfect patience and perfect logic. *Machines make a man's life longer in terms of time to think.*

In a society which has accepted labor-saving machines such as automatic reapers, and time-saving machines such as airplanes, it is not strange that science and industry have accepted a mind-saving machine, the computer. It would be just as sensible to harvest a field by hand, or walk from New York to California, as it would be to spend precious years in calculations which can be done in just a few minutes on a computer.

There is no question about the *need* for computers. The only question is *when* computing should be taught and *to whom.* It is apparent that a serious student in mathematics, science, or economics should learn to use a computer as soon as possible. Can students of first-year calculus learn to program the computer for problems in mathematics and the sciences?

Thomas J. Watson, Jr., of IBM, had the intuition and the confidence to launch the experiment on fifteen-year old high school seniors at the Bronx High School of Science, where calculus is given as a senior-level course. His intuition was correct and his confidence fully justified. The course in Numerical Analysis, of which computing is a part, has been more than successful in stimulating the work in mathematics and the sciences. The course has supplied hundreds of qualified programmers in a civilization starved for trained personnel.

Now we are secure. We can pause to express our deep appreciation to the man who has served not only us, but also his country and the university of knowledge by inspiring students to think. For these reasons, this book is dedicated, with his permission, to Mr. Thomas J. Watson, Jr., of IBM.

Irving Allen Dodes

Introductory Remarks

The purpose of this book is to introduce mathematicians, scientists and students to the theory and practice of the programming of a stored-program digital computer. This book employs as illustrative material programs for the basic IBM 1620 (with automatic division, but no other special features).

There are many books on "general programming". You may wish to know why yet another is needed. There are three main reasons:

1. We feel that it is as impossible to learn "general programming" with no specific machine in mind as it is to learn "performing on a musical instrument" with no specific musical instrument in mind.

2. The basic IBM 1620 is a typical variable-length random-access digital computer. The illustrations in this book are immediately applicable to larger machines like the IBM 7090; and, in fact, most machines of today are at least similar to the IBM 1620. To continue our "musical" analogy, this book teaches you the piano, but, as a result, you should have a fairly good idea of techniques for the xylophone and the pipe organ.

3. Books on general programming emphasize mainly the theory of programming without admitting the student to three great mysteries: (*i*) which buttons to push, (*ii*) what the limitations of the machine are, and (*iii*) what the language of the machine really is. We shall not make this error.

We shall say a few words about the last of these items. It is true, we admit, that experienced programmers invariably use symbolic language in their programs. In other words, if they wish to add two numbers represented by *A* and *B*, they write something like

Add A,B

and the machine accomplishes the addition. What could be easier? There are books which teach only symbolic language, such as that used on FORTRAN. However, it is our opinion that it is impossible to understand symbolic language unless machine language is first understood. The idea that the computing machine is a "black box" into one side of which a problem is inserted and from the other side of which the correct solution appears is the purest nonsense. This thought would have some sense if the machine were intelligent, i.e., if the machine could really understand and interpret the instructions. But machines can not and do not understand instructions.

They actually use a device to translate the symbolic instruction into machine language (numbers) and continue from there. It is well known that no programmer, no matter how experienced, is able to write a set of instructions for a real program without one or more errors. The correction of the program — *always necessary* — is easier if the programmer understands the language of the machine. The corrections made are incomprehensible if he does not understand machine language.

It is for these reasons that a considerable amount of time is spent in the learning of a language which is seldom used later, except for corrections. There are too many programmers today who do not really know what they are doing.

One further question remains to be answered. Why was the basic IBM 1620 chosen as a model? The answer is that it is a popular, high-speed, electronic, stored-program digital computer with features characteristic of all modern computers. It is large enough to permit the solution of any normal program and, with some ingenuity, of any program. It is fast enough to accomplish most students' programs almost instantaneously (within fractions of a minute), even if they entail thousands of steps. The *basic* machine with 20,000 memory "cells", automatic division, and no special features is ideal pedagogically. Special features make it easier to program but, without them, the pedagogy is more straightforward and more easily understood. Once the basic machine is understood, the special features (indirect addressing, automatic floating point, etc.) can be read in the manual which is supplied with whatever machine you have.

This book deals with four areas of computing, namely, *numerical analysis, machine language, a symbolic programming system (SPS)*, and *the "Formula Translation System" (FORTRAN)*. Part One is a quick summary of the material discussed in Dodes, I. A. and Greitzer, S. L., *Numerical Analysis*, Hayden Book Co., Inc., 1964. Readers will find it helpful to skim through this section of the book even if they are well-acquainted with numerical analysis. Detailed information on this indispensable topic can be found in the aforementioned work, and more sophisticated information can be found in such well-known advanced sources as:

Hastings, Cecil, *Approximation for Digital Computers*, Princeton Press, 1955.

Hildebrand, F. B., *Introduction to Numerical Analysis*, McGraw-Hill Book Company, 1956.

Karman, T. and Biot, M., *Mathematical Methods in Engineering*, McGraw-Hill Book Company, 1940.

Ralston, A. and Wilf, H., *Mathematic Methods for Digital Computers*, John Wiley and Sons, 1960.

Scarborough, J. B., *Numerical Mathematical Analysis*, John Hopkins Press, 1958.

We have already mentioned the omission of "special features" and the pedagogical reasons for their omission. We have also omitted a discussion of *time-and-space* requirements for programs, i.e., how long a program takes, and how much machine space is required for the program. There are three reasons for the latter omission:

1. Students' programs, even if they seem long to the students, are usually finished in times varying from a fraction of a minute to a few minutes by *any* computing machine. The *time* calculation is, therefore, unnecessary for the beginner and usually unnecessary for other programmers. From the standpoint of economy, it does not usually "pay" to spend hours in revising a program merely to save a minute, or a fraction of a minute, on the machine. Of course, if the program is very long, or if it is a "work-horse" program which is going to be used over and over again, the expenditure of programming time may be worthwhile. We shall say a word about this in a moment. As for *space* requirements, you will find that the symbolic programs are set up so that the machine will compute the amount of space used. Ordinarily, this does not concern you unless the machine does not have enough space to accommodate your data. This problem is discussed at the end of the book, in the section on FORTRAN where this is most likely to occur.

2. Each kind of machine differs in its time-and-space limitations. This kind of information is tabulated in manuals which come with the specific machine.

3. Even the most standardized machines are subject to constant improvement, so that any time-and-space limitations given in a book are, very likely, out of date by the time the book is published. Even the manuals which come with the machine are likely to be out of date in this matter, and the most reliable information is obtainable, if it is needed, from the company which produced the machine. To emphasize this fact, the time requirement may be off by *ten* times in a manual and by more than that in a book.

Many thanks are due to IBM for much help and guidance in the preparation of the manual which preceded this book. In particular, the author is grateful to the following executives of IBM who have been of material assistance: Mr. John Lawrence, Manager of the University Training Program; Mr. David Plank, former Manager of Data Processing; Dr. James Kearns, Special Representative for Education; and Dr. William Cain, Special Representative for Education. Sincere gratitude is also due to Mr. Milton Cluff, of the IBM Education Center, who gave so freely of his time and wisdom in reading and criticizing the orginal manual from which this book was written; to Mr. Samuel Alexander, of the Department of Mathematics of the Bronx High School of Science who read and taught from the manuscript, making corrections as he did so; to Dr. Louis Cohen, Department of Mathematics of the Bronx High School of Science who read and criticized the manuscript; and to the many students in the Computing class of the Bronx High School of Science who read, criticized, and improved the manuscript. Special mention is due Messrs. Henry Laufer, Alex Nagel, and Barnet A. Wolff of the Class of 1962 who were most helpful in this respect.

We acknowledge with gratitude the kind permission of IBM to reproduce tables and pictures from various IBM machine manuals.

IRVING ALLEN DODES, *Chairman*
Department of Mathematics
The Bronx High School of Science

New York, N. Y.

Contents

CONTENTS

APPENDIX MATERIAL

PART ONE
A Review Of
Numerical Analysis

Operations With Numbers

You are probably aware that electronic computers are incredibly fast. A calculation that takes a mathematician or a scientist an hour or so to do by hand (or minutes on a desk calculator) can be done in *microseconds* by a computing machine. (A microsecond is one *millionth* of a second.)

However, before the problem is ready for the computing machine, the mathematician or scientist must do three things:

1. He must prepare a *numerical analysis* of the problem.
2. He must write *instructions* for the machine.
3. He must compute, preferably on a desk calculator, some intermediate and final results for a simplified *test problem* in order to check his program.

You will note that a computing machine is not used until these three preliminary steps are taken. All three steps are absolutely essential. The programmer, therefore, must know—in addition to the obvious information about the computer—the theory of numerical analysis, and he must have some skill with the desk calculator.*

Section 1. Numbers Used In Computing

1.1 EXACT AND APPROXIMATE NUMBERS

Any number arrived at by an *estimate* or *measurement* will be called an *approximate number*. This means that the number, as written, is an approximation to a "true value" which we may or may not know. Some examples of approximate numbers are

---

*This part of the book is merely a brief summary of some of the important procedures of numerical analysis. For further information, and for an explanation of numerical analysis applied to desk calculator manipulations, the reader is referred to Dodes, I. A. and Greitzer, S. L., *op. cit.*, and to the more advanced books cited in the Introductory Remarks section.

physical measurements and statistics, and the representation of π by 3.14159.

All other numbers are *exact numbers*. Some examples are the number of windows in a specific room, π, sin 27°, log 2, and so on. Note that any number arrived at by an exact count is an exact number, and that there exist numbers like π and e (the base of natural logarithms) which are not the result of a count, but which are exact numbers.

1.2   MEASUREMENTS

In ordinary work, a measurement like "67.3 grams" is understood to be an approximate number. Since the smallest unit of measurement here is actually 0.1 gram, this measurement is said to have a *precision* of 0.1 gram. The number associated with this measurement, therefore, has a precision of 0.1. The number has three significant figures and this is called its *accuracy*. The following numbers also have an accuracy of three significant figures: 0.673, 0.0000673, 673., and 67.3. In considering a number like 3,156,200, it is often difficult to tell whether this has an accuracy of 5, 6 or 7 significant figures. In other words, the right-hand zeros may or may not be significant.

We may settle the question in one of two ways: (*i*) by writing the number in *scientific notation*, e.g., 3.15620×10^6, or (*ii*) by writing, in parentheses, how many significant figures (s.f.) the number has, e.g., (6 s.f.).

1.3   RANGE OF A MEASUREMENT

The most precise way to express the probable limits between which a measurement lies is *range number* notation. For example, the fact that 67.3 grams is a rounded number as small as 67.25 (grams) or almost (but not quite) as large as 67.35 (grams), is expressed in the notation.

$$[67.25, 67.35)$$

In this symbolism, the bracket means that the left-hand value is *included* in the range. The parenthesis means that the right-hand value is *not included*.

ILLUSTRATIVE PROBLEM I

Express 41.8° as a range number, and explain.
Solution: [41.75°, 41.85°) is the range number. This means that the "true value" may be as small as 41.75° or may be almost as large as 41.85°. If it were really as large as 41.85°, we would round it off to 41.9°.

Negative approximate numbers can also be expressed in range number notation. For example, the approximate number −2.74° corresponds to the range number, (−2.745, −2.735]. Notice that the bracket and parenthesis are interchanged.

ILLUSTRATIVE PROBLEM II

Express −5.667° as a range number, and explain.

Solution: $(-5.6675°, -5.6665°]$ is the range number. This means that the true value may be almost as small as $-5.6675°$ or quite as large as $-5.6665°$. If the number were really as small as $-5.6675°$, it would have been rounded off to $-5.668°$.

To be consistent, the approximate number, $0.00°$, corresponds to the range number $(-0.005°, +0.005°)$.

1.4 STATISTICS

The accuracy and precision of *statistics* are handled a bit differently, by reference to the *standard error* of the statistic. We postpone, to Subsection 6.5, a brief description of this method.

EXERCISES

Express as a range number and explain the meaning of the resulting symbol:

1 2.9   **2** -3.67

3 -32.465 **4** 156.2229

Write an approximate number which represents the range number given:

5 [35.35, 35.45)   **6** [127.515, 127.525)

7 $(-98.25, -98.15]$ **8** $(-30.105, -30.095]$

Section 2. *Addition and Subtraction of Measurements*

2.1 RANGE OF A SUM

What is the sum of the two approximate numbers, 67.3 and 12.98? In arithmetic, you might write

$$
\begin{array}{r}
67.3 \\
+\ 12.98 \\
\hline
80.28
\end{array}
$$

The sum corresponds to [80.275, 80.285), which would appear to guarantee that the "true value" lies between 80.275 and (not quite) 80.285. However, if the original approximate numbers are rewritten as range numbers, then added, we obtain

$$
\begin{array}{rl}
67.3 & = [67.25,\ 67.35) \\
12.98 & = [12.975,\ 12.985) \\
\hline
\text{Result} & = [80.225,\ 80.335)
\end{array}
$$

This shows that the "true value" lies somewhere between 80.225 and (not quite) 80.335. Comparing this correct answer with the result previously obtained by a "straight" addition, we see that they do not agree. *The range number method always gives the correct answer*, so that the "straight" addition method is incorrect.

The same conclusion would be reached for a subtraction problem.

2.2   RULE OF PRECISION

There is no perfect way for dealing with the addition or subtraction of measurements, except by the range number method. This is somewhat cumbersome for ordinary work. However, there is a very useful *rule of thumb* which is found to be satisfactory in all but the most exacting scientific work.

Rule of Precision for Addition and Subtraction: After adding or subtracting approximate numbers, round off the answer so that its precision *is the same as that of the least precise addend.*

Applying this rule to the situation in Subsection 2.1, we have, as a result of the straight addition, 80.28. The least precise addend has a precision of 0.1. The answer should therefore be rounded to the nearest tenth. The rounded answer is now 80.3, instead of 80.28. This rounded answer corresponds to the range number [80.25,80.35). The correct answer is given by [80.225,80.335). They do not agree exactly, and that is why the rule is called a *rule of thumb*. It is just a convenient way of obtaining a more reasonable answer which is not, unfortunately, perfectly correct in its range but which ordinarily is close enough.

ILLUSTRATIVE PROBLEM I

Subtract 46.1 from 96.609, where both numbers are the results of measurements. *Solution:* The straight subtraction yields 50.509. The rounded answer is 50.5, which has the same precision as 46.1.

2.3   HALF-ADJUSTING

In computer language, "rounding off" is called *half-adjusting*. The reason is that you can accomplish your purpose by adding or subtracting a "5" in the first position to be dropped. The following examples will clarify the method:

ILLUSTRATIVE PROBLEM I

Half-adjust 50.509 to the nearest tenth.

Solution:
$$
\begin{array}{r}
50.509 \\
\downarrow \\
+\quad 5 \\
\hline
50.5\cancel{09}
\end{array}
$$

The answer is 50.5.

ILLUSTRATIVE PROBLEM II

Half-adjust 50.509 to the nearest hundredth.

Solution:

$$50.509$$
$$+ \quad 5$$
$$\overline{50.514}$$

The answer is 50.51.

ILLUSTRATIVE PROBLEM III

Half-adjust −27.789 to the nearest hundredth.

Solution:

$$-27.789$$
$$- \quad 5$$
$$\overline{-27.794}$$

The answer is −27.79.

2.4 SCALING A SUM

In problems which are programmed for an electronic computer, the number of addends may be two, or may be hundreds, thousands, or even more. It is of importance to us to know how many digits there will be left and right of the decimal point. For convenience, we shall use a simple symbolism to represent the *form* of a number. For the number 12.3456 (whether positive or negative), we shall use either

$$\text{xx.xxxx}$$

or ②.④

From the Rule of Precision, you know that a sum of the form ③.⑤ + ①.③ will give you *three* places to the right of the decimal point. How many would there be to the left of the decimal point? The "worst" situation for the numbers of the form ③.⑤ and ①.③, is

$$999.99999$$
$$+ \quad 9.999$$
$$\overline{1009.99899}$$
$$\quad\quad\quad 5 \quad\quad \text{(half-adjusting)}$$
$$\overline{1009.99949}$$

which is of the form ④.③ or xxxx.xxx. Notice that the intermediate sum (before half-adjustment) is of the form ④.⑤, or xxxx.xxxxx.

This entire calculation, involving the amount of *space* needed for the intermediate results, the position of the decimal point, the position of the digit to be half-adjusted, and the form of the answer, is called *scaling*. It is a calculation of the utmost importance in computation.

ILLUSTRATIVE PROBLEM I

   Scale the problem ③ . ④ + ④ . ② .

Solution:

$$
\begin{array}{r}
999.9999 \\
+\ 9999.99 \\
\hline
10999.9899
\end{array}
$$

$$
\begin{array}{r}
\downarrow \\
5 \\
\hline
10999.99\cancel{49}
\end{array}
$$

The intermediate answer will be of the form ⑤ . ④ , half-adjustment will take place at the second figure from the right, and the answer may be as large as ⑤ . ②.

   An alternate method for solving this problem is the following:

$$
\begin{array}{lll}
999.9999 & = & 1000-0.0001 \\
+9999.99 & = & 10000-0.01 \\
\hline
\text{Result} & = & 11000-0.0101
\end{array}
$$

which leads to the same answer. This may not seem easier, but it is much more convenient when there are many numbers.

ILLUSTRATIVE PROBLEM II

   Scale the problem: ② . ④ + ③ . ③ + ① . ⑤ + ② . ③ + ④ . ④ + ④ . ②.

Solution:

Method 1	Method 2
99.9999	100−.0001
999.999	1000−.001
9.99999	10−.00001
99.999	100−.001
9999.9999	10000−.0001
+ 9999.99	+ 10000−.01
21209.98779	21210−.01221

From either method, it is clear that the intermediate result is in the form ⑤ . ⑤ , or xxxxx.xxxxx. The half-adjustment is done on the third figure from the right and the final result is in the form ⑤ . ② , or xxxxx.xx.

   Notice that in scaling, no account is taken of the *signs* of the numbers. We are merely interested in the space requirement for the intermediate and final results. For this information, we do not have to know the signs and they may be disregarded. Of course, we must take the sign of the intermediate result into account for the half-adjustment.

2.5 MATRIX NOTATION

Much of the work that is done by a mathematician or scientist involves tables of values, such as the one shown in Table I. This table, like most tables, has *rows* (from left to right) and *columns* (from top to bottom). Table I has 13 rows and 8 columns.

We have headed the columns X_{k1} through X_{k8}. The little numbers k1, k2, etc., are called *subscripts* and are used to locate an entry in the table. The first of the subscript numbers refers to the *row*, and the second refers to the *column*. For example, Mr. Earwig's rating on the third test is given by $X_{53} = 1535$.

ILLUSTRATIVE PROBLEM I

Find X_{28} and explain.

Solution: X_{28} is the entry in the second row, eighth column, namely, Mr. Baker's score on the eighth test, 0.698.

ILLUSTRATIVE PROBLEM II

Find $X_{11} + X_{21} + X_{31} + X_{41}$.

Solution: Adding 501.99, 493.37, 545.06, and 566.59, we obtain 2107.01.

In Illustrative Problem II, instead of writing, "Find $X_{11} + X_{21} + X_{31} + X_{41}$" we could have made use of the fact that the *row number* was the only variable. We might say that k is "taking on" the values 1, 2, 3, and 4 in succession. Then the problem may be stated, "Find $\sum_{k=1}^{k=4} X_{k1}$," which means precisely the same thing.

ILLUSTRATIVE PROBLEM III

Find $\sum_{k=8}^{k=10} X_{k4}$.

Solution: Adding 1147, 712, and 702, we have the sum 2561.

Notice that the bottom value of k shows where k starts and the top value shows where it ends. These are called, respectively, the lower and upper limits for k. We should mention that k is a *dummy variable*. This means that k plays no part in the actual problem except to designate the place where 1, 2, 3, and 4 are to be substituted. Any letter could have been used. To make this perfectly clear, we note that

$$\sum_{k=1}^{k=4} X_{k1} = \sum_{j=1}^{j=4} X_{j1} = \sum_{p=1}^{p=4} X_{p1} = \sum_{i=1}^{i=4} X_{i1}$$

There is one further convention which we shall observe. The symbol ΣX_{k3} without the specification of upper and lower limits will always mean that the entire column is to be added.

Table I: THE SCORES OF VARIOUS MEN ON EIGHT TESTS

Name	X_{k1}	X_{k2}	X_{k3}	X_{k4}	X_{k5}	X_{k6}	X_{k7}	X_{k8}
Able	501.99	81.115	1562	727	926	1080	1237	1.815
Baker	493.37	73.990	1897	512	700	1231	1246	0.698
Cook	545.06	90.001	1559	915	831	1347	1058	−0.474
Davis.	566.59	96.024	1594	1047	989	999	1112	−1.637
Earwig	540.75	91.233	1535	947	819	1375	1013	−2.386
Firenze	648.43	115.278	2498	914	904	1009	1095	0.815
Grady	467.53	79.207	1065	920	517	704	676	0.298
Handsoff	652.73	116.211	1623	1147	823	1158	1229	−0.774
Irish	575.21	102.776	1727	712	752	1299	1158	−2.086
Janus	605.36	98.092	1576	702	889	1247	1102	0.991
Kelp	562.28	64.800	1562	710	889	1275	1050	−0.537
Llama	428.77	95.333	1998	712	850	1275	1050	−1.268
Man	536.44	89.919	1645	1022	869	1041	1761	−0.822

EXERCISES

Scale the following:

1 ②.⑤ ± ③.④   **2** ③.⑧ ± ⑤.②

3 ⑦.① ± ⓪.②   **4** ⑥.③ ± ⓪.④

5 ⑤.② ± ④.③   **6** ⑦.⓪ ± ③.④

7 One hundred numbers of the form xxx.xxxx are to be added and subtracted.

8 Four hundred numbers of the form xx.xxxx are to be added and subtracted.

Scale and find the sum on a desk calculator or by hand:

9 $\sum_{k=3}^{k=5} X_{k5}$ **10** $\sum_{k=1}^{k=2} X_{k7}$

11 $\sum X_{k1}$ **12** $\sum X_{k2}$

13 $\sum_{k=2}^{k=6} X_{k6}$ **14** $\sum_{k=1}^{k=13} X_{k2}$

Section 3. *Multiplication of Measurements*

3.1 RANGE OF A PRODUCT

We shall start our discussion by assuming that we are required to multiply the two approximate numbers, 2.43 and 368.7. Proceeding in the usual fashion, we obtain

$$2.43 \times 368.7 = 895.941$$

Using the usual convention for approximate numbers, this means that the true value of the product is between 895.9405 and 895.9415. The question is whether this answer is justified.

Let us re-examine the original problem. Expressing the approximate numbers as range numbers, we seek to find

$$[2.425, 2.435) \times [368.65, 368.75)$$

We shall now investigate the "worst" possibilities:

$$2.425 \times 368.65 = 893.97625$$
$$2.435 \times 368.75 = 897.90625$$

which means that the correct answer to the problem is really the range number [893.97625,897.90625). Clearly, the result of the "straight" multiplication, 895.941, is absurd because it gives us the wrong impression about the range of the answer. What approximate number will give the best possible range? We shall round off the "straight" answer and see which is the best of them:

$$895.941 = [895.9405, \ 895.9415)$$
$$895.94 \ = [895.935, \ 895.945)$$
$$895.9 \ \ = [895.85, \ 895.95)$$
$$896 \ \ \ \ = [895.5, \ 896.5)$$

Again we are confronted with the fact that no one of these possibilities expresses precisely the correct range of the answer. However, we shall compromise with another *rule of thumb* which is found to be satisfactory in most work (although not in very precise scientific work).

Rule of Accuracy for Multiplication: After multiplying approximate numbers, half-adjust the product so that the accuracy of the product is the same as that of the least accurate factor.

Another way of stating this is that the product should have as many significant figures as the factor which has the smallest number of significant figures.

ILLUSTRATIVE PROBLEM I

Find 2.7 × 1.32
Solution: The intermediate answer, 3.564, is half-adjusted to *two* significant figures, and the answer is expressed as 3.6. If 2.7 = [2.65, 2.75) and 1.32 = [1.315, 1.325). then the true range of the answer is [3.48475, 3.64375).

3.2   SCALING A PRODUCT

It is important for us to know what happens when we multiply a number of the form xxxx.xxx by another number of the form, for example, xx.xxxxxx. We shall abbreviate this in our usual fashion as $(4).(3) \times (2).(6)$.

Again, let us consider the "worst" case, namely,

$$9999.9999 \times 99.999999 = 999999.890000001$$

which is in the form $(6).(9)$. It is easy to see that the result of multiplying two approximate numbers, one of the form $(a).(b)$ by another of the form $(c).(d)$, is *at most* $(a+c).(b+d)$. There may, of course, be *nonsignificant zeros* on the left side of the number as in the multiplication

$$13.456 \times 391.4 = 05266.6784$$

and there may not, as in

$$93.456 \times 391.4 = 36578.6784$$

ILLUSTRATIVE PROBLEM I

What is the result of ⑤ . ② × ④ . ⑨?

Solution: The intermediate result is ⑨ . ⑪ . We are entitled to only seven significant figures, so that half-adjustment will take place at the figure which is eighth from the left, *counting from the first non-zero digit.*

3.3   ASTERISK NOTATION

Insteal of using × as a symbol of mulitiplication, we shall, from this point on, use the asterisk (*). This is a common convention in computing. Notice that 4 * 5 means 4 × 5, or 20. Double asterisks are used to indicate exponentiation, e.g.,

$$4 ** 5 = 4^5 = 1024.$$

3.4   CONTINUED PRODUCTS

There is really nothing new in the discussion of the range of a continued product that has not been implied in the Rule of Accuracy for a product. When the product

$$75.6688 * 36.999874 * 0.0008787655000$$

is to be considered, the range can be settled by multiplying in pairs. It should be perfectly obvious that the least accurate factor, in this case, is the first one, which has only six significant figures. Sooner or later, this factor will have to be used and therefore the final result can have only six significant figures. For greater accuracy and precision, the entire problem can be done (for very careful work) with the corresponding range numbers.

To scale a continued product, the problem can be considered, once again, in pairs. The example given above amounts to

$$② . ④ * ② . ⑥ * ⓪ . ⑬$$

Multiplying the first pair, we obtain a ④ . ⑩ . Multiplying this result by the third factor, we obtain a ④ . ㉓ . We are entitled to only six significant figures, so that we will count six figures from the first non-zero digit and half-adjust at the seventh figure from the first non-zero digit.

ILLUSTRATIVE PROBLEM I

Scale and solve the problem given in the text.

Solution: Multiplying the first two factors, we get 2799.7360657312, a ④ . ⑩ number as expected. We are entitled to only six significant figures in the answer, but it does not matter how many are kept in the intermediate stages of the calculation. In hand calculation, we usually retain one extra significant figure all through to the end, i.e., up to the final half-adjustment. In working with desk calculators, we usually fill the keyboard (ordinarily eight or ten places), then half-adjust at the end. In working with electronic computers, we do not actually see the intermediate products (unless we ask for them), and no general rule can be given for the number of figures to be retained. A good general rule for all problems, no matter how they are done, is to keep as many figures as are convenient, making sure that there is enough extra to provide for half-adjustment. In this case, we shall, for the moment, retain ten significant figures in the intermediate product, so that the problem has been reduced to

$$2799.736573 \quad * \quad 0.0008787655000$$

Performing the multiplication, we obtain 0002.4603119094406315000, which is half adjusted to 2.46031.

Notice that the left-hand zeros are not considered in counting off the six significant figures, even though they had to be considered in the scaling of the problem.

The product 38.9 * 38.9 * 38.9 can be written 38.9 ** 3, and the result of an exponentiation of this kind follows the usual Rule of Accuracy for Multiplication.

3.5   SUMS OF PRODUCTS

One of the most common problems in numerical analysis is one in which you have, two columns, as follows:

j	Y_{j1}	Y_{j2}
1	27.6	163.49
2	31.29	−58.418
3	−143.18	−3.27

and we are required to multiply each entry in Y_{j1} by the corresponding entry in Y_{j2}, then find the sum. The symbolism for this problem is

$$\sum_{j\,=\,1}^{j\,=\,3} Y_{j1}Y_{j2}$$

The intermediate calculations for this problem are as follows:

j	Y_{j1}	Y_{j2}	$Y_{j1} * Y_{j2}$
1	27.6	163.49	4512.324
2	31.29	−58.418	−1827.89922
3	−143.18	−3.27	468.1986
			3152.62338

How much of this answer are we entitled to?

Let us examine this little problem line by line. Using the Rule of Accuracy for Multiplication, we are entitled to only 3 s.f. for the first product, 4 s.f. for the second product, and 3 s.f. for the third product. Using the Rule of Precision for Addition, we are now entitled to only the first three digits in the final answer. In other words, the result should be stated as 3150 (3 s.f.) or 3.15 * 10^3.

Unfortunately, there is no easy way to shorten this procedure.

EXERCISES

The following summations refer to the data of Table I. Scale and, by use of an estimate, show where the half-adjustment will be made:

1 $\displaystyle\sum_{k=7}^{k=9} X_{k1}X_{k4}$ **2** $\displaystyle\sum_{k=3}^{k=5} X_{k2}X_{k5}$

3 $\displaystyle\sum_{k=1}^{k=5} X_{k2}X_{k3}$ **4** $\displaystyle\sum_{k=4}^{k=10} X_{k6}X_{k2}$

5 $\displaystyle\sum X_{k2}X_{k3}$ **6** $\displaystyle\sum (X_{k8})^2$

Section 4. Division Involving Measurements

4.1 RANGE OF A QUOTIENT

A division in applied mathematical work is represented by a slash (/). We shall consider 782/52628 where both the numerator and denominator are approximate numbers obtained by a measurement:

$$782 \quad = \; [781.5, \; 782.5)$$
$$52628 = \; [52627.5, \; 52628.5)$$

The "worst" cases are those where the smallest numerator is divided by the largest denominator, and where the largest numerator is divided by the smallest denominator:

$$781.5/52628.5 = 0.014849368\ldots$$
$$782.5/52627.5 = 0.014868652\ldots$$

Therefore, the true value of the quotient is in the interval between these two end-point quotients. The "straight" division 782/52628 yields 0.014859010 . . . . For reasons which should now be clear, the following *rule of thumb* is applicable in all but the most precise scientific work:

Rule of Accuracy for Division: After dividing two approximate numbers, half-

adjust the answer so that its accuracy (number of significant figures) is the same as that of the least accurate of the two numbers.

In the sample problem, therefore, the answer is 0.0149.

4.2   SCALING A QUOTIENT

We shall start with the problem

$$56.112/3.14159 = 17.861$$

In this case, we have ② . ③/① . ⑤ = ② . ③. If you know the approximate sizes of the numbers to be used, the easiest way to scale the quotient is to *estimate* the answer by ordinary arithmetic to find out how many places there are before the decimal point, then use enough decimal places to satisfy the Rule of Accuracy.

ILLUSTRATIVE PROBLEM I

In a certain practical problem, a series of divisions is to be done on numbers of the form xxx.xxx/x.xxxx. The numerators are all approximately 150 and the denominators are all approximately 3. Scale the problem.

Solution: The estimated answer (by arithmetic) is 50. We are entitled to *five* significant figures. The answer, therefore, will be in the form xx.xxx, with half-adjustment taking place in the fourth decimal place (the first digit to be dropped).

In other problems, we may have a series of divisions in which we have insufficient information to scale the problem completely. The procedure is shown in the following illustrative problem.

ILLUSTRATIVE PROBLEM II

In a certain practical problem, a series of divisions is to be done on numbers of the form xxx.xxx/x.xxxx. Scale the problem as far as possible.

Solution: The problem may be written as ③ . ③/① . ④. In the final answer, we are entitled to five significant figures. If we shift the decimal point in the denominator and numerator in the usual fashion, the problem becomes

$$\frac{\text{xxxxxx0}}{\text{xxxxx}}$$

where the 0 is written to show that a nonsignificant zero has been added as a place-holder. In the absence of other information, we must assume that the denominator may possibly be as small as 00001. Therefore, the quotient may have as many as *seven* digits before the decimal point. On the other hand, the numerator may be as small as 10 and the denominator may be as large as 99999, and the answer would be in the form 0.000xxxxx where, again, the zeros are place-holders. The best answer we can give, in this problem, is that we must allow space for *seven* digits before the decimal point and *nine* after the decimal point. This includes one extra space for half-adjustment. Half-adjustment is done on the *sixth* digit to the right of the first non-zero digit.

4.3 DIVISION INVOLVING APPROXIMATE AND EXACT NUMBERS

The Rules of Accuracy apply only to approximate numbers derived from a measurement. In some problems, one (or more) of the numbers is an exact number. For example, in finding the average of 157 measurements, if the sum of the measurements is xx.xxxx, the result of dividing by 157 will still have six significant figures.

The same remark holds for multiplication.

EXERCISES

A series of divisions is to be performed on numbers with approximate sizes as shown. Scale as much as possible.

1 xxxx.xx/xxxx.xxx. The numerator is about 2000, the denominator is about 1000.

2 xx.xxxxx/xxx.xxxxxx. The numerator is about 35, the denominator is about 700.

3 0.xxxxxxx/xxxx.xxx. The numerator is about 0.5, the denominator is about 5000.

4 0.00xxxxx/0.00xxx. The numerator is about 0.007, the denominator is about 0.002.

A series of divisions is to be performed on approximate numbers as shown. Scale as much as possible:

5 xxxx.xx/xxxx.xxx

6 xx.xxxxx/xxx.xxxxxx

7 0.xxxxxxx/xxx.xxx

8 0.00xxxxx/0.00xxx

In the following, the denominator is an exact number. Scale as much as possible:

9 xxxx.xxx/xxxx

10 xx.xxxxxxxx/ xxxxxx

Section 5. Combined Operations

5.1 ORDER OF OPERATIONS

With the information you already have, you should be able to do any problem which involves addition, subtraction, multiplication, division, and exponentiation with an integral power. The problem of square roots will be discussed for another purpose in Section 8, but the general problem of fractional powers (including roots) is solved by computers by use of the definition

$$a^b = e^{(b \ln a)}$$

where e is the base of natural logarithms, approximately 2.718, and ln a is read "the natural logarithm of a." Natural logarithms use the base e instead of base 10.

It still remains to discuss the order of operations in a problem which involves more than one operation. A good general principle in computing is that *division* is postponed as long as possible. In other words, in a problem like

$$\frac{94.67 \times 56.88}{6.388 \times 7.926}$$

which is (94.67 * 56.88)/(6.388 * 7.926) in computer terminology, we would perform the multiplication in the numerator, then the multiplication in the denominator, then we would divide the new numerator by the new denominator. *We would postpone all half-adjustments to the end of the problem.* In other words, we keep all the intermediate figures until the final result and then use the scaling instructions to half-adjust. In this sample problem, the numerator becomes 5384.8296 and the denominator becomes 50.631288. The division gives us 106.353794 ... which must be half-adjusted at the fifth digit from the first non-zero digit. The final answer is 106.4, having four significant figures.

If the problem involves addition and subtraction, the Rule of Precision must also be used, but not until the very end.

5.2   FORTRAN SYMBOLISM

We have already referred to the fact that * is used in place of × for multiplication, that ** is used for exponentiation, and that the slash is used for division in computer symbolism. These are all part of FORTRAN notation and are explained in Subsection 23.2, which deals with FORTRAN. We shall use this symbolism throughout the book. The reader is advised that it is important to familiarize himself with this symbolism.

In addition to the symbolism for the operations, the reader is asked to read that part of the material in Subsection 23.3 of the FORTRAN discussion which explains the concept of an *expression* and a *replacement*. We shall use the symbolism

$$N = N + 2$$

to mean "Replace N by N + 2" throughout the book.

EXERCISES

Scale and indicate the order of operations:

1   897.10 * 31.27/0.00299778

2   0.0233587 * 16.90073/0.07786179

3   250000 (5 s.f.)/(56.77044 * (−31.2290))

4   0.03007660 * 2.446798/(7.50002 * 308.007)

5   803.44668 * (−0.2256934) ** 2/((−17.000022) * (−0.00004598224))

6 3.468756 ** 3 * 4.55693/(−5.335689) ** 2 * (−7856.2245)

The reader is also advised to do the exercises following Subsections 23.2 and 23.3 at this time.

Section 6. Introduction to Statistics

6.1 PROBLEMS OF STATISTICS

It is very common in modern-day science, technology, industry, and business to collect thousands or millions of numbers related to some situation for one reason or another. Consider, for example, the punched cards used by utility companies, department stores, and so on. Each card may have your identification, the item purchased, and other pertinent information. Another example is one in which a medical research team collects data from thousands of people concerning the relative efficacy of two kinds of polio cure. A third example is one in which the free paths of millions of atomic particles are studied. These *statistics* may be approximate numbers (the result of a measurement of some kind) or they may be exact numbers (in this case, the result of a count).

In general, after the basic statistics have been gathered, it is necessary to do something with them before they can be made useful. We shall mention four important problems of statistics:

1. *The Problem of Condensation.* How can a large mass of statistics be *described* in such a manner as to give the essential characteristics of the entire distribution of numbers while using only a few numbers to do so?

2. *The Problem of Correlation.* If you have two or more distributions of statistics, how can the *similarities* between them be described?

3. *The Problem of Significant Differences.* If you have two or more distributions of statistics, how can the *differences* between them be described?

4. *The Problem of Prediction.* After you have amassed a large amount of information about the present data, how can you tell what is likely to happen for future data?

6.2 CENTRAL TENDENCIES

Table II contains three columns of fictitious statistics about seven items, or people. (These are not enough data for a real study. This table, like Table I, is displayed for illustrative purposes only.)

The first column contains an array of *exact numbers*, each number being obtained by an actual count. The second and third columns contain arrays of *approximate numbers*, each obtained by a measurement of some kind.

Table II. STATISTICAL DATA

j	X_{j1}	X_{j2}	X_{j3}
1	3	25.762	44.514
2	5	−17.418	−40.846
3	5	36.335	65.660
4	5	−28.519	−63.048
5	4	41.663	76.316
6	2	20.003	33.996
7	6	−32.957	−71.723

We wish, at this time, to give a single *datum* which expresses what statisticians call the *estimate of maximum likelihood* for the distribution in each column in Table II.

The usual datum employed by mathematicians and scientists is the *Arithmetic Mean*, M, defined by the equation

$$M_k = \sum_{j=1}^{j=N} X_{jk}/N$$

where N is the number of "scores" in the column. To find M_1, the mean of the first column, we add the numbers and obtain

$$M_1 = 30/7$$

Now, since these are exact numbers, we are apparently entitled to an exact number as an answer. However, this makes no sense. The exact answer, $4\frac{2}{7}$, is of no use to a statistician. We are left with the problem of choosing a logical and useful representation for the Arithmetic Mean.

We shall postpone (to Subsection 6.5) the explanation of the procedure for scaling the answers to statistical problems. For the present, we mention, as a *rule of thumb*, that the Arithmetic Mean is ordinarily written with one more place than the original data. Using this rule of thumb for Table II, $M_1 = 4.3$, $M_2 = 6.4099$.

An interpretation of the Arithmetic Mean is as follows: If a great many experiments were done in a similar way, it is probable that the Mean in each experiment would be 4.3 for the first column and 6.4099 for the second column. It is in this sense that the Mean is sometimes called the "most probable value."

The Arithmetic Mean is one of many measures called *central tendencies*. The phrase, central tendency, is intended to suggest that the value calculated is at the middle of the array. Of course, it may or may not be an actual datum. In Table II, the Means are not actual data. If a column had been 1,2,3,4,5,6,7, then the Mean would have been 4, an actual datum.

There are other central tendencies used in scientific work, but the Arithmetic Mean is the most convenient for computers and the most attractive for most statistical experiments.

6.3 DISPERSION TENDENCIES

The Arithmetic Mean for the third column of Table II, M_3, is 6.4099. This is precisely the same as that for column 2, yet the data are not at all alike. Notice that in column 2, the *range* of data is from -32.957 to $+41.663$, whereas in column 3, the range of data is from -71.723 to $+76.316$.

It should be perfectly clear that a central tendency, all by itself, does not suffice to describe adequately a distribution of data. As an absolute minimum, we need to know one other measure, a measure which describes the *spread* or *dispersion* of the scores. Also, if there is anything unusual, so to speak, about the *shape* of the distribution, we must have a way of expressing this fact. We cannot go into this latter phase of the description of a distribution. This involves the *moments* of a distribution.*

For many reasons, the most satisfactory measure of dispersion is the one called the *standard deviation*, represented by the Greek letter *sigma*, σ. In the definition of σ, difference

$$x_{jk} = X_{jk} - M_k$$

is calculated for each score. The lower-case letter, x, is defined as the *deviation* of a score from its Mean, and X_{jk} and M_k have their customary meaning. For example, in column 2 of Table II,

$$x_{52} = X_{52} - M_2 = 41.663 - 6.4099 = +35.253$$
$$x_{42} = X_{42} - M_2 = -28.519 - 6.4099 = -34.929$$

After the deviations are calculated, the *variance*, σ^2, may be found by the formula

$$\sigma^2 = \frac{\sum x^2}{N}$$

where N is the number of data in the column, and the summation is understood to be over the entire column. For column 2 of Table II, the variance, $\sigma^2 = 862.15978\ldots.$

The standard deviation, σ, is simply the square root of the variance, i.e.,

$$\sigma = \sqrt{\frac{\sum x^2}{N}} \qquad \text{(definition of } \sigma\text{)}$$

For column 2 of Table II, using the definition, $\sigma = 29.3626$, where the standard deviation has been half-adjusted to have the same precision as the Arithmetic Mean of the same distribution, $M_2 = 6.4099$.

The combination, $M_2 = 6.4099$, $\sigma_2 = 29.3626$, describes the distribution displayed in column 2 provided it is a *normal distribution*.** If column 2 is such a distribution, these two *tendencies* inform us that:

1. The mean of X_{j2} is 6.4099.

---

*This is discussed somewhat more fully in Dodes, I. A. and Greitzer, S. L., *op. cit.*, and with great thoroughness in books on advanced statistics.

**See Dodes, I. A. and Greitzer, S. L., *op. cit.*

2. 68.26% of the universe of which column 2 is a sample lies within one σ of the mean, i.e., between (-22.9527) and $(+35.7725)$.

3. 95.46% of the universe of which column 2 is a sample lies within two σ of the mean, i.e., between (-52.3153) and $(+65.1351)$.

4. 99.75% of the universe of which column 2 is a sample lies within three σ of the mean, i.e., between (-81.6779) and $(+94.4977)$.

6.4   COMPUTATION FORMULA FOR σ

A computer has absolutely no difficulty in subtracting M from X to find x, squaring each x, adding the squared deviations, then dividing by N. However, for many reasons beyond the scope of this book, this is not the most efficient procedure. One obvious reason is that a division is needed to find M and, as we mentioned previously, it is best to have the divisions as late in the computation as possible. Another reason is that original data (in this case, the original scores) should be used in preference to derived data (in this case, the deviations) whenever possible.

For the computation of σ, it is easy to calculate a formula which utilizes the original data and which postpones division to the very end. This is done, as an example of the thinking done in numerical analysis of a computation problem, in the following. Note that subscripts have been omitted, with the understanding that we are using X_{jk}, x_{jk}, M_k and σ_k, and that summations are over all j, from $j = 1$ to $j = N$, where N is the number of items, or subjects, in the sample.

$$\sigma^2 = \frac{\sum(x^2)}{N} = \frac{\sum(X - M)^2}{N} = \frac{\sum(X^2 - 2MX + M^2)}{N}$$

$$\sigma^2 = \frac{1}{N}\left[\sum(X^2) - 2M\sum X + NM^2\right]$$

$$\sigma^2 = \frac{1}{N}\left[\sum(X^2) - 2\frac{\sum X}{N}\sum X + N\frac{(\sum X)^2}{N^2}\right]$$

$$\sigma^2 = \frac{1}{N^2}\left[N\sum(X^2) - 2(\sum X)^2 + (\sum X)^2\right]$$

$$\sigma^2 = \frac{N\sum(X^2) - (\sum X)^2}{N^2}$$

Let $L = \sqrt{N\sum(X^2) - (\sum X)^2}$

then $\sigma = L/N$

The formula just derived is called a *computation formula*. Observe that it uses the original scores and postpones the division until the very end. It is easier, faster, and more accurate than the definition, even on a desk calculator. For column 2 of Table II, the desk calculator results are

$$\sum(X^2) = 6322.722381$$
$$N\sum(X^2) = 44259.056667$$
$$\sum X = 44.869$$
$$(\sum X)^2 = 2013.227161$$
$$L^2 = 42245.829509$$
$$L = 205.53790$$
$$\sigma = 29.3626$$

In this case, the answer from the definition and the answer from the computation formula came out the same. However, in general, round-off errors in the use of definitions may cause errors; thus it is *always* safer to use the computation formula.

6.5   RELIABILITY OF A STATISTIC

Reliability refers, in general, to the accuracy and precision of a statistic. An *experiment* is said to be reliable if (*i*) you would obtain approximately the same results after repeating the experiment, and (*ii*) another experimenter would also obtain the same results. The reliability of a *test* refers to the likelihood that the same test, given over and over, would bring about the same distribution of scores.

These are general concepts. Mathematically, the reliability of any statistic refers to the magnitude of its *standard error*. The standard error of a score, such as one of the data in Table I or Table II, is the standard deviation, σ, of the column in which the score appears. The standard error of a mean, σ_M, is calculated from the formula

$$\sigma_M = \sigma/\sqrt{N - 1}$$

where σ is the standard deviation for the column.* The standard error of a standard deviation, σ_σ, is given by the formula,

$$\sigma_\sigma = \sigma/\sqrt{2N}$$

In any kind of statistical work, the number of significant figures in the original data depends upon the way the measurement was made. The original data are usually approximate numbers obtained by measurement. The Arithmetic Mean is a calculated quantity, however, and the number of significant figures in this *parameter* and in other calculated statistics (parameters) must be decided by some sort of rule.

We shall point out that it does not make much difference how many figures are reported for any statistic or parameter *provided only that the standard error of the statistic is given with it*. The statistic, along with its standard error, makes up a "package" somewhat like a range number.

The general practice is to keep enough figures in each statistic so that its standard error will have three or four significant figures. As an example, if a statistic is calculated as 531872.6119823... and its standard error is calculated as 2.7182457... it would usually be written as 531872.61 with a standard error of 2.72. However, as we have remarked, this "rule" is not an important one. Remember only to express each statistic together with its standard error.

---

*This formula, and others mentioned in Part One, are derived in Dodes, I. A. and Greitzer, S. L., *op. cit.*

6.6   OPERATIONS WITH STATISTICAL NUMBERS

In working with statistics, retain as many figures as are convenient. Use computation formulas which retain original data and postpone division. In the older statistics books, you will find methods of "grouping" data into tables. These methods are still of interest for the drawing of graphs and charts, but are of no interest to the person who has access to a computer. The grouping of statistics *always* introduces errors based upon assumptions which may or may not hold. Along with "grouping methods" go "grouping corrections" based upon other assumptions. All these ideas were indispensable when calculations were done by hand or by slow calculators, but they are indefensible now. Use the original data.

EXERCISES

Find M_k, σ_k, $\sigma_{M,k}$ and $\sigma_{\dot\sigma,k}$ for each column of Table I, using the computation formula for σ_k. You will find these figures useful in checking the programs to be written for the digital computer, in later chapters.

Section 7.   Statistical Problems

7.1   SIMILARITY BETWEEN TWO ARRAYS

The similarity between two columns of data is usually expressed by the *coefficient of linear correlation*, or *Pearson's r*, defined by

$$r_{12} = \frac{\sum (z_1 z_2)}{N} \qquad \text{(definition of r)}$$

where z_1 is the set of *standard scores* for column 1, and z_2 is the set of corresponding standard scores for column 2. For any column, the standard score, z, is found by the formula

$$z = \frac{x}{\sigma} \qquad \text{(definition of z)}$$

where x is the deviation from the mean of the column, and σ is the standard deviation of the column. When this formula is applied to columns 1 and 2 of Table I, it is found that $\sum z_1 z_2 = 8.1540363$ and $r = +0.62723356$. If this is the final result, the coefficient of correlation is usually expressed to two decimal places, i.e., $r = +0.63$. If it is not the final result, all the figures are retained, in the usual fashion, until the final result is attained.

The computation formula for r is

$$r_{12} = \frac{N \sum (X_1 X_2) - (\sum X_1)(\sum X_2)}{L_1 \, L_2}$$

where

$$L = \sqrt{N \sum (X^2) - (\sum X)^2}$$

When this formula is applied to columns 1 and 2 of Table I, the result is that $r = +0.62723356$. A difference may be caused by round-off errors when the definition is used.

Unlike most statistics, the standard error of r, σ_r, is seldom used. Experience has brought about a simpler criterion for deciding whether or not a correlation is a good one:

1. When $-0.4 < r < +0.4$, we say that the correlation is insignificant or negligible.
2. When $0.4 \leqslant |r| < 0.7$, we say that the correlation is significant and substantial.
3. When $0.7 \leqslant |r| < 0.8$, we say that the correlation is significant and high.
4. When $0.8 \leqslant |r| < 0.9$, we say that the correlation is significant and very high, or very significant.
5. When $|r| \geqslant 0.9$, we say that the correlation is significant and extremely high, or extremely significant.

Another approach to the meaning of r is through the notion of *communality*, C. Communality refers to the extent to which two arrays overlap or intersect. It has been shown that

$$r^2 \leqslant C \leqslant |r|$$

so that when $r = 0.62$, the communality, C, is between $(0.62)^2$ and 0.62, i.e., between 38 and 62 percent.

The coefficient of correlation, r, may be anywhere between -1 (for perfect negative correlation) to $+1$ (for perfect positive correlation).

7.2   DIFFERENCE BETWEEN TWO ARRAYS

There are many methods for comparing two or more arrays of data. Among the most important are the t-method (critical ratio), the chi-square (χ^2) method, and the F-method (analysis of variance).* We shall mention only the first method, since it is the most common in simple experiments. This method depends upon the fact that, like simple scores, Means vary (yielding a standard error, σ_M), and the *difference* between two Means also varies (yielding a standard error, $\sigma_{\Delta M}$). For two groups designated as X and Y, the standard error of the difference of their Means is given by the formula

$$\sigma_{\Delta M} = \sqrt{\sigma^2_{M,X} + \sigma^2_{M,Y} - 2r_{XY}\ \sigma_{M,X}\sigma_{M,Y}}$$

If the groups being compared for difference are perfectly matched (so that r, for all practical purposes, is equal to $+1$), then a simpler formula can be used:

$$\sigma_{\Delta M} = \frac{\sigma_d}{\sqrt{N - 1}}$$

where σ_d is the standard deviation of the difference between matched pairs.

---

*The first two methods are explained in detail in Dodes, I. A. and Greitzer, S. L., *op. cit.*; the last method is dealt with in specialized books on statistics.

Now, the critical ratio, t, of the difference of means, ΔM, is computed from the formula

$$t = \frac{\Delta M}{\sigma_{\Delta M}} \quad \text{(definition of critical ratio)}$$

In *biology, psychology* and *education*, we say that the difference, ΔM, is statistically significant if $t \geqslant 2$. In the *physical sciences*, we say that the difference, ΔM, is statistically significant if $t \geqslant 3$.

7.3   LEAST-SQUARES LINES

We shall illustrate the procedure for obtaining a least-squares line by three examples. In a general way, a least-squares line is a straight line which appears to "fit" experimental data in a satisfactory manner.

ILLUSTRATIVE PROBLEM I

X	−11.0	−8.00	−5.00	−3.00	0.00	+3.00	+6.00	8.00	11.0	12.0	14.0
Y	−40.0	−15.0	−10.0	+10.0	20.0	40.0	50.0	70.0	70.0	90.0	91.0

We are given the table of values (shown above), and we would like to find a formula, $Y = f(X)$. The first step is to plot these values. The plot shows that the relationship appears to be a straight-line dependence. Therefore, we seek a formula of the form $\tilde{Y} = b_1 X + K$ where $\tilde{Y}$ is read "the predicted value of Y," b_1 is "the regression coefficient of Y on X," and K is a constant to be determined. It is, as will be obvious, the value of Y when $X = 0$. The basic equations are

$$\begin{cases} \sum Y = b_1 \sum X + NK \\ \sum XY = b_1 \sum (X^2) + K \sum X \end{cases}$$

the summations being taken over the entire array. For this problem, the result of the arithmetic (done on a desk calculator) is

$$\begin{cases} 376 = 27\, b_1 + 11\, K \\ 4684 = 789\, b_1 + 27\, K \end{cases}$$

from which $b_1 = 5.204$ and $K = 21.408$. The *least-squares line* is, therefore,

$$\tilde{Y} = 5.204\, X + 21.408$$

The regression coefficient, b_1, is related to the coefficient of linear correlation, r, by the relationship

$$b_1 = r_{XY} * \frac{\sigma_Y}{\sigma_X}$$

ILLUSTRATIVE PROBLEM II

X	1.052	1.848	3.083	3.921	5.161
Y	8.614	23.62	63.08	171.9	470.4

A plot of these values shows that no straight line would be likely to fit them.

However, a plot on *semi-log* paper shows that $\ln Y = f(X)$ is a possible straight line relationship of the form

$$\ln \tilde{Y} = b_1 X + K$$

To find the least-squares line by computer, we merely have the machine calculate $\ln Y$ and proceed as in the first illustrative problem. For a desk calculator, it is more convenient to use common logarithms. The method is shown here because it is always important to calculate one sample problem when a program is written for the large computer.

X	1.052	1.848	3.083	3.921	5.161
log Y	0.93520	1.37328	1.79989	2.23528	2.67247

We now find the relationship

$$\log \tilde{Y} = b_1 X + K$$

using

$$\begin{cases} \sum(\log Y) = b_1 \sum X + NK \\ \sum(X \log Y) = b_1 \sum(X^2) + K \left(\sum X\right) \end{cases}$$

$$\begin{cases} 9.01612 = 15.065 \ b_1 + 5 \ K \\ 31.62786 = 56.037 \ b_1 + 15.065 \ K \end{cases}$$

from which $\log \tilde{Y} = 0.41919 X + 0.54017$.

Now we use $\ln \tilde{Y} = 2.302\ 585\ 092\ 994 \log \tilde{Y} = M^{\ell} \log \tilde{Y}$ and obtain $\ln \tilde{Y} = 0.96522 X + 0.54034M'$ which, in *exponential form*, is

$$\tilde{Y} = 3.470 \ e^{0.96513X}$$

This is the least-squares equation for the data given.

ILLUSTRATIVE PROBLEM III

X	1.802	3.979	7.016	15.03	24.96	41.08	49.87	71.22
Y	200.7	97.23	38.83	19.26	8.418	5.938	3.104	2.878

When these data are plotted on ordinary axes, or on semi-log axes, they do not appear to fall along a straight line. However, when they are plotted on *log-log* paper, the points seem to approximate a straight line. On a computer, each value of X and Y may be transformed to $\ln X$ and $\ln Y$, respectively. In calculation by desk calculator, it is more convenient to use common logarithms:

log X	0.25575	0.59977	0.84609	1.17696	1.39724	1.61363	1.69784	1.85260
log Y	2.30255	1.98780	1.58917	1.28466	0.92521	0.77364	0.49192	0.45909

The two equations to be used are

$$\begin{cases} \sum(\log Y) = b_1 \sum(\log X) + n \ K \\ \sum(\log X * \log Y) = b_1 \sum(\log X)^2 + K \sum \log X \end{cases}$$

and the actual data lead to

$$\begin{cases} 9.81404 = 9.43988 \; b_1 + 8 \; K \\ 8.86449 = 13.39710 \; b_1 + 9.43988 \; K \end{cases}$$

the solution of which is

$$\log \tilde{Y} = -1.20271 \log X + 2.64593$$

or, in exponential form,

$$\tilde{Y} = 442.5 \; X^{-1.20271}$$

7.4   LEAST-SQUARES SURFACES

These problems* involve the calculation of partial correlations, partial standard deviations, and partial regression coefficients. The result is called a *multiple regression equation,* and the standard error of the predicted quantity is called the *standard error of estimate.* The similarity relationship between the predicted array and the array of variables which are used to make the prediction is called the *multiple correlation.*

7.5   OTHER STATISTICAL PROBLEMS

From the few examples given in the two sections of this chapter devoted to statistical problems, it is evident that the use of a computer is almost indispensable for the convenient solution of problems involving condensation, comparison, and prediction. We cannot spare any more space for examples, but some machine programs are included in Parts Three and Four which demonstrate the calculation of tables, condensation, and the formation of least-squares formulas for three variables. In addition to these, the computer is invaluable for all sorts of statistical computations involving the processing of a great mass of data.

EXERCISES

For each of the following sets of data, plot the points and decide what kind of least-squares line is probably correct:

1	X	−1.933	−1.652	−0.755	−0.400	+0.195	+1.773	+2.753
	Y	−61.813	+17.314	+93.817	132.188	147.981	158.040	57.225

2	X	0.600	1.200	2.100	3.002	3.806	4.495	5.314	5.787
	Y	300.0	150.0	78.85	32.50	18.95	8.915	5.000	3.016

3	X	1.513	7.225	14.89	30.23	59.91	91.06
	Y	8.035	19.84	35.01	51.63	82.18	100.9

---

*The reader is referred to Dodes, I. A. and Greitzer, S. L., *op. cit.,* for the solution of the least-squares problem for three variables, and to other, more specialized books for least-squares formulas involving more than three variables.

4

X	−11.56	−8.47	−6.17	−3.88	−1.86	+1.18	3.99	6.83	8.59
Y	83.18	67.75	42.38	27.62	2.43	−14.27	−49.97	−63.00	−89.10

In a certain experiment, the following condensed data was obtained for 36 pairs of mice:

	Control	Experimental
Mean	465.339	507.060
σ	80.362	134.947

5 Calculate σ_M and σ_σ for each group.

6 Assuming $r = 0$, find $\sigma_{\Delta M}$ and t. What are your conclusions?

7 Assuming $r = 0.54501995$, find $\sigma_{\Delta M}$ and t. What are your conclusions?

Section 8. Square Root: Introduction to Iterative Methods

8.1 MEANING OF ITERATION

The word *iterative* merely means *repeating* or *repetitive*. In this section, we shall explore the kind of systematic repetition of a process which is so easy for a computer. It is the thing which the computer does best, and (fortunately) it is the kind of thing that a mathematician or scientist likes least. Our emphasis is on *square root* because it is an easy approach. However, the methods we are going to mention are applicable to a vast variety of problems ranging from arithmetic to the most advanced calculus.

8.2 USE OF BINOMIAL THEOREM

The binomial theorem states that

$$(a + b)^n = a^n + \binom{n}{1} a^{n-1}b + \binom{n}{2} a^{n-2}b^2 + \binom{n}{3} a^{n-3}b^3 + \ldots$$

where the symbol $\binom{n}{k}$ refers, in the usual fashion, to $\dfrac{n!}{k! \, (n-k)!}$, when n is an integer, and $\dfrac{n(n-1)(n-2)\ldots(n-k+1)}{1*2*3*\ldots k}$ for all cases.

If $n = \dfrac{1}{2}$, this series can be used to find the square root of $(a + b)$. If b is a number smaller than one, then successive terms may become sufficiently small so that, after a while, they have little influence on the result to a given number of places. This is not necessarily a good method; we are using it only to introduce the general idea.

ILLUSTRATIVE PROBLEM I

Find $\sqrt{101.7}$.

Solution: We shall find $\sqrt{1.017}$, then multiply the result by 10. In this case, $a = 1$, $b = 0.017$. The expansion is:

$$(1 + 0.017)^{1/2} = (1)^{1/2} + \frac{(1/2)}{1} (1)^{-1/2} (0.017) + \frac{(1/2)(-1/2)}{1*2}(1)^{-3/2}(0.017)^2 +$$

$$\frac{(1/2)(-1/2)(-3/2)}{1*2*3}(1)^{-5/2}(0.017)^3 + \ldots$$

It is easy to see that successive terms are found by a rather simple procedure. The first term is 1. The second term is 0.0085. To obtain the third term, multiply the *second* term by $\frac{(-1/2)}{2} * (0.017)$ or -0.00425. The third term is, therefore 0.0085 * $(-0.00425) = -0.000036125$. The fourth term is found by multiplying the *third* term by $\frac{(-3/2)}{3} * (0.017)$, i.e., by -0.0085. The fourth term is, therefore, $+0.0000003070625$. Here is what we have, so far:

First contribution	1.0000000000000
Second contribution	0.0085000000000
Third contribution	−0.0000361250000
Fourth contribution	+0.0000003070625

It is evident that the successive terms are becoming smaller and are alternating in sign. It can be proved that the difference between the true answer and the answer obtained by taking only the first few contributions is less than the first contribution neglected. This theorem is, in general, true only for an *alternating* series in which successive terms are becoming smaller.

In this example, if we take only the first three terms, we find that $\sqrt{1.017} = 1.008\ 463\ 875$ with an error less than the fourth term (the first term neglected), i.e., with an error less than 0.000 000 307 0625. The original problem required $\sqrt{101.7}$, and we can now say that the answer is 10.084 638 75 with an error of less than 0.000 003 070 625.

It is important to notice the iterative procedure employed to obtain successive terms in this problem. It involves the establishment of a *recursion relationship*, i.e., a formula which tells what a term is when preceding terms are known. This is a very common procedure in writing programs for computers. For this reason, we shall explore just a little bit further.

Let the kth term of the binomial series be called u_k, and let the $(k + 1)^{st}$ term be called u_{k+1}. (The series starts with $k = 0$, for convenience). Then

$$u_k = \binom{n}{k} a^{n-k} b^k$$

$$u_{k+1} = \binom{n}{k+1} a^{n-(k+1)} b^{(k+1)}$$

We would like to express u_{k+1} in terms of u_k:

$$\frac{u_{k+1}}{u_k} = \frac{\binom{n}{k+1} a^{n-(k+1)} b^{(k+1)}}{\binom{n}{k} a^{n-k} b^k}$$

$$\frac{u_{k+1}}{u_k} = \frac{\dfrac{n(n-1)(n-2)\ldots(n-k)}{1*2*3*\ldots*(k+1)} a^{n-k-1} b^{k+1}}{\dfrac{n(n-1)(n-2)\ldots(n-k+1)}{1*2*3*\ldots*k} a^{n-k} b^k}$$

from which it is evident that

$$u_{k+1} = \frac{(n-k)}{(k+1)} * \frac{b}{a} * u_k$$

In the sample problem, using $a = 1$, $b = 0.017$, we might find successive terms by using this *recursion formula,* as shown in the following.

k	$\dfrac{n-k}{k+1}$	u_{k+1}
0	(1/2)	$(1/2)(0.017) = 0.0085$
1	$\dfrac{-1/2}{2}$	$(-1/4)(0.017)(0.0085) = -0.000031625$
2	$\dfrac{-3/2}{3}$	$(-1/2)(0.017)(-0.000031625) = +0.0000003070625$
3	$\dfrac{-5/2}{4}$	$(-5/8)(0.017)(0.0000003070625) + -0.00000000326253906$

and so on.

8.3   ODD-NUMBER METHOD

It is shown * that

$$\sum_{k=1}^{k=n} (2k-1) = n^2$$

In other words, when n successive odd numbers (beginning with *one*) are added,

---

*Dodes, I. A. and Greitzer, S.L., *op. cit.*

the result is n². As an example, $1 + 3 + 5 + 7 + 9 = 25$, i.e., the sum of the first *five* odd numbers is 25. If we wished to find the square root of 25, we might *subtract* odd numbers (beginning with one) and find out how many times it takes to return to zero:

25	subtract	1	result is	24
24	subtract	3	result is	21
21	subtract	5	result is	16
16	subtract	7	result is	9
9	subtract	9	result is	0
0	subtract	11	result is	−11

This is how the computer is usually programmed to find square root (but not other roots). It subtracts odd numbers until the result is negative. Then it counts how many odd numbers were subtracted *before* the result became negative. If the original number was a perfect square, this *count* is the square root. If the original number is not a perfect square, the machine result approximates the square root. To obtain greater precision, *pairs* of zeros are appended to the original number.

Notice, once again, the repetitive procedure used in machine calculations.

8.4   TRIAL-AND-ERROR METHODS

A trial-and-error method is one in which a *guess* is made about the right answer, and then the guess is "refined" by successive approximations. The trial-and-error method is very common in computing because the computer does arithmetic so quickly that millions of trials can be made in just a few minutes. There are many kinds of trial-and-error procedures. We shall illustrate the result of finding $\sqrt{101.7}$ by trial-and-error, using a desk calculator to demonstrate the intermediate results.

Our *program*, or plan of action, is as follows:

1. We shall guess, first, that $\frac{1}{2}$ the original number is the square root.
2. We shall square this guess.
3. We shall form the difference: $(\text{guess})^2$ − original number.
4. If this difference is *positive*, we shall take our second guess as half the previous one.
5. We shall repeat this procedure until we have a *negative* difference.
6. Whenever the difference is *negative*, we shall make a new guess by averaging the present one with the last one that was too large (i.e., had a *positive* difference).
7. We shall *terminate* the trials, when the difference between two successive guesses is less than some predetermined constant, δ (lower case Greek letter, *delta*).

In Table III, we show the results of the first few trials, starting with $\sqrt{101.7} = (\text{guess}) \frac{1}{2} (101.7)$.

This procedure is very tedious by hand, and even by desk calculator, but it is child's-play for an electronic computer. These twenty-one trials would have been completed by the time you walked a few steps from the card reader to the typewriter output mechanism!

Table III. TRIAL-AND-ERROR RESULTS FOR SQUARE ROOT

Trial	Guessed Root	(Guess)^2	(Guess)^2 − 101.7	Result
1	50.85000000	2585.7225000	+2484.02250	+
2	25.42500000	646.4306250	+544.73063	+
3	12.71250000	161.6076563	+59.90765	+
4	6.35625000	40.4019140	−61.29809	−
5	9.53437500	90.9043066	−10.79569	−
6	11.12343750	123.7308618	+22.03086	+
7	10.32890625	106.6863043	+4.98630	+
8	9.93164062	98.6374854	−3.06251	−
9	10.13027343	102.6224398	+0.92244	+
10	10.03095702	100.6200987	−1.07990	−
11	10.08061522	101.6188032	−0.08120	−
12	10.10544432	102.1200049	+0.42000	+
13	10.09302977	101.8692499	+0.16925	+
14	10.08682249	101.7439879	+0.04399	+
15	10.08371885	101.6813858	−0.01861	−
16	10.08527067	101.7126845	+0.01268	+
17	10.08449476	101.6970346	−0.00297	−
18	10.08488271	101.7048593	+0.00486	+
19	10.08468873	101.7009468	+0.00095	+
20	10.08459174	101.6989906	−0.00101	−
21	10.08464023	101.6999686	−0.00003	−

8.5 NEWTON'S METHOD

Newton's Method is a more reasonable trial-and-error method than the previous one. In this method, the basis is the fact that if you had exactly the right answer, $\sqrt{a}$, for the square root of a, then the result of dividing $\sqrt{a}$ into a would be precisely $\sqrt{a}$. In other words, the divisor and the quotient would be precisely the same. However, if the wrong answer, say b, is guessed for $\sqrt{a}$, then the quotient, c, and the divisor, b, will not agree; one will be larger than the other. For example, if we guess $\sqrt{25} = 6$, and if we then divide 25 by 6, the quotient will be 4 and a fraction; but if we guess $\sqrt{25} = 5$, and then divide 25 by 5, the quotient will also be 5.

In Newton's Method, we make a succession of guesses, each successive guess being the *average* of the preceding divisor and quotient.

ILLUSTRATIVE PROBLEM I

Find $\sqrt{751.48}$.

Solution: We shall start with a guess of 20:
Guess 1: 20
Quotient 1: 751.48/20 = 37.574

Sum 1: 20.000 + 37.574 = 57.574
Average 1 = Guess 2 = 28.787
Quotient 2 = 751.48/28.787 = 26.105
Sum 2 = 28.787 + 26.105 = 54.892
Average 2 = Guess 3 = 27.446
Quotient 3 = 751.48/27.446 = 27.380
Sum 3 = 27.446 + 27.380 = 54.826
Average 3 = Guess 4 = 27.413
Quotient 4 = 27.413

Since the fourth divisor (guess 4) and the fourth quotient agree, the answer is correct to the number of places shown. This is much faster than the previous method.*

8.6   RULE OF ACCURACY FOR SQUARE ROOT CALCULATIONS

The ultimate check for a square root calculation is the "reverse" calculation, i.e., multiplying the answer by itself. It should be immediately evident that the Rule of Accuracy for Multiplication applies to roots, as well. As an example, we are entitled to five significant figures in the result of the calculation of $\sqrt{751.48}$, since the radicand has five significant figures.

EXERCISES

Using the methods explained in this section, find the square roots of 64.0185 and 48.998. Check by multiplication.

Section 9.   Iterative Problems

9.1   NATURE OF ITERATIVE PROBLEMS

We have illustrated, in Section 8, the iterative process as applied to square root computation. All iterative problems share a certain *form*, so to speak. The machine is instructed to *begin* at some value, make *systematic changes* of some kind, then *test* the result, then *go back* and do the same thing (or a similar thing) all over again until the problem has been completed. As an example, consider the search for a root of

$$y = ax^2 + bx + c \sin \frac{n\pi}{2} = 0$$

where a, b, and c are given to the machine and we wish to find (for example) non-negative values of x correct to the nearest hundred-thousandth (10^{-5}). The *program*

---

*The reason for the *speed of convergence* is explained in Dodes, I. A. and Greitzer, S. L., *op. cit.* (a discussion of the Error Analysis of Newton's Method).

for this problem might be something like the following:

1. Read the values of a, b, and c into the machine.
2. Let x = 0, 1, 2, . . . and compute y until there is a change of sign, or until it is evident that such a change will not occur.
3. If the change will not occur, stop computing and write, "No solution in the permissible domain."
4. If there is a change in sign in going from x = 7 to x = 8, have the machine return to x = 7, then increment by one-tenth of the previous value. The next trials will, therefore, be 7.0, 7.1, 7.2, . . .
5. If there is a change in sign in going from x = 7.5 to x = 7.6, have the machine return to x = 7.5, then increment by one-tenth of the previous value. The next trials will, therefore, be 7.50, 7.51, 7.52, . . .

This procedure is continued until the increment, or Δx, is satisfactorily small. In this case, it is well to keep trying until $\Delta x = 10^{-6}$ (one millionth), then half-adjust the result. The value, 10^{-6}, is a *criterion*, and the instruction which tells the machine when to stop computing is called a *termination instruction*. The entire sequence of operations is called *terminating on precision*. It plays a very important part in the mathematical work of science.

There are other methods for terminating on precision. Another will be mentioned in Subsection 9.4 and illustrated in Subsections 21.2 and 21.3.

Another *iterative* problem, somewhat simpler, is one in which a table of values is desired for, let us say, the same relationship as the one just discussed. The *program* might be somewhat as follows:

1. Read the values of a, b, and c into the machine.
2. Starting with $x = x_1$, compute and type $y = y_1$.
3. Increase x by Δx to obtain the new value, x_2. Using this value of x, compute $y = y_2$.
4. Continue until $x = x_f$, the final value of x.

These iterative procedures are used for curve-fitting, solution of equations, summation of series, generation of tables of constants (such as the specific values of the *gamma function* for various values of the argument), evaluation of integrals, numerical solution of differential equations, the production of tables, and, in general, in all those problems which are so tedious and error-prone in the hands of a mathematician or scientist.

When iterative procedures are considered in the machine solution of a problem, it is absolutely essential that the method chosen have associated with it an estimate of the *error of truncation*, E_n, which can be calculated. We remark in passing that the solution of iterative problems by methods like *Simpson's Rule*, for example, without the calculation of E_n, leads to incorrect results. (In a program written by a pupil, the calculation of π by Simpson's Rule was correct to *seven* places when 16 intervals were chosen, and correct to *three* places when 1000 intervals were chosen.) We shall illustrate the calculation of E_n in the following sections.

9.2 MACLAURIN SERIES

It is explained in any elementary book on the Calculus that for any infinitely differentiable function, $f(x)$, the following series can be written:

$$f(x) = f(0) + \frac{f'(0)}{1!} x + \frac{f''(0)}{2!} x^2 + \ldots + R_n$$

where R_n is the *remainder after n terms*. If $\lim R_n = 0$ as $n \to \infty$, the power series is said to be *convergent*, and the power series (in the interval of convergence) represents the same function as $f(x)$.

If the series is *alternating* as well as convergent, then the *error of truncation*, E_n, after n terms, is less than the absolute value of the first term neglected. The use of an alternating, convergent Maclaurin Series is shown in Illustrative Problem I.

ILLUSTRATIVE PROBLEM I

Find sin 22°13′ to the nearest millionth.

Solution: The Maclaurin Series for sin x, with x in radians, is:

$$\sin x = x - \frac{x^3}{3!} + \frac{x^5}{5!} - \frac{x^7}{7!} + \ldots + R_n$$

The steps in the solution of the problem on a desk calculator are shown in the following, as an illustration of the computer procedure:

1. Convert 22°13′ to radians. By calculator, $13′ = 13/60° = 0.21666666666666666666$ ... degrees, so that x (in degrees) $= 21.6666667°$. Using $\pi = 3.14159\,26536$, we have x = 22.216666667 * 3.1415926536/180 = 0.3877540 radians.
2. As a first approximation, we obtain

$$\sin x = x = 0.3877540$$

The error of truncation, E_1, is less (in absolute value) than $\frac{x^3}{3!}$ which equals 0.00971667.

3. As a second approximation, we obtain

$$\sin x = x - \frac{x^3}{3!} = 0.38780373$$

$$E_2 \leqslant \left| \frac{x^5}{5!} \right| = 0.000,073,049,69$$

so that the error of truncation after two terms is of the order of seven hundred-thousandths. We should remark, at this time, that successive terms in a series are found by a *recursion formula* (as explained in Subsection 8.2) so that the time-and-space requirements on the computer are rather small, in general.

4. As a third approximation, we obtain

$$\sin x = x - \frac{x^3}{3!} + \frac{x^5}{5!} = 0.3781103$$

$$E_3 \leqslant \left| \frac{x^7}{7!} \right| = 0.000,000,261,495,32$$

so that the value of sin 22°13′, as found, is certainly in error by much less than one millionth, as required. This completes the problem.

If the Maclaurin Series is convergent but does not alternate, more heroic measures are needed to find the error of truncation. To assist us, we use the *Lagrange Remainder Theorem*, which assures us that

$$R_n = \frac{f^{(n)}(\theta)}{n!} x^n$$

where θ is a number between 0 and x. The error of truncation, E_n, is found as follows. We choose a value of x, x_1, such that $f^{(n)}(x_1)$ is the *largest* value in the interval [0,x]. Then, certainly, $f^{(n)}(\theta)$ is less than or equal to $f^{(n)}(x_1)$. Therefore,

$$0 \leqslant E_n \leqslant \left| \frac{f^{(n)}(x_1)}{n!} x^n \right|$$

For example, in Illustrative Problem I, if we had to use the Lagrange Error Estimate, we would have had to consider the interval [0°, 22°13′]. In this case, the derivative, $f^{(n)}$, is either a sine or a cosine, and the maximum value of a sine or cosine is *one*. Therefore,

$$0 \leqslant E_n \leqslant \left| \frac{1}{n!} x^n \right|$$

which happens to be the same result we obtained previously.

Let us consider a problem which is not quite so obvious.

ILLUSTRATIVE PROBLEM II

Find e to the nearest millionth, given that it is a number somewhere between 2 and 3.

Solution: The Maclaurin Series for e^x is:

$$e^x = 1 + x + \frac{x^2}{2!} + \frac{x^3}{3!} + \ldots + R_n$$

and we wish to evaluate this for x = 1. Consider the error of truncation, E_n. We know that all the derivatives of e^x are the same, namely, e^x. Therefore, $f^{(n)}(x_1) = e^{x1}$. What is the "worst" situation for $f^{(n)}$? Well, we know (from the given information in the problem) that e < 3. Therefore, $f^{(n)} < 3^1$. Therefore,

$$\theta \leqslant E_n \leqslant \frac{3}{n!}$$

Substituting n = 1, 2, 3, ..., we find that the first *nine* terms are more than enough to guarantee the precision required. In programming this problem for a computer, we would have the machine calculate $\frac{3}{n!}$ after each partial sum, and *iterate* until this quantity was less than the desired criterion.

ILLUSTRATIVE PROBLEM III

We wish to find $e^{1.3}$ correct to the nearest 10^{-4}.

Solution: The procedure is similar to that of Illustrative Problem II. However, in estimating E_n, we must consider $f^{(n)}$ in the region from 0 to 1.3. Let us suppose that we do not know much about the behavior of this function, e^x, except that it always increases as x increases. Clearly, the maximum value for $f^{(n)}$ occurs when it equals $f^{(n)}$ (1.3) $= e^{1.3}$. Isn't this somewhat circular? Yes, it is, and so we will not be able to proceed exactly this way. However, things are not so bad. All we need is a criterion, not an exact value. Remembering that $e < 3$, and $1.3 < 2$, we certainly know that $e^{1.3} < 3^2 = 9$. The Lagrange Error Estimate is therefore

$$0 \leqslant E_n < \left| \frac{f^{(n)}(x_1)}{n!} x^n \right| < \frac{9(1.3)^n}{n!}$$

After each calculation of a partial sum, the machine tests this quantity. When the absolute value of E_n becomes less than 10^{-4}, the program is complete.

9.3   TAYLOR SERIES

The Maclaurin Series is said to be an *expansion about zero* because it starts with $f(0)$ and corrects this first estimate by a subsequent series of terms. The Taylor Series starts with $f(a)$ and is therefore an *expansion about a*:

$$f(x) = f(a) + \frac{f'(a)}{1!} (x - a) + \frac{f''(a)}{2!} (x - a)^2 + \ldots + R_n$$

The Lagrange Error Estimate is given by

$$R_n = \frac{f^{(n)}(\theta)}{n!} (x - a)^n$$

where θ is in the interval $[a,x]$. The *error*, E_n, is therefore

$$0 \leqslant |E_n| \leqslant \left| \frac{f^{(n)}(x_1)}{n!} (x - a)^n \right|$$

where x_1 is chosen in such a way that $|f^{(n)}|$ is maximized in the interval under consideration, $[a,x]$.

ILLUSTRATIVE PROBLEM I

Find $e^{1.3}$ to the nearest millionth.

Solution: The series for e^x *about a* is

$$e^x = e^a + \frac{e^a}{1!} (x - a) + \frac{e^a}{2!} (x - a)^2 + \ldots + R_n$$

and

$$0 \leqslant |E_n| \leqslant \frac{e^{x_1}}{n!} \left| (x - a)^n \right|$$

Since we have already calculated e^1, we may choose $a = 1$. In each case, therefore, $(x - a) = 0.3$. It is found that only *five* terms are needed, and the value of $E_5 \leqslant 0.00000075$.

9.4 USING TAYLOR SERIES FOR SOLVING AN EQUATION

In Subsection 9.1 we mentioned a simple criterion for terminating the search for a root of an equation. Sometimes, Taylor Series calculations (or else the *Mean Value Theorem*) can be invoked to discover the precision of x.

We know that

$$f(x) = f(r) + R_1$$

where r is the root of the equation. Therefore,

$$f(x) - f(r) = f'(\theta) \cdot (x - r)$$
$$\frac{f(x) - f(r)}{(x - r)} = f'(\theta)$$

In this problem, $f(x)$ is the computed value and equals y; $f(r)$ is zero, by definition of a root. The quantity $| x - r |$ is the error, E. Substituting and solving, we find that

$$E = \left| \frac{y}{f'(\theta)} \right|$$

Let us find the value of x_1 in $[r,x]$ which makes the denominator as *small* as possible in absolute value. Then, obviously,

$$0 \leqslant E \leqslant \left| \frac{y}{f'(x_1)} \right|$$

This can be used to control the precision of x, provided that $| f'(x_1) |$ is not too close to zero. If it is, another method must be used.

ILLUSTRATIVE PROBLEM I

Find an expression to be employed in solving

$$x \ln x - k = 0$$

given that there is a root in $[2,3]$. (The derivative of $\ln x$ with respect to x is $\frac{1}{x}$.)

Solution:

$$f(x) = x \ln x - k$$
$$f'(x) = x \left(\frac{1}{x} \right) + \ln x = 1 + \ln x$$

In the interval $[2,3]$, $| f'(x) |$ is obviously a minimum at $x = 2$, where (from a handbook) $\ln 2 = 0.69315$. Therefore,

$$0 \leqslant E \leqslant \left| \frac{y}{1.69315} \right|$$

ILLUSTRATIVE PROBLEM II

Find an expression for the error in x in the solution of

$$x^2 + 4 \sin x = 0$$

given that there is a root in $[-2, -1]$.

Attempted Solution:

$$f(x) = x^2 + 4 \sin x$$
$$f'(x) = 2x + 4 \cos x$$

In the interval $[-2, -1]$, $f'(x)$ goes from approximately -5.66 to approximately $+0.16$. Therefore, the minimum value of $|f'(x_1)|$ is zero. This method cannot be used. Some comments about an alternative method are made in Subsection 24.1 where this equation is discussed.

In some cases, one more term of the Taylor Series can be employed:

$$f(x) = f(r) + \frac{f'(r)}{1!} (x - r) + \frac{f''(\theta)}{2!} (x - r)^2$$

Substituting $f(x) = y$, $f(r) = 0$, $(x - r) = E$, we obtain

$$[f''(\theta)] \ E^2 + [2 \ f'(r)] \ E - y = 0$$

Using the quadratic formula,

$$E = \left| \frac{-f'(r) \pm \sqrt{[f'(r)]^2 + y \ f''(\theta)}}{f''(\theta)} \right|$$

so that

$$0 \leqslant |E| \leqslant \left| \frac{-f'(x_1) \pm \sqrt{[f'(x_1)]^2 + y \ f''(x_1)}}{f''(x_1)} \right|$$

where x_1 is chosen in such a way as to maximize the right member in absolute value. However, this is such a difficult method that it should not be used except in emergency!

9.5   OTHER ITERATIVE PROBLEMS

We have merely touched upon some of the more common problems which can be attacked by iterative techniques. Iterative techniques for solving systems of equations are quite important. They may be solved by methods discussed in advanced books on numerical analysis, such as those mentioned in the preface. There, too, can be found methods for solving *differential* and *integral* equations. The great speed of the computer makes iterative techniques particularly applicable for these problems, and, in many cases, a perfectly random approach (the *Monte Carlo* method, for example) leads to quick, accurate, and perfectly satisfactory solutions.

EXERCISES

1 Find sin 4°27′ using a Maclaurin Series (nearest 10^{-6}).

2 Find cos 7°45′ using a Maclaurin Series (nearest 10^{-6}).

3 Find $e^{-0.5778}$ to the nearest 10^{-4}.

4 Find $e^{-1.7889}$ to the nearest 10^{-4}.

5 Find sin 31° to the nearest 10^{-6}, using a Taylor Series.

6 Find $e^{1.1156}$ to the nearest 10^{-6}, using a Taylor Series.

PART TWO

Machine Language Programming

Basic Computing Center

If someone asks you to add 57 and 45, you must accept the information in your memory via your eyes or ears (this is the *Input Phase*). You must *transmit* the information to that part of your brain which does arithmetic. Next, you must use *Arithmetic* and *Logic* to develop an answer. Finally, you tell the answer (this is the *Output Phase*). Computers are designed to go through the same steps.

The most interesting facets of computer programming are those dealing with arithmetic and logic. Unfortunately, the knowledge of arithmetic and logic are useless unless the programmer knows how to put the information into the machine, move it around, and get it out again. For this reason, Sections 10, 11, and 12 deal with the part of programming which experts call *housekeeping*, i.e., input, data transmission, and output.

Before launching into this explanation, we shall describe the components of a *basic computing center*. A basic computing center has a minimum of seven functions, some of which are in a single machine:

1. A device to prepare input material, e.g., keypunch, typewriter, tape punch.
2. A reading device to accept the input, e.g., card reader, tape reader.
3. A memory or storage to "store" the input, e.g., drum storage, magnetic cores, magnetic tape, disk storage.
4. An arithmetic unit.
5. A logic unit, e.g., switching circuits designed in accordance with Boolean algebra.
6. A device to prepare output material, e.g., card punch, typewriter, tape punch, printer.
7. A device to list output material, e.g., typewriter, "accounting machine."

We shall assume that the reader has access to the following four machines or their equivalents:

1. *IBM 026 Printing Card Punch (Fig. 1).* This machine prepares the IBM cards for the computer.

Fig. 1.   The IBM 026 printing card punch.

2.   *IBM 1620 Computer (Fig. 2).* We shall assume, for our purposes, that the *basic* machine (20,000 positions of storage) with *automatic division* but no other special features (such as indirect addressing, or automatic floating point) is available. The basic machine is adequate for most programs in mathematical and scientific work. Of course, it is easier to program a machine with greater storage and with other special features. The principles are precisely the same, however, and we shall content ourselves with the more limited machine and capacity.

The IBM 1620 has, as a part of its console, a typewriter which can be used for input-output (I-O) operations. The remainder of the machine is the memory and the arithmetic and logic unit.

3.   *IBM 1622 Read-Punch Unit (Fig. 3).* There are two *hoppers*, one at the right, and one at the left of the machine, not shown in the figure. The right hopper is used to hold IBM punched cards which are to be *read into* the computer. If read properly, they emerge into the rightmost of the five front hoppers, as shown in the figure. If a card is read incorrectly for one reason or another, it emerges into the front hopper second from the right. The hopper at the left side is filled with blank cards for punched-card output. If the card is punched correctly, it emerges into the leftmost front hopper; if punched incorrectly, it emerges into the front hopper second from the left. The middle front hopper is usually inoperative.

4.   *IBM 407 Accounting Machine (Fig. 4).* This machine is used to list program and data cards. Since the accounting machine is, in effect, a small electronic computer equipped to do business problems, it contains a great many components which we

Fig. 2. The IBM 1620 console.

Fig. 3. The IBM 1622 read-punch unit.

Fig. 4.   The IBM 407 accounting machine.

shall not need. However, it is possible to obtain a "stripped-down" version of the IBM 407 which does not duplicate the arithmetic and logic functions of the IBM 1620 to any great extent.

In addition to these four machines, which fulfill all the basic needs of a minimum computing center, there are three *peripheral machines* which, although not essential, make life much easier for the programmer:

1. *IBM 519 Document-Originating Machine (Fig. 5).* This machine duplicates a deck of cards. There is a left hopper (for the cards to be duplicated) and a center hopper (for blank cards). It is most useful for making copies of *work-horse programs,* i.e., tested programs which are to be used over and over again. It can also be used to compare two decks of punched cards, one deck in each read hopper.

Fig. 5.   The IBM 519 document-originating machine.

2. *IBM Interpreter (Fig. 6).* When a deck of punched cards is placed in the read hopper, this machine (one of several models) will read the holes in the card and print the equivalent letters and numbers at the top of the card. If all eighty columns are to be interpreted, two passes are needed.

3. *IBM Sorter (Fig. 7).* In this machine, most of the cards used in mathematical and scientific programming are keypunched with consecutive numbers in card columns 76 through 80. From time to time, the cards become disarranged and the sorter can be used to re-order them. It is such an inexpensive machine that it is worth the cost in money and space even if it is used much less often than the other machines in a computing center. Another use for the sorter is the separation of two kinds of cards in decks compiled by the SPS program (discussed in Part Three). A third use

Fig. 6.   The IBM interpreter.

Fig. 7.   The IBM sorter.

for the sorter involves the use of the counter on some models; the number of cards in a deck can be found in seconds by the use of this device.

Except for the computer, this book does not include an explanation of the operation of the machines or their wiring. (There is, however, a small description of the keypunch drum card.) In most cases, the programmer has the machines set up for permanent operation and he is not concerned with anything but the programming and operation of the computer itself. Pardonable curiosity can be satisfied by examining the IBM reference manuals supplied with each machine.

Section 10. Input-Output (I-O)

10.1 METHODS OF I-O FOR IBM 1620

There are various ways to get information in and out of the memory of the IBM 1620. In this book, we are assuming that the programs are of a mathematical or scientific nature. For this kind of program, the following input-output procedure is most convenient:

1. In general, information will be read into the memory via punched cards.
2. The typewriter may be used for input involving small amounts of data (like the single number, "578") or for short corrections in the program.
3. In general, the output will be in the form of punched cards.
4. Short output (a small table) may be typed on the console typewriter.

10.2 IBM CARD

A typical General Purpose IBM card is shown in Fig. 8. The card in the figure has an upper right corner cut. However, it may have a cut in some other corner, or no cut at all. The purpose of having a corner cut is to make sure that all the cards in a deck are facing the same way.

The IBM card has eighty card columns, numbered from 1 through 80 at the bottom. It has thirteen rows, identified from top to bottom as follows:

1. The top row is the space in which the keypunch types the equivalent of the holes (as shown in the figure).
2. The next three rows are called the *zone punching area*. Notice that they are, in order, the "12 punch," "11 or X punch," and "zero punch."
3. Rows 0 through 9 constitute the *digit punching area*. Notice that 0 is both a zone punch and a digit punch.
4. The digits 0 through 9 are represented by single punches in the card. These are called *numeric* characters.
5. The alphabet (A through Z) is represented by a double punch in the same column, one punch being a *zone punch* (12, 11, or 0), and the other being a *digit punch* (1 through 9, but not zero).

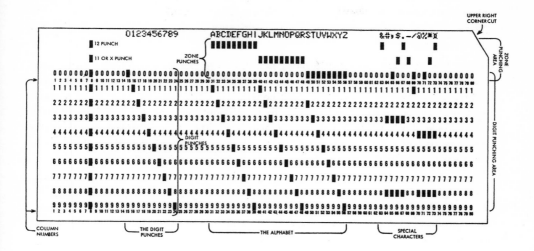

Fig. 8. A general-purpose IBM card.

6. The special characters, as shown in the figure, are represented by one, two, or three punches in a single column. There are different type-bars for different keypunches, and the special characters are not the same in print. The following equivalence should be noted:

Business Type	Scientific Type
& (ampersand)	+ (plus)
# (number sign)	= (equals)
@ ("at" sign)	− (hyphen)
% (percent)	((left parenthesis)
⊐ (box)	) (right parenthesis)

The computer reads only the holes (not the typing), so it doesn't matter how the typing appears on the keypunch. However, for mathematical and scientific work, the scientific type-bars make it easier to check the cards.

The alphabetic and special characters, together, are often called *alphameric* characters. However, under certain conditions to be explained soon, numeric characters become alphameric inside the machine.

7. The top of the card is called the *twelve-edge,* and the bottom of the card is called the *nine-edge.*

8. There is one other special character, not shown in the figure, which will be used throughout this book. This is the *record mark,* for which we shall use the conventional symbol, $\ddagger$. A record mark consists of a triple-punch $\{0,8,2\}$ in a single column. To make this triple punch in a card column, the MULTIPLE PUNCH key is held down while the three numeric keys $\{0,8,2\}$ are pressed in succession (in any order). The printing at the top looks like a smudge when this special character is made.

9. We shall have need for *flagged* numbers, which we shall represent, conventionally, as a digit with a minus sign above it, e.g., $\bar{0}, \bar{1}, \bar{2}, \ldots \bar{9}$. A flag one is made, for example, by holding down MULTIPLE PUNCH while the 1 and the *skip-minus* key are depressed (in either order). The printing at the top looks like a one with a minus sign right through the middle: $\pm$.

When the IBM cards are placed in the read hopper of the basic IBM 1622, they are read in, eighty columns at a time (simultaneously), at the rate of approximately 250 cards per minute. In other words, approximately 20,000 digits of information can be read into the machine each minute.

EXERCISES

Punch each digit, flagged digit, alphabetic character, and special character (including the record mark) on an IBM card.

10.3   MACHINE LANGUAGE PROGRAM CARD FORMAT

In order to introduce input procedure, we shall have to anticipate later explanations by stating that *every* input procedure involves three parts:

1. A *load program* which instructs the machine how to place your instructions in its memory, and which contains arithmetic tables.

2. A set of *program cards* which instruct the machine how to solve the problem.

3. A set of *data cards* which contain the information for the numerical part of the problem.

The load program is the same for all machine language programs in a computing center. We shall explain this phase of the operation in greater detail later; for the present, we merely remark that the load program cards used in the Computing Center of the Bronx High School of Science are listed in Appendix I. Each student is supplied with this deck.

Program cards are made for each problem. The form of a machine language program card depends upon the load program. Assuming that the load program from Appendix I is used, the actual instruction consists of 12 digits in card columns (cc) 1 through 12, an optional explanatory comment in the card columns beginning with cc 30, and the number of the card in cc 78-80.

Data cards are explained in Subsection 10.4.

For keypunching machine language program cards, you will find it convenient to make a keypunch *drum card* as follows:

cc 1	leave blank
cc 2-12	+ (plus or ampersand)
cc 13	— (skip-minus)
cc 14-29	+ (plus or ampersand)
cc 30	1 (one)
cc 31-77	A
cc 78	leave blank
cc 79, 80	+ (plus or ampersand)

When this card is placed on the drum of the keypunch with the program switch ON, print ON, and skip switch ON, each card typed will be numeric in the first twelve spaces (as if the numeric shift key were held down). The card will then automatically shift to cc 30 and the spaces from 30 to 77 will be alphameric (as if the alphabetic shift key were held down). If there is no comment on the card, or if the comment is finished, a tap on the SKIP key will make the card shift to cc 78. Card columns 78, 79, and 80 will be numeric. If only a single number is desired (in cc 80), the card may, of course, be spaced by use of the space bar, as on any typewriter. If it is desired to type a numeric character in a field which has been defined as alphameric, or an alphameric character in a field which has been defined as numeric, the drum instruction can be overridden by holding down the appropriate shift key.

EXERCISES

Using the drum card demonstrated above, prepare the following program cards. (They will be used in a later exercise.)

In cc 1-12	In cc 30, etc.	In cc 80
360600100500	READ A CARD	1
210600506010	ADD B TO A	2
220600506014	SUBTRACT C FROM (A + B)	3
15060060000≠	SET A RECORD MARK	4
340000000102	RETURN CARRIAGE	5
380600100100	TYPE THE ANSWER	6
490100000000	GO BACK	7

In order to distinguish between the *letter*, O, and the *numeral*, 0, we shall (wherever necessary) write the letter as follows: Ø. This is done on the program instruction sheet, but not on the cards or typewriter. On the input devices, there is no confusion, since the numeral is represented by a zero-punch, and the letter is represented by double-punched {11,6}, on a card, and by the even-odd pair (5,6) in the memory.

10.4   MACHINE LANGUAGE DATA CARD FORMAT

There is no special format for a data card. Ordinarily, it consists of digits (including flagged digits) somewhere in cc 1-77, with a number in cc 78, 79, and 80. The data may be in adjacent columns, or there may be spaces. The keypunch drum card should be adjusted to make it convenient to type the data cards without holding down the numeric shift key. In some cases, it will be convenient to include automatic skips in the drum card. If there are only a few data cards, it may not be worth the trouble to make a drum card and the result may be attained by switching the drum program OFF and using the numeric shift and space bar, as needed. Unless there are special requirements, the following drum card will at least hold down the numeric shift key, and will skip to cc 78 when the data have been typed:

cc 1	leave blank
cc 2-77	+ (plus or ampersand)
cc 78	leave blank
cc 79, 80	+ (plus or ampersand)

With this drum card on, the data may be typed without holding down the numeric shift key. When the end of the data is reached, a touch on the SKIP key will send the card to cc 78. The number of the data card should be placed at the end of the card.

To distinguish between program cards and data cards, if this is necessary, cards with different corner cuts, or of different colors, may be used. The computer does not, of course, pay attention to anything but the actual holes punched in the card.

EXERCISES

Type the following three data cards. (They will be used in a later exercise.)

In cc 1-14	*In cc 80*
$\overline{2}$1746358002$\overline{2}$173	1
$\overline{5}$922341$\overline{7}$7763$\overline{8}$14	2
$\overline{6}$1114$\overline{2}$23097$\overline{1}$114	3

10.5   MACHINE LANGUAGE PROGRAM PROCEDURE

We shall suppose that you have prepared the program cards and the data cards in the exercises of the previous two sections, and that you have a load program equivalent to the one in Appendix I. These cards will be used in the procedure listed below.

NOTE: The phrase "Check Switches" refers to three switches at the left side of the console and marked *PARITY, I-O* (input-output), and *O'FLOW* (overflow). These have two positions: "Program" (off) and "Stop" (on). The phrase "Program Switches" refers to four switches, numbered "1" and "2" in the upper row, and "3" and "4" in the lower row. Each switch has an "on" position and an "off" position. Check Switches will be discussed in Subsection 16.2, and Program Switches will be discussed in Part Three.

1. Clear Computer. Clearing the computer involves seven steps. (*i*) set Check Switches to "Program," (*ii*) press RESET, (*iii*) press INSERT, (*iv*) type 260000200003, (*v*) press R-S (Release and Start) key on the typewriter, (*vi*) press INSTANT STOP on the console, and (*vii*) press RESET. Step (*i*) allows the computer to accept the instruction in step (*iv*). In some cases, if a previous program has caused incorrect information to remain in the memory, and if the Check Switches are on STOP, the machine will not accept the instruction. Step (*ii*) turns off ("resets") all the logical switches in the machine. Step (*iii*) prepares the typewriter to receive an instruction. Step (*iv*) is an instruction, to be explained later, which commands the computer to place a zero in every memory "cell." Step (*v*) is a signal to the computer that you have finished your instruction (therefore: release) and that the computer should begin executing the command (therefore: start). It takes the computer approximately 4/5 of a second to execute this command for each 20,000 positions of storage in the computer. The basic IBM 1620 has 20,000 positions, but two additional modules are available, each with 20,000 more positions. In the basic machine, the execution is so rapid that you may do step (*vi*) almost immediately after step (*v*). Step (*vi*) stops the machine. Step (*vii*) sets the switches internally so that the computer can read cards.

2. Set Switches. The Check Switches should be set to STOP. This means that the machine will stop if there is an error. If the load program in Appendix I is to be used, then turning Program Switch 1 to its "on" position will cause the instructions to be listed on the typewriter. This is satisfactory for a very short program. If the program is long, however, it is better to list the program cards on the IBM 407 before the cards are placed in the machine, and to turn Program Switch 1 "off." The use of the typewriter always slows up the procedure because the typewriter prints only about 600 characters per minute, whereas the card reader is ready to read about 20,000 characters per minute.

3. Clear Read-Punch Unit. On each side of the IBM 1622, lift out the cards (if any) and depress the NON-PROCESS RUN-OUT key. Any blank cards which "run out" should be discarded. This operation resets the logic switches for the IBM 1622.

4. Load Program. Place the load program in the read hopper, face down, nine-edge forward. Place the program cards on top of these, face down, nine-edge forward; be sure that the edges are straight and that none of the cards are bent. Press the LOAD button on the IBM 1622; all the cards should now feed in except the very last one, and the READER NO FEED light on the console will now go on.

Press READER START on the IBM 1622; the last card will now read in and the typewriter will type PROGRAM LOADED. Take the program cards and the load program out of the hopper.

5. *Press CONSOLE START*. The computer now begins to execute your instructions. Usually, your instructions will include one or more commands to read a data card. If so, the READER NO FEED light will go on. If this is the case, place your data cards in the read hopper, face down, nine-edge forward, and press READER START. All the data cards will read in except the last one. For the last one, press READER START again.

6. *Preparation for Punched Cards*. If your program involves the production of punched-card output, the PUNCH NO FEED light will go on. (Be sure there are blank cards in the punch hopper.) Press PUNCH START. All the cards will punch, and all but the very last one will emerge in the leftmost front hopper. In order to obtain the last punched card, lift the cards in the punch hopper, and press NON-PROCESS RUN-OUT. The last punched card and two blank cards will run out in the leftmost front hopper. Discard the two blank cards.

These steps become quite automatic on the part of the machine operator. It is impossible to explain all of them at this point in the book, beyond the few comments which are made above. They will become very clear in a little while.

EXERCISES

Using the program cards and data cards prepared previously, go through the above six steps until they become somewhat familiar. If you do them correctly, the typewriter will type three numbers on three separate lines. If this does not happen, check your cards carefully. The machine does not make mistakes.

10.6 MEMORY, OR STORAGE UNIT

A programmer need not know the precise structure of the internal "hardware" of a computing machine. However, a short explanation of the structure of the *memory* or *storage* unit of the IBM 1620 will be helpful in explaining why instructions are written in a certain way, and how certain types of errors occur.

First, we shall discuss *numeric* information, such as the digits (0 through 9), the record mark (multiple-punched 0,2,8) and the numeric blank (multiple-punched 8,4). Every number from 0 through 9 can be represented by using combinations of only *four* digits, e.g., 8,4,2,1. If you will imagine four electric light bulbs with "8," "4," "2," and "1" painted on them, you can see that a "7" can be represented by a "4," "2," and "1" bulb on ("set") but the "8" bulb off ("reset"). If all the bulbs are reset, the number represented will be a "0." If all the bulbs are set, the number represented will be a "15."

In the machine, the same effect is produced by magnetic cores (see Fig. 9). When the current flows in one direction, a magnetic field is produced upwards; when it flows in the other direction, the magnetic field is produced downwards. (This is an applica-

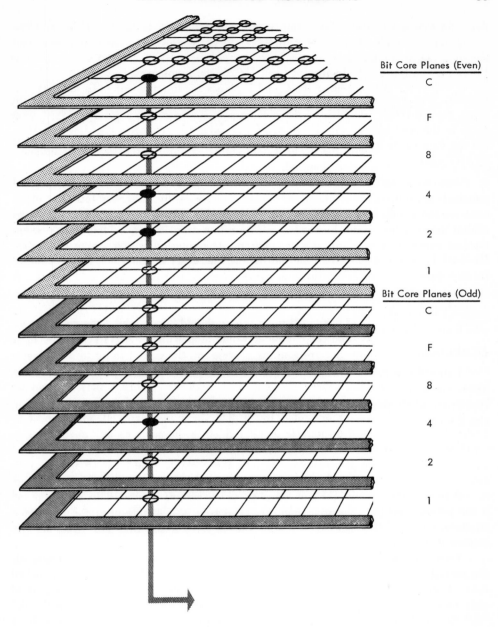

Fig. 9. Sets of six "Bit Core Planes".

tion of the "Right-hand Rule" familiar in elementary physics.) **One direction is identified as** *set* **and the other as** *reset.* In Fig. 9, two sets of magnets are shown. The set position is the one in which the cores have been drawn as filled-in ellipses, while the reset cores are not filled in. **Two memory cells, each with six magnets, are** shown in the figure. Since the memory cells are numbered from 00000 up to 19999 in the basic machine (up to 39999 or 59999 in the augmented machines), these two sets of bit cores could, for example, have the *addresses* 15026 for the upper set, and 15027 for the lower set. In memory cell 15026, the number represented is evidently $4 + 2 = 6$. (We are neglecting the C and F planes for the moment.) In memory cell 15027, the number represented is simply 4. You can see how every digit from 0 through 9 can be represented by these magnetic cores. (The word, *bit*, is a contraction of *bi*nary dig*it*, and refers to the fact that a magnet may be either set or reset.)

We shall now explain the C and F bits before explaining the way other numeric and alphameric information is stored.

Once in a while, for one reason or another, a card is read correctly but the information is transmitted incorrectly because one of the magnets fails to set or reset correctly. We say a bit has been "dropped." Thus, a "six," which contains a 4-bit and a 2-bit, would be read as a "four." A way had to be found to prevent such an error from entering any calculation. The solution was a stroke of genius. The machine was informed, via internal wiring, that every memory cell had to contain an *odd* number of bits. We say that every memory cell must have *odd parity*. A nonnumeric plane, called the C-plane (C for *check*), was added to each set of planes. A number like "6" is actually represented internally by ⁻{C,4,2}⁻. The C-bit has no "value" but maintains *odd* parity. If the machine should "drop a bit," the memory cell would have *even* parity, and the computer would stop with a PARITY CHECK light on. If this happens while you are running a program, the easiest thing to do is begin again. If there are continued parity checks (and if your program is correct), it is likely that you need the services of a customer engineer. A brush may be bent or broken in the reader, for example.

The *record mark* is represented by ⁻{C,8,2}⁻ in a memory cell, although it is ⁻{0,8,2}⁻ on the card; and a *numeric blank* (which is the same as an "at-sign" on a card) becomes a ⁻{C,8,4}⁻ internally.

There is one more plane containing bits, the F-plane. The F-bit (F for *flag*) is used for two purposes in programming (one of which we shall mention now and the other in Section 11). The one purpose which we are interested in at this point is the designation of a negative number. The rule is a simple one: the *low-order* (rightmost) digit of a negative number should have a flag-bit. For example, the number "−235" is typed on a card as 23$\bar{5}$. Suppose it enters the machine in memory cells 12345, 12346, and 12347. The memory cells would then contain the following configuration:

Cell	Configuration
12345	⁻{2}⁻
12346	⁻{C,2,1}⁻
12347	⁻{F,4,1}⁻

Notice that odd parity is maintained in memory cell 12347 by using the F-bit instead of a C-bit. If the input number had been +235, memory cell 12347 would have contained ⁻{C,4,1}⁻.

We shall now turn to alphameric information. You already know that an "A" is represented by a double-punched "12" and "1" in an IBM card (see Fig. 8). *All alphameric information must enter the machine with each character occupying an even-odd pair of memory cells in that order.* In other words, "A" may be read into memory cells 17436-17437, but not into 17437-17438. When the computer is informed that the information to be read is alphameric, it transforms the "12-punch" into a "4" in the even position, the "11-punch" into a "5" in the even position, and the "0-punch" into a "6" in the even position. Thus, an "M" becomes a (5, 4) in the machine, with configuration ⊰C,4,1⊱ in the *even* memory cell, and the configuration ⊰4⊱ in the *odd* memory cell. Figure 10 shows how various characters are translated internally. You may note, at the end of this table, that numbers sometimes occupy an even-odd pair of cells. We shall go into the reason for this later on. For the present, notice that when positive numbers are entered alphamerically, the actual values of the digits are shown in the *odd* memory cells, and that all the *even* memory cells contain sevens. However, a negative seven, which is (11,7) on a card, enters the machine as (5,7), i.e., the same as a "P."

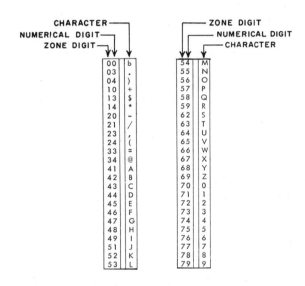

Fig. 10. Alphameric translations.

EXERCISES

Represent the following in terms of their bits, assuming that each begins in memory cell 15000. Give the memory address of each set of bits.

1 23

2 45

3 −57

4 −678

5 (ABLE)

6 X = B

7 $23.57 (where each character is alphameric)

8 5 + 7 = 12 (where each character is alphameric)

9 What alphameric character would the configuration of bits in the two memory cells of Fig. 9 represent?

10.7   INSTRUCTION FORMAT

A machine language instruction consists of twelve (numeric) digits located in twelve memory cells, of which the first one must be even-numbered. The load program in Appendix I automatically places the first digit of your first instruction in memory cell 01000, which means that the entire instruction will be in memory cells 01000 through 01011. The second instruction in your program will start at 01012 and occupy cells 01012 through 01023. (There was no special reason for selecting 01000 as the starting point. Instructions are given in Appendix I for shifting the starting point to some other even position.)

Each instruction has three parts, as follows:

1. The first two digits of the instruction tell the machine what operation to perform. This is called the *opcode*. An example is "36" which means "Read Numerically." The position of the first two digits is referred to by the symbols O_0O_1, where the O means "opcode" and the subscripts, 0 and 1, tell the placement within the instruction. For the example given, 36, the "3" corresponds to O_0 and the "6" corresponds to O_1.

2. The second set of digits contains *five* digits. They are almost always the address of a memory cell. We shall call these five digits the *P-field*. The positions are $P_2P_3P_4P_5P_6$. The "P" identifies the field and the subscript tells the position of the digit within the instruction. If the instruction is 360600100500, then

$$P_2 = 0, \ P_3 = 6, \text{ and } P_6 = 1.$$

3. The third set of digits also contains *five* digits. They are usually the address of a memory cell, a machine switch or a machine component. These five digits are called the *Q-field*. The five digits are designated as $Q_7Q_8Q_9Q_{10}Q_{11}$. Note that the placement of the individual digits is given by numbers from *zero* through *eleven*. In the instruction 360600100500, the "5" is Q_9.

10.8   DN 35: DUMP NUMERICALLY

The first instruction we shall explain is the *dump* instruction. This is used in actual programming for the purpose of *debugging* (removing errors from) a program. We shall use this instruction in the exercises in order to show exactly what is happening within the machine's memory cells.

The command DN350507600100, when separated into its three parts, means the following:

35	Dump Numerically
05076	from memory (starting at memory cell 05076)
00100	via the typewriter.

If we wish to know what is in the memory in a certain region, we press RESET, then INSERT, then we type 35xxxxx00100 (where xxxxx is the address of the *leftmost* memory cell of the region in which we are interested), then press the R-S button. (R-S stands for "Release the typewriter, and start executing the instruction.") When you type the instruction, it is automatically entered into memory cells 00000 through 00011. When you press R-S, the machine "looks" into 00000-00011, and executes that command. This means that the typewriter will immediately begin to type everything in the memory, starting at the memory cell addressed in the P-field, and going "to the right" in the memory. It will type numbers, flags, record marks, and so on, *numerically*. It is important to understand that a *numeric* command means that *each memory cell is interpreted individually*. Therefore, you cannot possibly obtain *letters*, e.g., A, B, C, in a numeric command. Remember that alphameric information requires *pairs* of cells.

The "dump" of the memory continues until the end of the memory is reached (19999 in the basic machine), or until INSTANT STOP is pressed.

Throughout this book we shall, for convenience, write commands in separated form, and with a mnemonic prefix, e.g.,

DN   35   05076   00100

where the DN (Dump Numerically) is intended to help you remember the meaning of the opcode. However, in typing the command on the typewriter or cards, this would be written without the mnemonic and without spaces, e.g., 3505076000100.

Occasionally, the programmer wishes to save time by dumping the memory onto IBM cards which may then be listed on the IBM 407 or a similar machine. This may be done with the command

35	Dump Numerically
xxxxx	from (leftmost address of memory area)
00400	via the card punch.

Notice that the typewriter is addressed in the Q-field by 00100, and the card punch is addressed in the Q-field by 00400. If this command is typed, and the R-S button pressed, the memory will dump, eighty memory cells at a time, on IBM cards until the end of the memory is reached, or until INSTANT STOP is pressed. Remember that the typewriter will dump only 600 cells per minute, but the punch will dump 10,000 cells per minute.

10.9   RN 36: READ NUMERICALLY

Numeric information may be typed into the computer memory by the instruction, RN 36 xxxxx 00100, where xxxxx is the address of the leftmost memory cell to be used. For example, the command RN 36 18000 00100 is translated

36	Read Numerically
18000	into memory (starting at memory cell 18000)
00100	via the typewriter.

The faster and more efficient method for entering numeric information into the memory is via the card reader, which has the Q-address 00500. For example, the instruction RN 36 14001 00500 is translated

36	Read Numerically
14001	into memory (starting at memory cell 14001)
00500	via the card reader.

Each such command will read, simultaneously, all eighty columns of a single card into eighty consecutive memory cells. In this case, the information on the card will occupy memory cells 14001 through 14080. The numeric information in cc 27 can be found in memory cell 14027. *Blank spaces on the card, when read in numerically, will be translated as zeros.* If you really want the memory to contain the equivalent of a blank space, you will have to fill the card columns with multiple-punched {4,8} signs. However, this is troublesome, and we shall find a better way in Subsection 12.3.

We remind you at this time that the machine will follow your instructions, but will not interpret them. If the letter "A" is on a card, and the card is read ·in *numerically*, the computer will "look" at the {12,1} punch which represents an "A"; will disregard the zone punch, 12; and will place a "1" in the memory. If the next letter is a "J," and the card is read in numerically, the computer will "look" at the {11,1} punch which represents the "J"; will read the zone punch as a "minus-sign"; and will place a flag-one, "$\bar{1}$," in the memory. If "AJ" is read numerically and is dumped numerically, it will read out as "1$\bar{1}$."

EXERCISES

1　Translate RN 36 19020 00100. How is this written on a card? If five digits are entered into the memory, what positions will they occupy?

2　Translate RN 36 15067 00500. How is this written on a card? If this command is executed, what positions in storage are occupied?

PROJECTS

Prepare the following data card: blank spaces in the first ten columns, 234$\bar{5}$ in cc 11-14, {0,8,2} in cc 15, {8,4} in cc 16, and the words READ NUMERIC TEST in card columns beginning with cc 30. Prepare the following program card: RN 36 15067 00500. (Remember to omit the mnemonic, and remember that the twelve digits of the command are punched in cc 1-12 of a card, with no blank spaces between the three fields.) Using your LOAD PROGRAM and the procedure described in Subsection 10.5, enter your one-card program, then press the START button on the IBM 1620. The READER NO FEED LIGHT will go on. Place your data card in the read hopper of the IBM 1622 and press READER START. (Hold it until the card emerges.) The CHECK STOP light will now go on because the machine will be "looking" for the next command and cannot find it; but this will not interfere with our present project. We would like to know exactly how this card was entered into the memory. Before doing anything else, try to visualize the situation. What will be in each of the eighty memory cells? Now dump the memory, starting at the leftmost position (where the card was read in), and press INSTANT STOP when you have enough data. Compare the actual contents of the memory with your guess. Be sure that you understand exactly what happened. Save your cards. We shall use them again in a later section.

10.10   WN 38: WRITE NUMERICALLY

Numeric information in the memory can be typed out or punched out using the WN 38 command. WN 38 01377 00100 will cause the computer to examine each memory cell, beginning at memory cell 01377, and type the *numeric* equivalent. It will continue to type until it reaches a record mark, ⧧, in the memory. Then it will stop typing and continue to the next instruction. In other words, *a function of the record mark is to stop the execution of a WN 38 typing command.*

The command WN 38 01377 00400 will cause the computer to examine eighty memory cells, beginning at memory cell 01377, and to punch the *numeric* content of all eighty cells in a single card. Unless precautions are taken (these will be described in Subsection 12.3) every card column will be punched. There will be no blank columns.

EXERCISES

1   Translate the command WN 38 00356 00100. What will be written from memory, and when will the writing stop?

2   Translate the command WN 38 00789 00400. What will be written from memory, and when will the writing stop?

PROJECTS

Figure 11 shows a machine language program instruction sheet with the instructions for two different programs, labeled (a) and (b). Prepare the program cards for each of these projects. (You may or may not wish to type the comments on your program cards, but be sure to number the cards in cc 80.) In each of these projects, the last command, H48, is an *unconditional halt* which informs the machine that there are no more commands in this program. Now prepare a data card punched as follows:

$$1\ 2\ 3\ 4\ 5\ 6\ 7\ 8\ 9\ 0\ A\ B\ C\ D\ E\ F\ b\ b\ b\ b\ \{8,4\}\ \{0,8,2\}$$

where the "b" stands for a blank space in the data card. Run the program for each of the two projects, using your data card, and make a record of the results. It will be of interest to run the program for each of these projects with the data card of the project in Subsection 10.9.

If you have any difficulty with machine check lights or card jams, refer to Subsections 12.5 and 12.6.

The abbreviations in the "Comments" column of Fig. 11 are as follows:

RNCD = Read a card numerically.

WNTY = Write numerically on the typewriter.

WNCD = Write a card numerically.

BOARD OF EDUCATION OF THE CITY OF NEW YORK

THE BRONX HIGH SCHOOL OF SCIENCE
DR. ALEXANDER TAFFEL, PRINCIPAL

1620 Data Processing System
PROGRAM INSTRUCTION SHEET

DEPARTMENT OF MATHEMATICS
DR. I. A. DODES, CHAIRMAN

IBM

Application: *WN 38 PROJECTS*　　　　　　　Date: *10-6-62*　Page: *1* of *1*

Routine: _____　　　Written by: *I. A. DODES*

LOCATION	OPERATION MNEM.	NUM.	P	Q	COMMENTS
				PROJECT (a)	
01000	RN	36	19020	00500	RNCD INTO 19020-19099
01012	WN	38	19020	00100	WNTY
01024	WN	38	19020	00400	WNCD
01036	H	48	00000	00000	HALT
				PROJECT (b)	
01000	RN	36	19021	00500	RNCD INTO 19021-19100
01012	WN	38	19021	00100	WNTY
01024	WN	38	19021	00400	WNCD
01036	H	48	00000	00000	HALT

Fig. 11. Writing numerically.

10.11 RA 37: READ ALPHAMERICALLY

We have already explained that every alphameric character occupies *two* adjacent memory cells: an even one and the next higher odd one. For example, the letter "S" becomes a (6,2) in the computer memory (see Fig. 10). To read alphameric data in and out correctly, the command must therefore work with *pairs* of memory cells.

The RA 37 command is one which informs the computer that it must regard the holes punched in a single card column as the contents of *two* cells. If a single card is read into memory, its eighty columns will occupy 160 memory cells *beginning* with an even one. We are emphasizing this fact because a misunderstanding will cause incorrect programming and lead to *check stops*.

Now suppose that there is an "A" in cc 1 of a data card. The machine has been instructed to expect alphameric information in this card, and every card column will be assigned two spaces. To be specific, we wish to read the card into spaces beginning with (even) memory cell 16000. The "A" must then occupy memory cells 16000 and

16001. However, there is a small problem here. You must have noticed, by this time, that the cards are inserted into the read hopper nine-edge first. This means that the brushes on the reader will read the "1" punch before it reads the "12" punch. (Remember that an "A" consists of a {12,1} double-punch in a single card column.) The "1" punch must be read into 16001, and the "12" punch in 16000. Because the command must tell the machine where to *begin,* all alphameric commands are addressed at the *odd* end of the first alphameric character. In this case, the command to read a card would be

$$RA \ 37 \ 16001 \ 00500$$

and the card would read into memory cells 16000 through 16159.

Similarly, the command RA 37 16001 00100 would accept data from the typewriter, entering the characters in pairs beginning with 16000-16001.

In reading the zone information into memory, the following changes are made:

12-punch	becomes	a 4-bit
11-punch	becomes	a 5-bit
0-punch	becomes	a 6-bit
No-punch	becomes	a 7-bit

For this reason, when unflagged *numbers* are read in alphamerically, they are changed to pairs of the form (7,x). For example, a "9" read in alphamerically becomes (7,9) in an even-odd pair of memory cells.

A blank space on a card reads in as (0,0), and a record mark, $\ddagger$, reads in as (0,$\ddagger$).

To summarize, we list a few of the differences between numeric and alphameric storage:

Input	Numeric Storage	Alphameric Storage
A	1	(4,1)
J	$\bar{1}$	(5,1)
9	9	(7,9)
$\bar{3}$	$\bar{3}$	(5,3)
b	0	(0,0)
$\ddagger$	$\ddagger$	(0,$\ddagger$)

"$\bar{3}$" reads in alphamerically as an "L" which becomes (5,3).

If the words SCHOOL 78 are read into storage alphamerically by the command RA 37 19021 00500, then, assuming that the words are typed in cc 1-9, the memory will appear as follows:

19020	6
19021	2

19022	4 ⎫
19023	3 ⎭
19024	4 ⎫
19025	8 ⎭
19026	5 ⎫
19027	6 ⎭
19028	5 ⎫
19029	6 ⎭
19030	5 ⎫
19031	3 ⎭
19032	0 ⎫
19033	0 ⎭
19034	7 ⎫
19035	7 ⎭
19036	7 ⎫
19038	8 ⎭

Notice that the following pair of instructions may cause trouble:

RN 36 19001 00500

RA 37 19081 00500

The first of these instructions will read a card numerically into 19001-19080 and it might seem that the second instruction should not cause an overlap. Actually, the second instruction does cause an overlap, because the information read in alphamerically would start at 19080 (not 19081) and would extend through 19239.

EXERCISES

Translate RA 37 15021 00500. How is it written on an IBM card? If a card is read in, what positions in storage will be occupied? If the data card has blank spaces in the first ten columns, $234\overline{7}$ in cc 11-14, ⧑0,8,2⧒ in cc 15, ⧑8,4⧒ in cc 16, and the words READ ALPHAMERIC TEST in columns beginning at cc 30, how will these appear in storage?

PROJECTS

Prepare the program card mentioned in the above exercise and prepare an H48 card. Read the two program cards in by means of your load program; then press START. The READER NO FEED light should go on. Read in the data card. Now dump the memory to see what it contains.

10.12   WA 39: WRITE ALPHAMERICALLY

Alphameric information in the memory can be typed or punched using the WA 39 command.

WA 39 15463 00100 will cause the typewriter to select *pairs* of memory cells beginning with 15462-15463 and to type the alphameric equivalent *if it exists*. It will continue to pick up pairs and translate them into alphameric equivalents until an *alphameric record mark* is reached. An alphameric record mark consists of a zero in an even memory cell and a $\neq$ in the odd memory cell adjacent to it (one higher).

WA 39 15463 00400 will cause the computer to read eighty even-odd pairs of memory cells beginning with the pair at 15462-15463 and ending with the pair at 15620-15621. These are translated alphamerically, simultaneously, *if the alphameric equivalent exists*, and eighty card columns are punched simultaneously. A (0,0) in even-odd positions inhibits the punch so that the corresponding card column is left blank.

It is important to know that the computer recognizes the nature of information from the *command*, not from the contents of the memory. For example, if the spaces beginning with 15462 are

15462	4
15463	9
15464	4
15465	2
15466	5
15467	4
15468	0
15469	0
15470	7
15471	1
15472	7
15473	6
15474	7
15475	2
15476	7
15477	0
15478	0
15479	$\neq$
15480	2
15481	0
.	.
.	.

then the command WN 38 15463 00100 would type

$$9425400717672700$$

whereas the command WA 39 15463 00100 would type

IBM 1620

Also, the command WN 38 15463 00400 would punch eighty columns of a card with all the digits from 15463 to 15542, inclusive. The command WN 39 15463 00400 would punch eighty columns of a card with the eighty *pairs* from 15462 through 15641, beginning with IBM 1620+ and continuing to the end of the card.

What happens if the even-odd pair does not constitute a defined alphameric symbol, or if the computer is given an even address for an alphameric read-in or read-out? Under ordinary circumstances, the I-O and PARITY switches on the console are set to "Stop," and that is what the machine will do. However, if these switches are set to "Program," mistyping and mispunching will occur and the contents

BOARD OF EDUCATION OF THE CITY OF NEW YORK

THE BRONX HIGH SCHOOL OF SCIENCE
DR. ALEXANDER TAFFEL, PRINCIPAL

1620 Data Processing System
PROGRAM INSTRUCTION SHEET

DEPARTMENT OF MATHEMATICS
DR. I. A. DODES, CHAIRMAN

IBM

Application: WA 39 PROJECTS   Date: 10-7-62 Page: 1 of 1

Routine: _____   Written by: I. A. DODES

LOCATION	OPERATION MNEM.	OPERATION NUM.	P	Q	COMMENTS
			PROJECT(a)		
01000	RA	37	19021	00500	RACD
01012	WA	39	19021	00400	WACD
01024	H	48	00000	00000	
			PROJECT (b)		
01000	RA	37	19021	00500	RACD
01012	WA	39	19021	00100	WATY
01024	H	48	00000	00000	
			PROJECT(c)		
01000	RA	37	19020	00500	RACD
01012	WA	39	19020	00400	WACD
01024	H	48	00000	00000	
			PROJECT(d)		
01000	RA	37	19020	00500	RACD
01012	WA	39	19020	00100	WATY
01024	H	48	00000	00000	
			PROJECT(e)		
01000	RN	36	19020	00500	RNCD
01012	WA	39	19021	00100	WNTY
01024	H	48	00000	00000	

Fig. 12. Writing alphamerically.

of the memory will be damaged. In the following projects, leave the I-O and PARITY switches on "Program" to see exactly what happens.

PROJECTS

Prepare the five programs shown in Fig. 12. With each of these programs, use the data card prepared in the exercise of Subsection 10.11 and explain the results. Be sure to clear the machine between programs, and to dump the memory beginning at 19020 in order to explain what happened.

The abbreviations in the "Comments" column of Fig. 12 are as follows:

RACD = Read a card alphamerically.

WACD = Write a card alphamerically.

WATY = Write alphamerically on the typewriter.

Section 11. *Transmitting Information Within the Memory*

11.1 WHY INFORMATION IS TRANSMITTED

Sometimes we may wish to copy the information from one set of memory cells to another set of memory cells. In the language of programming this copying operation is called *transmitting*. (It is important to realize that at the end of a transmission the information is in *both places*.) For example, we may have received the information on a card in the order AbBbCb57b32 and we may wish to punch a card or type a form in the order 32bAbCb57bB. (Remember that "b" stands for "blank space.")

There are three general types of transmitting:

1. A single digit is to be transmitted. This is always the contents of a single memory cell, such as a 9, or a $\overline{7}$ (flag seven), or a $\ne$ (record mark).
2. An entire set of memory cells is to be copied and (for some reason) it is convenient for us to use the address of the *rightmost* memory cell. If an area of memory is used in connection with its *right address,* we shall call it a *field.* This is the usual method for transmitting arithmetic information because we ordinarily do arithmetic from right to left, so that we think of the *right* end as the "beginning" of the area.
3. An entire set of memory cells is to be copied, and (for some reason) it is convenient for us to use the address of the *leftmost* memory cell. If an area of memory is used in connection with its *left address,* we shall call it a *record.* This is the usual method for transmitting material to be used in reading or writing because we read and write from left to right, so that we think of the *left* end as the "beginning" of the area. Alphameric information which, of course, is not the type of data used in arithmetic, is usually treated as a record, and is addressed at the left-plus-one address for reasons explained in Subsection 10.11.

It is very important that the procedure for transmitting (copying) information be learned thoroughly. It tends to be a little confusing at first and most errors in programming, at least for the beginner, occur at this point.

If it is any consolation, we remark that mathematical work on the computer (which we shall begin to discuss in Section 13) is extremely easy.

11.2   TD 25: TRANSMIT DIGIT

The command TD 25 06051 07022 copies the contents of memory cell 07022 (the Q-field) into memory cell 06051 (the P-field). Remember that the copying goes *from Q to P*. This command can be used to copy anything which is in the field, even a numeric blank. If a letter exists in 07022-07023, and the command is the one just mentioned, this command will copy the part which is in 07022. For example, if a B has been read into 07022-07023, then memory cell 07022 will contain a "4" and memory cell 07023 will contain a "2." The command will copy the "4" into memory cell 06051. It will not copy the B.

11.3   TDM 15: TRANSMIT DIGIT IMMEDIATE

In every command mentioned so far, the Q-field has been the *address* of either a position in memory or else an I-O device, e.g., 00400 for the card punch, 00500 for the card reader, and 00100 for the typewriter. In the *Immediate* instructions, the Q-field itself provides the data, not the address of the data.

The TDM 15 command copies the digit in Q_{11} into the address given by the P-field. The following examples give the difference between TD 25 and TDM 15:

TD   25 06049 13456   Takes the digit in the *address* 13456 and places a copy in memory cell 06049.

TDM 15 06049 13456   Takes the "6" in position Q_{11} of the instruction and places a copy in memory cell 06049. The digits in $Q_7Q_8Q_9$ and Q_{10} are completely disregarded.

Here are some further examples:

TDM 15 06049 0000$\ddagger$ Places a record mark at 06049.

TDM 15 06049 $\overline{2}$354$\overline{8}$ Places a "$\overline{8}$" at 06049.

TDM 15 06049 0000@   Places an "at-sign" at 06049. This is a numeric blank.

11.4   AREAS IN MEMORY

We have already mentioned that a machine language program is always inserted into memory by means of a load program, and that there are many variations possible. We cannot explain the instructions in the load program yet, but it is necessary that you know some of the things it does. The load program in Appendix I places your first instruction in 01000-01011, your second instruction in 01012-01023, your third instruction in 01024-01035, and so on. In Fig. 12, the "Location" column at the left of the program instruction sheet shows the address of the first digit, O_0, of the instruction. For example, in the second instruction of project (a), the address of the "39" is 01012-01013. The address of the "4" in Q_9 of the same instruction is 01021.

You may copy any information in the machine for which you have the address, and it is essential that the programmer know exactly where, in memory, all the instructions and data are. At the same time, it is important not to transmit information into areas which are being used for something else. When this is done, the original information is *erased*, so to speak, and the copy takes its place. The load program in Appendix I sets aside the following areas for your use:

00100-00401 contains arithmetic tables.

00402-00657 contains expendable material.

00658-00682 has zeros, with $\bar{0}$ in 00658.

00683 has a record mark.

00684-00700 contains expendable material.

00701-00780 contains eighty numeric blanks, $\{4,8\}$.

00781 contains a record mark.

Unless your program does not involve arithmetic, the region 00100-00401 should always be avoided. As for the other areas set aside, these are for your convenience and may be used for any purpose you may require.

There is one other region in memory which is used for special purposes and which should be avoided by the programmer. This is the region 00000-00099. When the INSERT key is pressed and information is typed into the memory, it enters via this region. Therefore, if the programmer has any instructions or data in this region, they will be erased and written over. The region from 00080-00099 is also used to form machine language products and quotients (to be discussed in Section 15).

11.5   TF 26: TRANSMIT FIELD

We mentioned that, in general, numerical information is conveniently handled as a *field*, i.e., an area in memory addressed at its rightmost memory cell. The contents of this rightmost memory cell may be any information which has a numeric translation, such as a number, a flagged number, a record mark, or a numeric blank.

The command TF 26 17058 06025 copies the information in 06025 into memory cell 17058 (from Q to P), then continues leftwards, as follows:

From	To
06024	17057
06023	17056
06022	17055
•	•
•	•

It continues to copy from the Q-field into the P-field *until it senses a flag.* Then it copies the digit with the flag, stops copying, and goes on to the next instruction. In other words, the leftmost digit of a field must have a flag or else the machine will continue to copy forever, or until it senses a flag someplace in the machine (or until INSTANT STOP is pressed).

The second use of a flag is therefore to stop transmission of a field. Remember that the first use was to indicate a negative number. The field consisting of the number, −603, must therefore be in memory as $\bar{6}0\bar{3}$. The flag on the low-order (rightmost) digit is a *negative flag,* and the flag on the high-order (leftmost) digit is a *termination flag.* A field always has at least two digits, so that there is never any confusion about the flag and its purpose.

We shall now have to learn two simple commands which *set* (place) and *clear* (remove) the flag. These are shown in the illustrative problem, following:

ILLUSTRATIVE PROBLEM I

A card has 51$\bar{7}$ in cc 15, 16, 17. Read the card into memory, beginning at 19001. Transmit the number into cells 17056-17058.

Solution: (See Fig. 13.) The first step reads the card into the eighty memory cells 19001-19080. The entry, 51$\bar{7}$, is now in 19015, 19016, 19017. In order to

BOARD OF EDUCATION OF THE CITY OF NEW YORK

THE BRONX HIGH SCHOOL OF SCIENCE
DR. ALEXANDER TAFFEL, PRINCIPAL

1620 Data Processing System
PROGRAM INSTRUCTION SHEET

DEPARTMENT OF MATHEMATICS
DR. I. A. DODES, CHAIRMAN

IBM

Application: ILLUS. PROB., SECTION 2.5 Date: 10-7-62 Page: 1 of 1

Routine: Written by: I. A. DODES

LOCATION	OPERATION MNEM.	NUM. (0 1)	P (2–6)	Q (7–11)	COMMENTS
01000	RN	36	19001	00500	RNCD INTO 19001-19080
01012	SF	32	19015	00000	SETS FLAG: $\bar{5}1\bar{7}$ IN 19015-19017
01024	TF	26	17058	19017	TRANSMITS: $\bar{5}1\bar{7}$ TO 17056-17058
[01036	CF	33	17056	00000	CLEARS FLAG: 51$\bar{7}$ IN 17056-
⋮	⋮	⋮	⋮	⋮	⋮ 17058]

Fig. 13. Transmitting a field.

transmit it, there must be a termination flag at the leftmost memory cell of the field. The *Set Flag* command, SF 32, places a flag at the address given in the P-field of the instruction. The Q-field is disregarded. Therefore, the second command places a flag in memory cell 19015. (If there is already a flag in that cell, no harm is done.) In the third command, transmission takes place as follows:

1. The $\bar{7}$ in memory cell 19017 is copied into cell 17058. Since the flag is on the rightmost digit, it is recognized as a *negative* flag, not a *termination* flag.
2. The 1 in memory cell 19016 is copied into cell 17057.

3. The $\bar{5}$ in memory cell 19015 is copied into cell 17056. Sensing the flag on the leftmost digit of the field, the computer proceeds to the next instruction.

In Fig. 13, brackets have been placed about the fourth instruction to indicate that it is usually unnecessary to remove the termination flag at this point. However, if it is desired to do so, the *Clear Flag* command, CF 33, removes the flag at the address given in the P-field of the instruction. The Q-field is disregarded. (If there is actually no flag there, no harm is done.) At the end of the program shown in Fig. 13, there is still a flag in 19015, but none in 17056.

The same sort of transmission can be accomplished for alphameric information. For example, suppose the word SCHOOL is in memory beginning with (leftmost) cell 14356. Then the S occupies 14356-14357. SCHOOL has six letters, so that it occupies twelve positions. You will find it easy, at this point, to count on your fingers. C begins at 14358, H begins at 14360, the first O begins at 14362, the second O begins at 14364, and the L begins at 14366 and ends at 14367. Remember that so far as the computer is concerned, this is a set of twelve digits, i.e., 624348565653.

To transmit the word to memory from 14178 to 14189, we would merely execute the following short program:

SF 32 14356 00000	Sets a flag over the zone portion of the S..
TF 26 14189 14367	Transmits $\bar{S}$CHOOL.
CF 33 14178 00000	Clears the flag from the copy.

EXERCISES

1 Write a series of commands to read a card numerically into memory beginning with (left address) 06011. What locations in memory are taken by a five-digit number beginning in cc 15? Transmit the number to memory beginning with (left address) 19004, and remove the termination flag.

2 Write a series of commands to read a card alphamerically into memory beginning with (left address) 07512. What locations in memory are taken by a seven-letter word beginning in cc 27? Transmit the word to a location in memory with left address 19102, and remove the termination flag.

3 We have already mentioned that the computer is "cleared to zeros" by the type-written command 26 00002 00003. (*i*) Explain why this command places a zero in each memory cell. (*ii*) Would 26 00007 00008 do the same thing? (*iii*) Would 26 00003 00002 do the same thing? (*iv*) What would happen if you used the command 26 0$\bar{0}$002 00003? You may check your answers by trying these commands, then dumping from 00000. The dump command will, of course, occupy memory from 00000 through 00011, but the remainder of the machine memory will reflect the effect of your command.

11.6 TFM 16: TRANSMIT FIELD IMMEDIATE

The TFM 16 instruction copies the actual data beginning at Q_{11} into the address given in the P-field of the instruction, and continues leftwards until a termination flag is reached. The following examples should clarify this command:

1. TFM 16 02117 13$\bar{5}$78. The computer will copy the "8" into memory cell 02117, the "7" into 02116, and the "$\bar{5}$" into 02115. It will then stop and proceed to the next instruction. The "1" and "3" in Q_7 and Q_8 are disregarded.
2. TFM 16 021$\bar{1}$7 13578. The computer will copy as follows:

8	into 02117
7	into 02116
5	into 02115
3	into 02114
1	into 02113
7	into 02112
$\bar{1}$	into 02111

Notice that the copying will continue until a termination flag is reached. If the programmer forgets to place a termination flag, the copying will continue throughout the memory, one cell at a time, until (accidentally) a flag is reached. Then it will stop. (By this time your program has probably been ruined. There is a moral here, somewhere.)

A common use of this command is to place an alphameric record mark, 0$\ddagger$, in some required location. Suppose, for example, you wish to type the word SCHOOL which is in memery in cells 14356 through 14367. In order to stop the typewriter you will need the alphameric record mark in positions 14368-14369. The following portion of a program accomplishes the desired end:

TFM 16 14369 000$\bar{0}\ddagger$

WA 39 14357 00100

(Remember that alphameric data is read in or out in its left-plus-one address.)

PROJECTS

Punch a data card with the sentence, "1984 IS AN INTERESTING BØØK." Now write a program to do the following: (*i*) Read the sentence into memory. (*ii*) Transmit "1984 IS A" to another available space. (*iii*) Transmit "BØØK." next to it. (*iv*) Type the sentence, "1984 IS A BØØK." This process is called *editing*.

11.7 TR 31: TRANSMIT RECORD

The TF and TFM commands transmit from *right* to *left*, stopping at the first termination flag, but not influenced by anything else. It will, for example, copy record marks.

In contrast, the TR command transmits from *left* to *right*, copying flags as well, and stops only when a record mark is reached. It copies the record mark, too.

Suppose the following is in memory at locations beginning with 05001:

1 2 $\bar{3}$ 4 $\bar{5}$ 6

and we wish to transmit this to positions beginning at 17126. Counting on our fingers, we see that the "6" is in memory cell 05006. We shall want a record mark in 05007:

TDM 15 05007 0000+

TR   31 17126 05001

The record now occupies positions 17126-17131 with a record mark in 17132.

As a further example, suppose we have the words "SCHOOL 25" in cc 1-9 of an IBM card. It is read into memory beginning at 05000 and we wish to transmit it to memory at locations beginning with 19100. The program is simple:

RA   37 05001 00500

TFM 16 05019 000$\bar{0}$+

TR   31 19100 05000

The first of these three instructions reads the information into 05000 through 05019 as follows:

05000-05001	S	(=62)
05002-05003	C	(=43)
05004-05005	H	(=48)
05006-05007	Ø	(=56)
05008-05009	Ø	(=56)
05010-05011	L	(=53)
05012-05013	b	(=00)
05014-05015	2	(=72)
05016-05017	5	(=75)

The second instruction places the record mark as follows:

05018-05019	+	(=$\bar{0}$+)

If, instead of the second instruction, the following had been used:

TDM 15 05018 0000+

then the record mark would have occupied the wrong half of the even-odd pair, and invalid results would ensue.

Although the TF and the TR commands perform the same ultimate task (transmitting information from one portion of the memory to another), there is sometimes an advantage in the use of one rather than the other.

The TF command will copy record marks inside an area, but no flags except a low-order (negative) flag. The TR command will copy flags, but will copy only the first record mark reached.

The TF command will copy (for example) a 24-position field into a 24-position area. If the TR command is used, space must be allowed at the right end for a numeric or alphameric record mark. From time to time, this may cause some difficulty. For example, suppose an area in memory contains the following information:

$$\ldots 123456789 \ldots$$

and we wish to replace the 456 by 654. We can easily accomplish this by a TF (or a TFM) command, removing the flag, if necessary, after the transmission. However, if we use TR, the record mark will erase the 7, so that the memory will contain

$$\ldots 123654\ddagger89 \ldots$$

and nothing will remedy the situation except another (digit) transmission to replace the record mark by a "7."

The TR command is very useful in establishing an area of numeric blanks. Let us say that we wish to set aside 19001-19080 as an area of numeric blanks. Then the command

$$\text{TR } 31 \ 19001 \ 00701$$

will (with the Appendix I load program) place numeric blanks in the required area, with a record mark in 19081.

11.8   CALCULATING ADDRESSES

Suppose a card is read into memory beginning with position 19224, and suppose there is information in cc 5-7, 23-45, 56, and 78-80. Where is it in memory?

The calculation clearly depends upon how the card was read into the memory. We take both cases:

1. It was read in by an RN 36 command. Then the eighty card columns go in as follows:

cc 1	enters memory at 19224
cc 2	enters memory at $19224 + 1$
cc 3	enters memory at $19224 + 2$
•	•
•	•
cc 80	enters memory at $19224 + 79 = 19303$

The card, in other words, occupies memory cells 19224 through 19303. Notice that the *eightieth* column is in $19224 + 79$. The fifth column will be in memory cell $19224 + 4$, the twenty-third column will be in $19224 + 22$, the fifty-sixth column will be in $19224 + 55$. To summarize:

cc 1	is in 19224
cc 5-7	are in 19228-19230
cc 23-45	are in 19246-19368
cc 56	is in 19279
cc 78-80	are in 19301-19303.

2. It was read in by an RA 37 command. Then the eighty card columns go in as follows:

cc 1	enters memory at 19224, 19225
cc 2	enters memory at 19226, 19227
cc 3	enters memory at 19228, 19229
• •	
• •	
cc 80	enters memory at 19382, 19383

where the last position is calculated by adding 159 $(= 160 - 1)$ to the left address 19224. Notice that the left address of each alphameric character can be found by adding $2(n - 1)$ to the left address of the first character, and the right address of each alphameric character can be found by adding $2(n - 1)$ to the right address of the character. Since the right address of the first character is 19225, the right address of the eightieth character is $19225 + 2(79) = 19225 + 158 = 19383$. The fifth card column will have a left address of $19224 + 2(4) = 19232$, and a right address of 19233. To summarize:

cc 1	is in 19224, 19225
cc 5-7	are in 19232 through 19237
cc 23-45	are in 19268 through 19313
cc 56	is in 19334, 19335
cc 78-80	are in 19378 through 19383.

This kind of calculation is also needed in internal transmissions, especially when the programmer has to know where to place a termination flag or a record mark. For our illustrations, we shall suppose that fourteen characters are in memory in positions with left address 14588, and we wish to transmit them to positions with left address 17034. We shall give one example where the characters are numeric and the other where they are alphameric.

1. The data are numeric. Then they presently occupy positions from 14588 to $(14588 + 13)$, i.e., from 14588 through 14601. Their final position should be from 17034 to $(17034 + 13)$, i.e., from 17034 through 17047. The commands are:

$$\text{SF} \ 32 \ 14588 \ 00000$$
$$\text{TF} \ 26 \ 17047 \ 14601$$

Both the original and the copy will have a flag at the high-order digit. If they are to be removed (usually this is unnecessary), the removal can be accomplished by the following commands:

$$\text{CF } 33 \ 14588 \ 00000$$

$$\text{CF } 33 \ 17034 \ 00000$$

2. The data are alphameric. Then they presently occupy fourteen pairs of positions in storage from (left address) 14588 to the right address calculated as (14589 + 26), i.e., 14615. The final position will be from left address 17034 to the right address, calculated as (17035 + 26), i.e., 17061. In both cases, "26" was added because it is 2(14 − 1). The transmission can be accomplished by the following commands:

$$\text{TFM } 16 \ 14617 \ 000\overline{0}\ne$$

$$\text{TR} \quad 31 \ 17034 \ 14588$$

The record will now occupy positions 17034 through 17061, with an alphameric record mark in 17062-17063.

In the latter example, the transmission can also be accomplished by using TDM 15 14616 0000$\ne$, but then the record mark will be in 17062. If it is desired to type the record, this will be unsatisfactory. With the alphameric record mark properly placed, the command

$$\text{WA } 39 \ 17035 \ 00100$$

will type the record correctly. Remember that for read-in or read-out alphamerically, the left-plus-one address must be used.

If it is desired to remove the flagged zero and record mark (this is usually unnecessary), this can be accomplished by the commands

$$\text{TDM } 15 \ 17062 \ 00000$$

$$\text{TDM } 15 \ 17063 \ 00000$$

which replaces the contents of 17062-17063 by zeros.

EXERCISES

1 A card has the numbers $2\overline{3}5\overline{7}\overline{8}$ in cc 15-19. Write a program to read the card into memory beginning at 12147, and then transmit the number into memory cells beginning at 19967.

2 A card has the information A2$\overline{7}$ in cc 35-37. Write a program to read the card into memory beginning at 18588, and then transmit the information into locations beginning with memory cell 19036.

PROJECTS

Test your programs and check by dumping the memory from appropriate places.

Section 12. Output Control

12.1 TYPEWRITER CONTROL

You already know that the typewriter will start writing at the address specified in the P-field of the command

WN 38 xxxxx 00100   (xxxxx is even or odd)

or at the address-minus-one of the P-field of the command

WA 39 xxxxx 00100   (xxxxx must be odd)

You also know that a numeric record mark must be used for stopping a WN 38 type-out and an alphameric record mark for a WA 39 type-out.

Control of the form of the typewriter output is given by three K 34 commands, the specific nature of each being indicated by the Q-field:

MNE	OP	P	Q	Comment
K	34	00000	00101	SPTY
K	34	00000	00102	RCTY
K	34	00000	00108	TBTY

The "comments" mean:

SPTY = Space once on the typewriter.

RCTY = Return the carriage of the typewriter.

TBTY = Skip to tabs set on the typewriter.

The computer, of course, pays no attention to the comments. It also pays no attention to the P-field in a K 34 command.

If the TBTY command is used, the tabs must be set at the proper places before the program is started.

EXERCISES

A data card has the following information punched, beginning at cc 1: 49425400717672700. Examine the program in Fig. 14, explain each step, and predict the output. You may check your answer by preparing the cards and running the program. For a complete check, you will also have to dump the memory at selected points.

You may note that a step could have been saved by using TF 26 16467 15473 in place of the instruction in 01096. Do you see why this is so?

PROJECTS

A card has the numbers 258, $\overline{587}$, and 1012 punched beginning in cc 7, 15, and 43, respectively. Write a program to read this card into memory, then type the three

BOARD OF EDUCATION OF THE CITY OF NEW YORK

THE BRONX HIGH SCHOOL OF SCIENCE   DEPARTMENT OF MATHEMATICS
DR. ALEXANDER TAFFEL, PRINCIPAL   1620 Data Processing System   DR. I. A. DODES, CHAIRMAN
IBM   PROGRAM INSTRUCTION SHEET

Application: _EXERCISE, SECTION 3-1_____ Date: _10-7-62_ Page: _1_ of _1_

Routine: _____ Written by: _I. A. DODES_____

| LOCATION | OPERATION | | P | Q | COMMENTS |
	MNEM.	NUM.			
0 1 0 0 0	R N	3 6	1 5 4 6 2	0 0 5 0 0	
0 1 0 1 2	S F	3 2	1 5 4 6 2	0 0 0 0 0	
0 1 0 2 4	T F	2 6	1 6 4 6 7	1 5 4 6 7	
0 1 0 3 6	C F	3 3	1 6 4 6 2	0 0 0 0 0	
0 1 0 4 8	T DM	1 5	1 6 4 6 8	0 0 0 0 ≠	
0 1 0 6 0	K	3 4	0 0 0 0 0	0 0 1 0 2	
0 1 0 7 2	W N	3 8	1 6 4 6 2	0 0 1 0 0	
0 1 0 8 4	S F	3 2	1 5 4 6 8	0 0 0 0 0	
0 1 0 9 6	T F	2 6	1 7 4 7 3	1 5 4 7 3	
0 1 1 0 8	C F	3 3	1 7 4 6 8	0 0 0 0 0	
0 1 1 2 0	T DM	1 5	1 7 4 7 4	0 0 0 0 ≠	
0 1 1 3 2	K	3 4	0 0 0 0 0	0 0 1 0 8	
0 1 1 4 4	W N	3 8	1 7 4 6 8	0 0 1 0 0	
0 1 1 5 6	K	3 4	0 0 0 0 0	0 0 1 0 8	
0 1 1 6 8	T DM	1 5	1 5 4 7 9	0 0 0 0 ≠	
0 1 1 8 0	W N	3 8	1 5 4 7 4	0 0 1 0 0	
0 1 1 9 2	K	3 4	0 0 0 0 0	0 0 1 0 1	
0 1 2 0 4	K	3 4	0 0 0 0 0	0 0 1 0 1	
0 1 2 1 6	K	3 4	0 0 0 0 0	0 0 1 0 1	
0 1 2 2 8	W A	3 9	1 5 4 6 3	0 0 1 0 0	
0 1 2 4 0	K	3 4	0 0 0 0 0	0 0 1 0 2	
0 1 2 5 2	H	4 8	0 0 0 0 0	0 0 0 0 0	

Fig. 14.   An Input-Output problem (Machine Language).

items in three columns in the following order: 58̄7, 1012, 258. There should be four spaces between the first and the second numbers and a large skip to the third number. Run your program.

12.2   ALTERNATE METHOD FOR SPACING TYPEWRITER

Any number of spaces can be provided by a series of one-space commands, K 34 00000 00101, but this is rather a nuisance if more than one or two spaces are desired. The alternative method for spacing the typewriter depends upon the fact that an alphameric blank is (0,0) in an even-odd pair of positions.

Recall that the load program (Appendix I) has zeros in 00658 through 00682, with a record mark in 00683. The command

WA 39 00679 00100

will, therefore, cause the typewriter to space twice, and the command

$$\text{WA \quad 39 \quad 00661 \quad 00100}$$

will cause the typewriter to space eleven times.

EXERCISES

What will be the effect of WA 39 00673 00100? of WA 39 00674 00100?

12.3   NUMERIC OUTPUT: CARD CONTROL

The command WN 38 15462 00400 will cause the card punch to punch eighty card columns simultaneously from 15462 through 15541. Whatever is in storage in these spaces will punch out whether or not we want it. Ordinarily, this will lead to a card with every column punched, but with no blank spaces. To make a "clean card," i.e., a card with the desired information on it in the desired spaces, and unpunched card columns on the remainder of the card, we must use *numeric blanks*.

We shall illustrate by a specific example. Suppose that we are going to do some computing and that the result will appear in memory cells 15466 through 15468, i.e., a number of the form xxx. The digit in 15466 will have a termination flag, and the digit in 15468 may or may not have a negative flag. We do not want the termination flag on the card. We do want the result to be punched in cc 23-25 of a clean card. We proceed as follows:

1. We decide, before writing the computing program, to set aside eighty spaces in memory as a punch zone. Ordinarily, when we assign spaces in a machine language program, we work backwards from the end of the machine memory (19999 for the basic machine). This means that the program instructions start at 01000 and work upwards (in blocks of twelve), and that the space assignments start at 19999 and work downwards (the blocks depending upon the needs of the program). We shall suppose that spaces have been assigned, for other reasons, from 19999 down to 19206, inclusive. We now wish to reserve eighty spaces for the punch zone. Subtracting 80 from 19206, we have 19126 as the beginning of the punch zone. The right address is 19126 + 79 = 19205. This would be fine, except that we are going to transmit numeric blanks to the punch zone by a TR 31 command and this will place a record mark in 19206, erasing whatever is there. Instead, we shall move down one and designate the punch zone as 19125 through 19204. This leaves memory cell 19205 for the record mark. (Note how carefully transmission must be done!)

2. Now we transmit eighty numeric blanks from 00701-00780 to 19125-19204.

3. Now we must transmit the contents of 15466-15468 to the proper place in the punch zone. Since we want the information to appear in cc 23-25, the transmission must be done to memory cells 19125 + 22 to 19125 + 24, i.e., 19147-19149.

4. Finally, we must clear the flag which appears in 19147.

BOARD OF EDUCATION OF THE CITY OF NEW YORK

THE BRONX HIGH SCHOOL OF SCIENCE   DEPARTMENT OF MATHEMATICS
DR. ALEXANDER TAFFEL, PRINCIPAL   1620 Data Processing System   DR. I. A. DODES, CHAIRMAN

IBM   PROGRAM INSTRUCTION SHEET

Application: *ILLUSTRATION, SECTION 3.3*   Date: *10-7-62* Page: *36* of *37*

Routine: _____   Written by: *I. A. DODES*

LOCATION	OPERATION		,	Q	COMMENTS
	MNEM.	NUM.			
0 6 7 2 4	T R	3 1	1 9 1 2 5	0 0 7 0 1	PREPARES 19125-19204 FOR PUNCHING
0 6 7 3 6	T F	2 6	1 9 1 4 9	1 5 4 6 8	PLACES X̄X̄X̄ IN CC 23-25
0 6 7 4 8	C F	3 3	1 9 1 4 7	0 0 0 0 0	XXX IN CC 23-25
0 6 7 6 0	W N	3 8	1 9 1 2 5	0 0 4 0 0	PUNCHES A CLEAN CARD

Fig. 15.   Punching a "Clean Card".

This portion of a program is shown in Fig. 15, where it is assumed that the first step in this sequence is in 06724.

PROJECTS

Punch the numbers 258, −587, and 1012 in a card, with the numbers in cc beginning at 7, 15, and 43. Write a program to read the card into memory and punch out a clean card with −587 beginning at cc 13; 258 beginning at cc 44; and 1012 beginning at cc 71. Run your program.

12.4   ALPHAMERIC OUTPUT: CARD CONTROL

The command WA 39 15463 00400 will cause the computer to read 160 memory cells (from 15462 through 15621) and punch eighty card columns with the alphameric interpretation of the even-odd pairs.

To prepare a "clean card," we must, therefore, set aside 160 spaces filled with *alphameric blanks*. This is fairly simple, since an alphameric blank is the even-odd pair, (0,0). You will remember that the machine is cleared to zeros before the program is entered. Therefore, it is merely necessary to reserve 160 of these clean spaces and exercise care not to trespass upon them.

For example, suppose that we are considering the same program as that in subsection 12.3, except that we now wish to punch a clean card with the words, "END OF PROGRAM" in cc 1-14. Our procedure is as follows:

1. We have already reserved spaces from 19999 down to 19204, inclusive, for other purposes. We now set aside 160 more spaces, i.e., from 19044 through 19203, for the alphameric punch zone. (Remember that this must begin with an *even*

memory cell to permit the alphameric interpretation to take place properly.)

2. We prepare a data card with the words, "END OF PROGRAM" on it, but nothing else. This is read in with the command

$$RA \quad 37 \quad 19045 \quad 00500$$

3. When the clean card is desired, we use the command

$$WA \quad 39 \quad 19045 \quad 00400$$

This completes the task.

There is a slight complication if we wish to punch a clean card with the information: X = 54, where the "54" is the result of a computation. In order to do this, we must have in memory (in even-odd positions) the following information:

$$(67) \ (00) \ (33) \ (00) \ (75) \ (74)$$

For the purpose of our illustration, we shall suppose that 18001-18160 is known to contain zeros, the alphameric information " X =" is in 14000-14007, and a positive two-digit number is in 13000-13001. We wish to punch "X = xx" in cc 1-6 of a clean card. One solution of this problem is shown in Fig. 16.

BOARD OF EDUCATION OF THE CITY OF NEW YORK

THE BRONX HIGH SCHOOL OF SCIENCE
DR. ALEXANDER TAFFEL, PRINCIPAL

1620 Data Processing System
PROGRAM INSTRUCTION SHEET

DEPARTMENT OF MATHEMATICS
DR. I. A. DODES, CHAIRMAN

IBM

Application: _ILLUSTRATION, SECTION 3.4_   Date: _10-7-62_ Page: _2_ of _5_

Routine: _NUMERIC FILL_   Written by: _I. A. DODES_

LOCATION	OPERATION MNEM.	NUM.	P	Q	COMMENTS
01432	SF	32	14000	00000	
01444	TF	26	18007	14007	
01456	TDM	15	18008	00007	
01468	TD	25	18009	13000	
01480	CF	33	18009	13000	
01492	TDM	15	18010	00007	
01504	TD	25	18011	13001	
01516	WA	39	18001	00400	

Fig. 16. Numeric fill.

The operation of inserting sevens in order to type or punch numeric material alphamerically is called *numeric fill*. If this is to be done frequently, the programming becomes a nuisance. Instead, a special feature can be installed on the machine to change numeric to alphameric form by inserting sevens (numeric fill), and conversely to change alphameric numbers to numeric form by removing the sevens (numeric strip.)

We have by no means solved the problem completely, even in this program. An alphameric write-out does not show the flags and it will become necessary for us to learn how to make logical decisions (Section 14) before we can really dispose of this problem.

EXERCISES

Explain each step of the above illustrative program.

PROJECTS

You have three data cards. Card 1 has "IF A =" in card columns beginning with cc 1; card 2 has a "3" in cc 5 and a "7" in cc 19; card 3 has "THEN B =" in card columns beginning with cc 1. Read the first and third cards in alphamerically, and the second card numerically. Now write a program to punch a clean card with the statement, "IF A = 3 THEN B = 7" beginning in cc 10. Run your program.

12.5   CHECK ERRORS

When a card enters the card reader, all eighty card columns are read by a set of brushes ("first read") then read again by a second set of brushes ("second read"). Sometimes the card is mispunched or bent, or a brush is broken, and the information is read incorrectly. If there is any error in reading, the two readings will not be the same. The card reader will stop and the READER CHECK light will go on.

There are other check points before the computer accepts the information. One of these is a check for *parity* which we have already mentioned (in Subsection 10.6). This guards against the loss of information by the machine while the information is traveling from the reader to the computer. If any information is lost, a check light will go on either on the reader or at the console (or both) and the machine will stop.

If a check light goes on, perform the following:

1. Remove your cards from the read hopper.
2. Depress the NON-PROCESS RUN-OUT key. The remaining cards will feed into the second front hopper from the right.
3. Take the cards out of the first hopper (front right).
4. Put the three sets of cards together as follows: first hopper (face down), second hopper (behind these), read hopper (last).
5. If the rejected cards were *program cards*, it is wise to clear the machine and start over again.
6. If the rejected cards were *data cards*, press RESET, then INSERT, then type 4901000, then press the R-S key, and read in the data cards again. (We shall explain the typewriter insertion in Subsection 13.7.)

If the rerun brings about another *check stop*, check your cards to see that they are correct. If the cards are bent at the edges, duplicate the cards and try again. If the machine refuses to accept your cards, you may require repair.

12.6   CARD JAMS

The card reader (and other machines) will not jam if the cards and brushes are in good condition. However, if the cards are bent or torn, an edge may catch on a brush and cause a card jam.

If this happens, there are two ways to proceed. First, we will describe the wrong way. The wrong way is to grasp a corner of the card and pull. This is a very successful method for bending the reading brushes and throwing the machine out of commission for an entire day. The other (correct) way is to turn off the machine, lift out or disengage the brushes carefully, then let the card pass through gently. This is the intelligent way, but it requires knowledge of the correct unlocking and locking devices. It is a good idea to learn how this is done for each machine in the Computing Center.

Section 13.   Programs Involving Addition and Subtraction

13.1   PLANNING A PROGRAM

The previous three sections have dealt with input, output, the transmission of information, and editing. All of these are ordinarily regarded as *housekeeping* by programmers. They are not too interesting, but they are absolutely essential. At any rate, if you have mastered housekeeping, you have a fairly good idea of the working of the machine and the source of errors. Also, you know which buttons to push. Now we can concentrate on the computing. This is really very interesting.

To begin, suppose you had to calculate

$$\sqrt{\frac{(2.7812) \; * \; (-4.6627)}{(-8.1552)^3}}$$

on a desk calculator. You might go about it as follows:

1. Read the problem.
2. Multiply (2.7812) by (4.6627).
3. Decide on the sign.
4. Write the answer.
5. Calculate 8.1552 * 8.1552.
6. Write the answer.
7. Multiply the answer by 8.1552.
8. Decide on the sign.
9. Write the answer.
10. Divide the result in step 4 by the result in step 9.
11. Decide on the sign.
12. Write the answer.

13. Find the square root of the result in step 12.
14. Round off.
15. Write the answer.

> **NOTE:** Steps 2, 5, 7, 10, and 13 actually comprise many program steps. Even a simple multiplication on a desk calculator involves some or all of the following: (*i*) clearing the machine, (*ii*) shifting the carriage, (*iii*) inserting the multiplicand, (*iv*) inserting the multiplier, (*v*) pushing the Multiply switch, (*vi*) reading the answer to the required number of decimal places, and (*vii*) checking the answer by repetition or inversion (in this case, by divison).

The plan of action in steps 1 to 15, as amended by the above Note, is called a *program*. There are two important differences in planning a program for a desk calculator and planing a program for a digital computer:

1. In the large computer, the entire program is entered and stored in the memory before any data are entered and before the computing is begun. For this reason, machines like the IBM 1620 are called *stored-program* computers.
2. In the large computer, the instructions are given in *general* form. This is the *program*. Every machine program is designed to work for an entire class of problems, not just one. The specific parameters (data) are fed to the machine to obtain a specific answer to a specific member of the class of problems.

To illustrate, we shall write (in English) the program for the very same illustrative problem as it might appear if we wrote it for the IBM 1620.

1. Read the three numbers, A, B, C, from a card.
2. Compute A * B.
3. Store the result. (Transmit the product.)
4. Compute C^2.
5. Compute C^3.
6. Store the result. (Transmit C^3 to a convenient location in the memory.)
7. Compute $A * B/(C^3)$.
8. Compute the square root of the result in step 7.
9. Half-adjust ("round off").
10. Write the answer (on the typewriter or card).

After this program is *loaded* into the machine, a data card is *read in*. On the data card are three numbers to inform the computer that A = 2.7812, B = −4.6627, and C = −8.1552.

In addition to the incredible speed and invariable accuracy of the computer, it should be noted that the *program* is perfectly general. If you wished to compute

$$\sqrt{\frac{(-9.1224) \ * \ (-5.9127)}{(2.7138)^3}}$$

you would merely read in another data card with this new information about A, B, and C. It would not even be necessary to load the program again! In other words, once you have solved a problem and *debugged* the program, the program can be used forever.

EXERCISES

In each of the following, indicate (in English) a program and the data. Use letters to represent the numbers. Each program should begin with a "read" and end with a "write."

1   $2.755 * \sqrt[3]{\dfrac{12.81 + 41.22}{16.92 - 18.61}}$

2   $9.5113 + 7.6229 * (-2.123) - 16.42 / 0.081177$

3   $(127.8) ** 5 - 31.66 - 14.68 / 8.8133 ** 2 + 0.0045$

4   For an array of numbers, X_i, program

$$\frac{N \sum(X_i^2) - (\sum X_i)^2}{N}$$

where there are understood to be thirteen entries in a column, as in Table I.

13.2   STEPS IN PROGRAMMING

We will suppose that you, as a mathematician or scientist, have a problem to be solved by computer. The problem may be like one of the following:

1. Find the Mean and the standard deviation of a set of one thousand ten-place numbers.
2. Find the correlation between two arrays of numbers, each array composed of 1500 eight-place numbers.
3. Solve to the nearest millionth the equation $x^4 + 2.185771\ x^3 + 0.772641\ x^2 - 1.427183\ x - 6.277004 = 0$.
4. Make a table of values for $e^x \sin x$, for x in $\left[-\dfrac{\pi}{2}, \dfrac{\pi}{2} \right]$ in increments of 0.001 radians.
5. Find the product of two 12 by 12 determinants.
6. Find the eigenvalues of a matrix.

Whatever the problem is, the programmer must go through certain steps. The following list is intended for reference. It will not be entirely clear to you until you have performed some actual programs.

1. Make a *flow chart*, or *block diagram*, to show the general sequence of instructions.
2. Test the flow chart with a simple problem for which you know the answer.
3. Code the program.
4. Test the program, as written, with a simple problem.
5. Punch cards for program and data.
6. List the program cards and data cards and check these against your program instruction sheet.
7. Input: load your program with data for a test problem to which you know the correct answer.
8. Run the program. For a long program, the testing should be done in segments. The sub-programs can be checked much more easily than the entire program.

9. Output: collect the results.
10. Check the results for the test problem.
11. Debug the program.
12. At last, run the actual data.

EXERCISES

For one of the six problems mentioned above, devise a simplified problem to which you know the answer. Although simplified, the problem must be of the same general type so that the program will really be tested. In some cases, several different test problems will have to be used.

13.3   RULES FOR ARITHMETIC

There are four rules which hold for *all* arithmetic commands, i.e., addition, subtraction, multiplication, and division. These are as follows:

Rule 1:   Arithmetic is done just as we do it on paper. Thus addition, subtraction, and multiplication are done from *right* to *left,* and division is done somewhat like the manual method, using repeated subtraction, from *left* to *right.*

Rule 2.   Arithmetic data always form a *field.* This means that every number used for arithmetic must have at least two digits (the first one may be zero, of course), and there must be a flag on the high-order digit. Arithmetic data are always addressed at the *right address* and are terminated by a termination flag at the left.

Rule 3:   A negative arithmetic datum must have a negative flag on the low-order (rightmost) digit. add + mult .

Rule 4:   In all arithmetic commands, the Q-data must not have more digits than the P-data.

EXAMPLES

1. $\overline{2}3$ is an arithmetic datum meaning -23.
2. 7 is meaningless as an arithmetic datum.
3. $\overline{7}$ is meaningless as an arithmetic datum.
4. $\overline{0}00576$ is an arithmetic datum meaning 576.
5. A command with P-data of $\overline{9}81$ and Q-data of $\overline{0}0023$ will cause an *overflow check stop* because the number of digits in the Q-data is larger than the number of digits in the P-data. Remember that it is not the relative *size* of the data which is considered, but only the number of *memory cells* in which the data are stored.

We pause to mention a convention which we shall use. If the number -487 is stored in a field with *right address* 15234, we shall say that the *contents* of field 15234 is -487. This is abbreviated as $C(15234) = \overline{4}8\overline{7}$ or as $C(15234) = -487$. In the latter case, it is understood that -487 is actually represented in memory as $\overline{4}8\overline{7}$. If the address is given in the P-field of an arithmetic command, we shall refer to the data as the P-data. If the address of the data is given in the Q-field, we shall refer to the data as the Q-data.

In all our machine language programs, the three Check Switches, I-O, PARITY, and O'FLOW, should be set to "Stop." There are certain situations in which the

O'FLOW switch is set to "Program," but we shall not need this in elementary programs (i.e., in this chapter).

13.4 A 21 AND S 22: ADDITION AND SUBTRACTION

The command A 21 15228 16067 adds C(16067) to C(15228), destroys the previous contents of 15228, and places the result in 15228. The *termination flag* for the result is at the same address as the termination flag for the P-data.

EXAMPLES

1. C(15228) = $\overline{1}$23456, C(16067) = $\overline{8}$901. The P-data have six memory cells; therefore, they extend from 15223-15228, and there is a flag in 15223. The Q-data are in four memory cells: 16064-16067, with a flag in 16064. The result, $\overline{1}$32357, erases the P-data and replaces them. The flag for the result is in 15223, and the result extends, like the P-data, from 15223 to 15228.

2. C(15228) = $\overline{0}$0000001234, C(16067) = $\overline{5}$67. The P-data are in 15218-15228 (eleven memory cells), with a termination flag in 15218. The Q-data are in 16065-16067, with a termination flag in 16065. The result destroys and replaces the P-data, retaining the termination flag. The result is, therefore, $\overline{0}$0000000667, in cells 15218-15228.

3. C(15228) = $\overline{0}$000000123$\overline{4}$, C(16067) = $\overline{5}$67. The result is $\overline{0}$000000066$\overline{7}$.

4. C(15228) = $\overline{1}$23$\overline{4}$, C(16067) = $\overline{0}$0567. This will lead to a *check stop* because the length of the P-data is less than that of the Q-data.

5. C(15228) = $\overline{9}$99, C(16067) = $\overline{9}$99. This will lead to a *check stop* because the result will not fit into the area reserved for the P-data.

Notice that the addition is an *algebraic* addition.

The command S 22 15228 16067 subtracts the Q-data from the P data, and destroys and replaces the P-data with the *algebraic* difference. The rules for subtraction are precisely the same as those for addition.

ILLUSTRATIVE PROBLEM

We are given A = xxxxxx in cc 1-6 of an IBM card, B = xxxxx in cc 7-11, and C = xxx in cc 12-14. We know that all values of A are near 200,000; all values of B are near 30,000; and all values of C are near 800. We wish to compute (A + B − C), then type A, B, C and (A + B − C) in four columns. (Notice that the numbers were chosen in such a way, in this problem, that the results will not cause an overflow check stop. We shall discuss the other case in Subsection 13.6.)

Solution: Even a problem as simple as this one requires some good thinking. One way to think about a problem involving computation and housekeeping is to imagine what the final result is to look like, then work backwards. In this case, we shall, for example, plan to have A typed at the left end of a line, then five spaces, then B, then five spaces, then C, then a bigger space controlled by a tab, then (at last) the result (A + B − C).

Now, let us go one step backwards. In order to type any of these, we shall have to have a record mark after each record to be typed. Looking at the problem again, we see that if we place a record mark after A, it will destroy the first digit of B. The same thing holds true if we place a record mark after B: we will destroy the first digit of C. As for the spaces after C, we are not told what is in cc 15-80 and it is not safe to assume that in a real problem we can place a record mark after C, either. (In this little problem, of course, it would be quite satisfactory.)

The moral is that we shall have to establish a special area in the memory, with a record mark following it, out of which we can type any record we wish. We shall call this a *type-out-zone*. For the data given, this will have to be at most six digits long, i.e., it will have to include six memory cells.

Now we are ready to start planning the housekeeping phase of this problem. (The solution will take twenty-five instructions, of which *two* will be computation, and *twenty-three* will be housekeeping!)

As a matter of good programming practice, we start the instructions at the left end of the memory (we are starting at 01000), and we start the *designated areas* at the *right end* of the memory, i.e., at 19999. We shall read-in the IBM card to the region, 19920-19999. Then we shall place a record mark in 19919. We shall reserve 19913-19918 for the type-out zone. This is shown in Fig. 17.

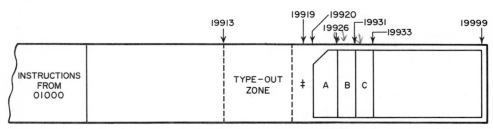

Fig. 17.   Designating areas in the memory.

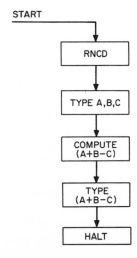

Fig. 18.   Flow chart for a simple problem involving arithmetic.

BOARD OF EDUCATION OF THE CITY OF NEW YORK

THE BRONX HIGH SCHOOL OF SCIENCE
DR. ALEXANDER TAFFEL, PRINCIPAL

1620 Data Processing System
PROGRAM INSTRUCTION SHEET

DEPARTMENT OF MATHEMATICS
DR. I. A. DODES, CHAIRMAN

IBM.

Application: *ILLUSTRATIVE PROB., SECTION 4.4*   Date: *10-8-62*   Page: *1* of *1*

Routine: _____   Written by: *I. A. DODES*

LOCATION	OPERATION MNEM.	NUM.	P	Q	COMMENTS
01000	RN	36	19920	00500	RNCD 19920-19999
01012	SF	32	19920	00000	Ā IN 19920-19925
01024	SF	32	19926	00000	B̄ IN 19926-19930
01036	SF	32	19931	00000	C̄ IN 19931-19933
01048	TDM	15	19919	0000≠	DEFINES END OF TYPE-OUT ZONE
01060	K	34	00000	00102	RCTY
01072	TF	26	19918	19925	Ā IN 19913-19918
01084	CF	33	19913	00000	A IN 19913-19918
01096	WN	38	19913	00100	TYPES A
01108	WA	39	00673	00100	5 SPACES
01120	TF	26	19918	19930	B̄ IN 19914-19918
01132	CF	33	19914	00000	B IN 19914-19918
01144	WN	38	19914	00100	TYPES B
01156	WA	39	00673	00100	5 SPACES
01168	TF	26	19918	19933	C̄ IN 19916-19918
01180	CF	33	19916	00000	C IN 19916-19918
01192	WN	38	19916	00100	TYPES C
01204	K	34	00000	00108	TBTY
01216	A	21	19925	19930	(A+B) IN 19920-19925
01228	S	22	19925	19933	(A+B-C) IN 19920-19925
01240	TF	26	19918	19925	(A+B-C) IN 19913-19918
01252	CF	33	19913	00000	(A+B-C) IN 19913-19918
01264	WN	38	19913	00100	TYPES (A+B-C)
01276	K	34	00000	00102	RCTY
01288	H	48	00000	00000	

Fig. 19.   Coding for a simple problem involving arithmetic (Machine Language).

We will not say that programmers invariably make a diagram of the contents of the memory. We will say, however, that it helps keep things straight in our own minds.

Now we shall plan the order of operations (the *flow chart*). Clearly, we shall read in the data, first. This is shown as the first block in Fig. 18. Then, after some house-keeping, we shall do the first type-outs, A, B, and C. (If we postponed the type-outs until after the computation, we would lose the "A," since this would be in the P-field of the arithmetic instructions.)

Then, after we have done the preliminary typing, we can complete the computation (in two steps!) and type the result.

The complete set of instructions is shown in Fig. 19. Notice that it is essential to know, at all times, just where the beginning and end of every area is. The "Comments" column should never be neglected. The few moments taken to fill in the information in this column is well repaid, both in program time and in debugging time.

PROJECTS

Using the same data card (with the same approximate values of A, B, and C), write a program to find A + C − B, then punch a clean card with A, B, C, and (A + C − B) beginning in cc 5, 15, 25, and 35, and with the code number 753 in cc 78-80.

13.5   AM 11 AND SM 12: ADD IMMEDIATE AND SUBTRACT IMMEDIATE

The AM and SM commands are exactly like the A 21 and S 22 commands except that (as in all Immediate commands) the data in the Q-field are used instead of the data at the Q-address.

EXAMPLES

1. AM 11 04602 002$\bar{3}$7.
2. SM 12 04$\bar{6}$02 00237.

In the first example, 37 is added to the data addressed at 04602. In the second example, 60200237 is subtracted from the data addressed at 04602. In both cases, the number of digits in the P-data must be at least as many as the number of digits in the Q-data. In both cases, the result destroys and replaces the P-data. The termination flag for the result is at the same address as the termination flag for the original P-data.

13.6   WORK CELLS AND SUM CELLS

A programmer frequently designates specific areas in which he plans to do certain things. We have already done this in setting aside eighty numeric blanks for a punch zone, six spaces plus a record mark (in the problem of Subsection 13.4) as a type-out zone, and we will find that this is a rather common occurrence in programming. These areas are called *work cells* (they should really be called work *areas*). A special case of a work cell is the *sum cell* (or sum *area*) which we shall discuss briefly.

Let us reconsider the problem of addition and subtraction. It should be clearly understood that the command

A 21 14567 12278

takes the contents of 12278 and adds them to the contents of 14567. At the end of the operation, the contents of the Q-field, 12278, are precisely the same as they were before. However, the contents of 14567 (the P-field) now consist of the *sum*, instead of the original number.

In performing an arithmetic operation, there are at least two circumstances in which you might wish to proceed somewhat differently. First, you may not wish to destroy the contents of the P-field. Second, the P-field may not be *long enough* to accommodate the sum or difference. In either case, you may proceed by establishing a *sum cell*. This is shown in the following illustrative problem:

ILLUSTRATIVE PROBLEM

You are given A = xxxxx and B = xxxx. You wish to compute A + B and then type or punch A, B, and (A + B). Assume that A is in 18000-18004, with a flag in 18000; and B is in 18005-18008, with a flag in 18005. The load program in Appendix I has a $\overline{0}$ in 00658, zeros in 00659-00682, and a record mark in 00683. We now proceed as follows:

TF	26 19999 00663	Places $\overline{0}00000$ in 19994-19999.
A	21 19999 18004	Adds A to the sum cell.
A	21 19999 18008	Forms (A + B) in 19994-19999.

Now, A, B, and (A + B) are in accessible positions. We know that the sum cell is long enough, because A = xxxxx and B = xxxx. The worst case is that in which A = 99999 and B = 9999. Then (A + B) = 109998, i.e., xxxxxx.

If (A + B) is to be typed, it is preferable to place the sum cell in 19993-19998, so that a record mark may be written in 19999.

If the sum is to be punched, a punch zone should be designated and the sum cell should be set up in the punch zone in order to reduce the amount of housekeeping.

Notice that the sums may look like $\overline{2}35678$ or may look like $\overline{0}00046$, depending upon the values of A and B in the illustrative example. We shall learn (in Subsection 14.4) how to eliminate nonsignificant zeros.

EXERCISES

Given A = xx, B = xxx, C = xxxx, D = xxxx, write a program to read a card into memory if these quantities are in adjacent positions on an IBM card, to find A + C, A + B + C − 3, and B + 75, and to punch the results in a clean card in the order, A, B, C, A + C, A + B + C − 3, B + 75, in cc beginning with 1, 10, 20, 30, 40 and 50, and with the code number 200 in cc 78-80.

13.7   B 49: UNCONDITIONAL BRANCH, THE SIMPLEST LOOP

The programs just demonstrated do a job once, then they stop. Ordinarily, it does not pay to go to so much trouble for this little job. However, suppose there were a hundred, a thousand, or a million data cards. How could we communicate to the machine our desire that the computer read another data card and do the entire job (or part of the job) again?

The simplest method is one in which the H 48 command is removed (as, for example, in Fig. 19) and a *branch* command, B 49 01000 000, is substituted. The interpretation of this command is, *Branch to instruction 01000 and execute it, then continue to 01012, . . .*

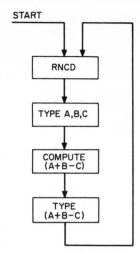

Fig. 20.   The simplest loop: B 49.

The flow chart for this situation is shown in Fig. 20. Compare it with the original flow chart in Fig. 18. Can you see why it is called a loop?

The effect of the B 49 command is to make the program branch to the instruction in the P-field. The Q-field is disregarded. If B 49 01012 00000 had been written, the program would have *branched* to instruction 01012. If B 49 01004 00000 had been written, the computer would have found, at that place, the invalid instruction 92 00050 03219. Since there is no instruction with the opcode 92, the computer would have stopped with a *check stop*.

Looking back at Fig. 18, note that the effect of the substitution of B 49 01000 00000 for H 48 00000 00000 is to make the program return endlessly to the beginning, to read another card, to do more typing, and to complete more calculations. In other words, this is a way of making a *table of values*. When the last data card has been read in, the computer will again return to the beginning and look in vain for another data card. THE READER NO FEED light will go on. We say that the program has "stopped on a READ." This is not the most elegant way to complete a program, and we shall discuss, in Section 14, how a neater termination can be made.

There is another inelegancy in this program, as we have changed it. Notice that step 01048 is done each time the computer goes through a *loop*. This is surely unnecessary. Once the record mark is in place there is no reason to have another one read over it. If we rearrange the steps just a little,

```
01000 TDM 15 19919 0000+
01012 RN   36 19920 00500
01024 SF   32 19926 00000

        •    •    •    •    •

01288 B    49 01012 00000
```

we see that the record mark is placed in position once, and only once. Time is saved every time the computer goes "through the loop." How much time is saved? See Appendix VII for a list of execution times. A rule-of-thumb states that each instruction requires about 160 microseconds in the 1962 model of the basic IBM 1620. According to the Appendix, a TDM instruction requires 200 microseconds in the 1962 model. This isn't much time (200 *millionths* of a second) but—apart from the pride that a good programmer takes in turning out an efficient program—there is the fact that even a very ordinary mathematics or science program may go through each loop millions of times. If 200 microseconds are saved each time, there is a *money* and *time* saving in the program as a whole. When you consider that the programs you will be doing *for practice* will have loops within loops within loops . . . , you can see that a practical program must be constructed carefully.

The steps from the beginning of a loop up to and including the branch instruction is called the *range of the loop*. We can summarize our present discussion by reminding you to avoid leaving within the range of the loop any steps which may be left outside that range.

PROJECTS

Make thirteen data cards with the information of Table I on them as follows:

X_{j1} in cc 1-5	X_{j5} in cc 26-28
X_{j2} in cc 7-14	X_{j6} in cc 30-33
X_{j3} in cc 16-19	X_{j7} in cc 35-38
X_{j4} in cc 21-24	X_{j8} in cc 40-43

In each case, disregard decimal points. Flag the low-order digits if the numbers are negative, but do not flag the high-order digits. In cc 60ff (ff means "and the following (columns)"), type ROW 1, ROW 2, . . . , ROW 8. We shall use these cards for later exercises as well.

Write a program to find successive partial sums as these data cards are read into memory. For example, after the first row is read in, the partial sums will be merely the entries for the first row. After the second row is read in, the partial sums will be the sums of the first and second rows. Following, are some hints to assist you in your program:

1. Each row is on a single data card. Therefore, each card can be read into memory over the previous card, then the partial sums can be computed and typed, and a branch can be made to read in the next card.

2. The sum cells must be scaled carefully. For a review of the scaling of sums, refer to Subsection 2.4. For each column, assume the "worst." For example, in column 2 of Table I, assume that each entry is of the form xxxxxx and use 999999 in scaling. By the time you reach the thirteenth row, the sum of the entries in column 2 may be as large as 13 * 999999 = xxxxxxxx. Therefore, the sum cell for column 2 should start with $\overline{0}0000000$.

3. If the sum cells are prepared carefully, they can be used as type-out zones. You need eight of them.
4. After writing your program the first time, see whether you can move any of the instructions out of the range of the loop, to save computer time.

Now run your program. If you have planned your designated areas carefully, and if you have not neglected to fill in the "Comments" column for each instruction, you should have no trouble. If you do have trouble, read Section 16 for help. Remember that your program will stop on a "Read," that you do not yet know how to place decimal points and minus signs, and that you may have nonsignificant high-order zeros. We shall take care of all these in the following section.

Section 14. Logical Decisions

14.1 BASIC MODULE IN PROGRAMMING

Figure 21 shows the *basic module* to be found in all programs except the very simplest. It will not be entirely clear to you until the end of this section. We are introducing this module at this point in order to give you an overall view of the circumstances under which decisions are made in computing.

You are already familiar with the housekeeping (which is ordinarily not shown in flow charts unless the programmer wishes to remind himself to do a special thing at a special point in the program) and with the *compute box* which, so far, has included only A 21, S 22, AM 11 and SM 12.

The *set* box refers to those instructions which must be accomplished in preparation for a loop. For example, in the exercise of Subsection 13.7, you had to prepare, for each column, a sum cell *set to zero*. In other words, in column 2, where each number might be as large as 999999, you had to allow for a sum of 13 * 999999 = xxxxxxxx. This means that you had to *set* the sum cell for column 2 equal to $\overline{0}0000000$. Then you added the entry for column 2 into the sum cell for column 2. (This is the *compute* box.) Then there was an unconditional decision, given by B 49, to return

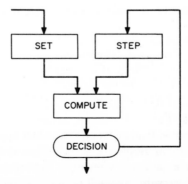

Fig. 21.   A basic module in programming.

to the beginning of the loop. The exercise does not have a *step* box, and we shall have to explain that later.

Figure 22 shows a flow chart suitable for the exercise of Subsection 13.7. As you can see, it is a variation of the basic module.

We shall discuss many *branch* instructions in this section. With the exception

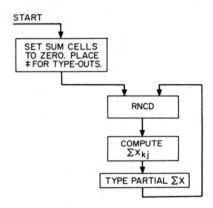

Fig. 22.   A modified basic module with a set box.

of B 49 which is an *unconditional* branch, all branches are logical decisions of the general form

$$(\text{OP}) \quad (\text{P-field}) \quad (\text{Q-field})$$

where the opcode and the Q-field, together, present a certain situation or condition. If the condition is satisfied, then the computer *branches* to the instruction whose address is given in the P-field. If the condition is not satisfied, then the computer *continues* to the next instruction, whatever that is. We realize this is a bit vague at this point, but everything will clear up as we go through the branch instructions.

14.2   BNF 44: BRANCH IF NO FLAG. USE IN HALF-ADJUSTING.

The command BNF 44 04536 19935 does the following:

1. The computer "looks" for a flag in memory cell 19935.
2. If there is no flag, the computer branches to the instruction in 04536.
3. If there is a flag, the computer continues to the instruction directly following the BNF instruction.

This logical decision has wide application. We shall apply it to a simple problem. Our problem is to half-adjust a number, xx.xxx, to two decimal places and punch it in a card in cc 52-55. The unadjusted number is in memory cells 15001-15005.

Before discussing the program, we shall consider four possibilities:

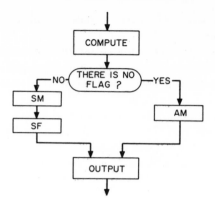

Fig. 23.   Flow chart of a portion of a program for half-adjustment at the flagged digit.

1. The number is in memory as $\overline{2}3459$. Then we may proceed as follows:

$$
\begin{array}{lll}
\text{AM} & 11 & 15005 \quad 000\overline{0}5 \\
\text{TF} & 26 & 19055 \quad 15004 \\
\text{WN} & 38 & 19001 \quad 00400
\end{array}
$$

The first of these instructions adds 5 to the third decimal place, so that the number in storage becomes $\overline{2}3464$. The second instruction transfers the field $\overline{2}346$ to positions 19052-19055. The third instruction punches a card with $\overline{2}346$ in the proper positions.

2. The number is in memory as $\overline{2}3452$. The same instructions operate correctly, and the half-adjusted result, $\overline{2}345$, appears on the card.

4. The number is −23.459, in storage as $\overline{2}3459$. The set of instructions shown in (1) will give incorrect results for two reasons. In the first place, the AM command will add .005 to −23.459, giving an answer of −23.454. The round-off will transfer $\overline{2}345$ instead of the correct answer, $\overline{2}34\overline{6}$. Notice that the negative flag was lost, and the wrong answer was obtained.

5. The number is −23.452, in storage as $\overline{2}345\overline{2}$. The instructions in (1) yield incorrect results.

It should be obvious that in the half-adjustment of negative numbers, the SM command should be used, rather than the AM command. For example, case (3) should be as follows:

$$
\begin{array}{lll}
\text{SM} & 12 & 15005 \quad 000\overline{0}5 \\
\text{SF} & 32 & 15004 \quad 00000 \\
\text{TF} & 26 & 19055 \quad 15004 \\
\text{WN} & 38 & 19001 \quad 00400
\end{array}
$$

The second command is necessary in order to replace the low-order flag which is needed in the result. The use of this sequence of instructions will give the correct result as $\overline{2}346$. (The original data in 15001-15005 is spoiled by these maneuvers. If this is unsatisfactory, the original data can be transmitted to a work cell, and the half-adjustment can be done in the work cell.)

This solution of the problem, i.e., using SM instead of AM, is perfectly satisfactory if we know whether the result is positive or negative. However, we usually do not know. We shall have to program the machine to use AM if there is no flag, and SM if there is.

The plan of action in this portion of a program is shown in Fig. 23. The logical decision to be made is indicated by the rounded box in the flow chart. If this statement is true (Yes), the program will *branch* (because the command is to branch if there is no flag). If the statement is false (No), then the program will *continue*. The program steps are shown in Fig. 24 and will repay careful study. Notice the use of the B 49 command.

There is one more case which is of considerable interest and importance.

BOARD OF EDUCATION OF THE CITY OF NEW YORK

THE BRONX HIGH SCHOOL OF SCIENCE
DR. ALEXANDER TAFFEL, PRINCIPAL

1620 Data Processing System

DEPARTMENT OF MATHEMATICS
DR. I. A. DODES, CHAIRMAN

IBM

PROGRAM INSTRUCTION SHEET

Application: ILLUSTRATIVE PROB., SECTION 5.2   Date: 10-12-62   Page: —— of ——

Routine: HALF-ADJUSTING   Written by: I.A. DODES

LOCATION	OPERATION MNEM.	OPERATION NUM.	P	Q	COMMENTS
\multicolumn{6}{l}{THE RESULT IS XX.XXXX IN 15051-15006 AND IS TO BE ROUNDED}
\multicolumn{6}{l}{TO XX.XXX. THIS PORTION OF A PROGRAM STARTS WITH AN}
\multicolumn{6}{l}{INSTRUCTION IN 06000. THE PUNCH-OUT ZONE IS 19001-19080.}
06000	BNF	44	{ }	15006	BRANCH IF NO FLAG
06012	SM	12	15006	00005	HALF-ADJUST BY SUBTRACTING
06024	SF	32	15005	00000	REPLACE NEGATIVE FLAG
06036	B	49	{ }	00000	
06048	AM	11	15006	00005	HALF-ADJUST BY ADDING
06060	TF	26	19055	15005	TF TO PUNCH-OUT ZONE
06072	WN	38	19001	00400	PUNCH A CLEAN CARD
\multicolumn{6}{l}{ }
NOTES:	\multicolumn{5}{l}{WHEN THE PROGRAM IS FIRST WRITTEN, YOU MUST LEAVE}
	\multicolumn{5}{l}{THE P-FIELDS BLANK IN INSTRUCTIONS 06000 AND 06036.}
	\multicolumn{5}{l}{AFTER THIS PORTION IS WRITTEN, YOU RETURN AND FILL}
	\multicolumn{5}{l}{IN AS FOLLOWS:}
06000	BNF	44	{06048}	15006	
06036	B	49	{06060}	00000	
06072	WN	38	19001	00400	

Fig. 24.   Half-adjusting at the flagged digit.

This is the case where a number in storage is of the form xxx.xxxxxx in 17005-17013, and is to be rounded to xxx.xx. *This is by far the most common case.* The first digit to be dropped is in 17010, *and this never has a flag.* In other words, if arithmetic is done on the part of the number which is in 17005-17010, then the computer will treat it as a positive number (since there is no flag on 17010). Therefore, half-adjustment can always be done by use of the AM command.

Of course, after the half-adjustment is done, the flag (if any) in 17013 must be placed on the low-order digit of the rounded result. The flow chart in Fig. 25

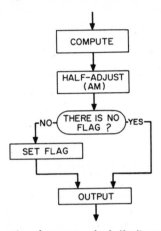

Fig. 25.   Flow chart for a portion of a program for half-adjustment not at the flagged digit.

shows the plan of action for this portion of the program, and the steps are shown in Fig. 26. If it is necessary to preserve the original (unrounded) number, the half-adjustment should be done in a work cell.

It is clear that this is much easier and more convenient. Therefore, it is always to our advantage to carry some extra digits beyond the one to be dropped.

PROJECTS

Re-examine your program for Subsection 13.7. Add steps to round each answer by one digit. Run the program.

14.3   DECIMAL POINTS AND MINUS SIGNS

For any mathematical purpose, an output like $\overline{0}02345\overline{6}$ is perfectly satisfactory (provided that we know where the decimal point is supposed to be). However, it certainly does not look good. We shall discuss, in this subsection, the problems of placing decimal points and minus signs, and (in Subsection 14.6) removing superfluous zeros.

Before doing this, we shall mention *packing*, a little trick that programmers use to save time and space. We have already mentioned that certain parts of certain instructions are not "read" by the computer. The following are some examples in

BOARD OF EDUCATION OF THE CITY OF NEW YORK

THE BRONX HIGH SCHOOL OF SCIENCE
DR. ALEXANDER TAFFEL, PRINCIPAL

1620 Data Processing System
PROGRAM INSTRUCTION SHEET

DEPARTMENT OF MATHEMATICS
DR. I. A. DODES, CHAIRMAN

IBM

Application: _ILLUSTRATIVE PROGRAM SECTION 5.2_ Date: _10-12-62_ Page: ___ of ___

Routine: _HALF-ADJUSTING, BEFORE THE FLAG_ Written by: _I. A. DODES_

LOCATION	OPERATION MNEM.	NUM.	P	Q	COMMENTS
			THE RESULT IS XXX.XXXXXX IN 17005-17013 AND IS		
			TO BE ROUNDED TO XXX.XX. THIS PORTION OF A		
			PROGRAM STARTS AT 05084.		
05084	AM	11	17010	00005	
05096	TF	26	19009	17009	
05108	BNF	44	05132	17013	
05120	SF	32	19009	00000	
05132	WN	38	19001	00400	

Fig. 26.   Half-adjusting, not at the flagged digit.

which the unread portions are represented by x:

01000	AM	11	12345	xxx$\overline{0}$5
01012	B	49	13456	xxxxx
01024	CF	32	12345	xxxxx
01036	H	48	xxxxx	xxxxx
01048	K	34	xxxxx	x01x8
01060	SF	32	12345	xxxxx
01072	TDM	15	12345	xxxx9

These are by no means all the examples. In general, I-O commands use only Q_8 and Q_9 in the Q-field of the instruction, and the same is true of all branch commands. In addition, there is a *No Operation* command, NOP 41, in which both P and Q-fields are unread. This command may be inserted anywhere. (It wastes 160 microseconds, so it should not be used inside a loop.)

All these unread spaces may be used for storage of numeric data. For example, consider the B 49 command in instruction 01012. Positions 01019 through 01023 are wasted. We may, if we like, *pack* data in this space. Suppose, for example, that we rewrite that instruction as

01012   B 49 13456 0200$\pm$

The instruction will still branch to 13456. We can, however, use the data in the Q-field. For example, the command

WA 39 01021 00100

will cause the typewriter to pick up the contents of (01020,01021), (01022,01023) . . . in pairs until an alphameric record mark is reached. What is in these locations? Looking back at Fig. 10, we see that (2,0) is an alphameric minus sign and (0,$\pm$) is an alphameric record mark. If the instruction is packed this way, we can therefore always use WA 39 01021 00100 to type or punch a minus sign.

Similarly, a decimal point is an alphameric (0,3) in even-odd positions. It is important, in packing, that you place the alphameric information in even-odd pairs. Remember that the address of the instruction is a *left address*, i.e., it is the address of the digit in O_0.

EXERCISES

The result of a certain computation is of the form xx.xxx in 19995-19999. There is a termination flag over 19995, and there may or may not be a negative flag over 19999. We wish to type it with a decimal point and, if necessary, with a minus sign, and without flags. In the following portion of a program, it is assumed that 19991-19993 has been reserved as a type-out zone, and that there is a record mark in 19994. Notice that the "whole number" part of the result is in 19995-19996, and the "decimal part" of the result is in 19997-19999. Explain each step of the program.

$$\begin{array}{ccc} \bullet & \bullet & \bullet & \bullet & \bullet \\ \bullet & \bullet & \bullet & \bullet & \bullet \end{array}$$

04644	BNF	44	04680	19999
04656	WA	39	04677	00100
04668	CF	33	19999	0200$\pm$
04680	TF	26	19993	19996
04692	CF	33	19992	0030$\pm$
04704	WN	38	19992	00100
04716	WA	39	04701	00100
04728	SF	32	19997	00000
04740	TF	26	19993	19999
04752	CF	33	19991	0140$\pm$
04764	WN	38	19991	00100
04776	WA	39	04761	00100

$$\begin{array}{ccc} \bullet & \bullet & \bullet & \bullet & \bullet \\ \bullet & \bullet & \bullet & \bullet & \bullet \end{array}$$

14.4 INDICATOR BRANCHES AND DECISIONS BY COMPARISON

After every arithmetic operation, the computer notes whether the result is positive, zero or negative. For example, when the command

A 21 18000 19000

is executed, there are three possibilities. Let p represent the original contents of the P-field and q represent the original contents of the Q-field. Then

$$p > -q \qquad (p + q) \text{ is positive}$$
$$p = -q \qquad (p + q) \text{ is zero}$$
$$p < -q \qquad (p + q) \text{ is negative}$$

Before discussing the indicators which distinguish between the above three cases, we shall also illustrate

$$\text{S } 22 \; 18000 \; 19000$$

$$p > q \qquad (p - q) \text{ is positive}$$
$$p = q \qquad (p - q) \text{ is zero}$$
$$p < q \qquad (p - q) \text{ is negative}$$

There are three indicators on the machine which can be interrogated about these three cases. The Q-addresses of these indicators are as follows:

01100 is the H/P (high-positive) indicator which is set (on) for the first case.

01200 is the E/Z (equal-zero) indicator which is set (on) for the second case.

01300 is the HP/EZ (high-positive or equal-zero) indicator which is set (on) for either the first case or the second case.

The *names* of the indicators (H/P, and so on) come from the *subtraction* command, reflecting the fact that the original intention was probably to compare the relative size of p and q. Note that after the A 21 instruction, the first condition exists even if $p < q$, provided that $(p + q)$ is positive.

To review:

1. When the result is positive, the H/P and HP/EZ indicators are *both* set.
2. When the result is zero, the E/Z and HP/EZ indicators are *both* set.
3. When the result is negative, all three indicators are reset (off).

The same stipulations apply to the other arithmetic operations, including the Immediate commands.

There are two *comparison* commands which are quasi-arithmetic. These two commands *simulate* a subtraction and adjust the indicators to the nature of the difference, $p - q$, but the actual subtraction is not done and the P-field is not destroyed or replaced. These two commands are

$$\text{C } \; 24 \; 14056 \; 13998$$

which *compares* C(13998) and C(14056) and adjusts the indicators according to C(14056) − C(13998), and

$$\text{CM } 14 \; 14056 \; 13\bar{9}98$$

which *compares immediately* the number 998 with C(14056) and adjusts the indicators according to C(14056) − 998.

The branch commands used in connection with these indicator settings are

BI   46 P Q = Branch to the P-address when the indicator addressed in Q is *set* (on)

BNI   47 P Q = Branch to the P-address when the indicator addressed in Q is *reset* (off)

Using these two commands, a logical decision can be made on the basis of a comparison.

In writing programs, we shall use the following abbreviations in the "Comments" column to make it easier to follow them:

{ BH   = Branch if p is "high" compared to q
{ BP   = Branch if p — q is positive

{ BE   = Branch if p = q
{ BZ   = Branch if p — q is zero

{ BNL = Branch if p is not "low" compared to q
{ BNN = Branch if p — q is not negative

{ BNH = Branch if p is "not high" compared to q
{ BNP = Branch if p — q is not positive

{ BNE = Branch if p is not equal to q
{ BNZ = Branch if p — q is not equal to zero

{ BL   = Branch if p is "low" compared to q
{ BN   = Branch if p — q is negative

The relationship of these *comments* to the BI ("Branch on indicator") and BNI ("Branch on no indicator") commands is shown in the following table:

Q-field	01100	01200	01300
BI 46	BH, BP	BE, BZ	BNL, BNN
BNI 47	BNH, BNP	BNE, BNZ	BL, BN

There are other indicators in the machine which may be addressed for one reason or another. A complete list is given in Appendix VI. However, we shall be concerned in this section with only one more:

$$\text{BI 46 xxxxx 00900 BLC}$$

which is a command to "branch on last card." You will remember that the last card of a deck does not feed in automatically. READER START button must be depressed. When this is done, Switch 9 is set, and a branch can be instituted on that basis.

PROJECTS

Your project for Subsection 13.7 stops on a "Read." Alter the program slightly so that it will branch to a "Halt" after the last data card is read in. Run your program.

14.5   ADDRESS MODIFICATION

Consider the problem of reading in 100 cards, each with xxxxx in cc 2-6. These cards are to be stored in memory in consecutive locations, beginning with 17000. How many instructions would be needed?

Let's start the program and see what happens:

01000	RN	36	14000	00500	RNCD into 14000-14079.
01012	SF	32	14001	00000	x̄xxxx in 14001-14005.
01024	TF	26	17004	14005	Transmits first entry to 17000-17004.
01036	RN	36	14000	00500	RNCD (second card) into 14000-14079.
01048	SF	32	14001	00000	x̄xxxx in 14001-14005.
01060	TF	26	17009	14005	Transmits second entry to 17005-17009.

.   .   .   .   .

.   .   .   .   .

It is clear that we would need 300 instructions just to read the cards and entries into the desired places in memory. Perhaps we can do with less!

Consider the first set of three instructions. They are precisely the same as the second set of three instructions and the third, and the fourth, . . . , except for the P-address in the third instruction of each set. If we could only tell the machine to repeat these three instructions until all the cards are read, increasing the P-address by five each time, then we would not need all these instructions.

There are many ways to accomplish this. The first way to be demonstrated is easiest in *this* problem, but all three methods are important for other problems we shall have.

In reading the following explanation, keep firmly in mind that the instruction in 01024-01035 actually contains a *number* in memory, 261700414005. In this number, the address of the "7," for example, is memory cell 01027.

METHOD I.   BY LAST CARD INDICATOR

In this method (see Fig. 27), six instructions will read in any number of cards, then proceed to the main body of the program. The only problem with this method is that if there is a card jam, and if the READER START button is depressed, Switch 9 will go on and the rest of the cards will not read in.

01000	RN	36	14000	00500
01012	SF	32	14001	00000
01024	TF	26	(17̄004)	14005
01036	BI	46	⊰{01072}⊱	00900
01048	AM	11	01030	000̄05
01060	B	49	01000	00000
01072	·	·	·	·

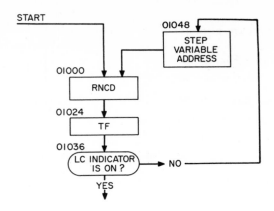

Fig. 27. Flow chart for BLC.

The braces in instruction 01036 means that the P-field would be left blank in writing the program until the programmer could calculate the proper address.

Notice the flag in instruction 01024 (the parentheses about the P-field remind the programmer that this is a variable address). If the number in that instruction were not flagged, the arithmetic instruction in 01048 would keep going until a flag was reached somewhere.

METHOD II. TERMINAL ADDRESS

We know that the first address for transfer is 17004, the second is $17004 + 5$, the third is $17004 + 2(5), \ldots$, the hundredth is $17004 + 99(5) = 17499$. We store the terminal address in work cell 19995-19999, thus setting the condition for our eventual comparison. In this example (see Fig. 28), we used the BNE condition to make the logical decision. However, we can save steps by using a slightly different arrangement. This will be left as an exercise at the end of this subsection.

```
01000 TFM  16  19999   00499
01012 RN   36  14000   00500
01024 SF   32  14001   00000
01036 TF   26  (17004) 14005
01048 C    24  19999   01042
01060 BNI  47  {01096} 01100
01072 AM   11  01042   00005
01084 B    49  01012   00000
01096  ·    ·     ·       ·
```

Although this method requires a little more thought than the BLC method, it is superior in that it provides a *positive termination* to the read-in (or other) portion of the program where the logical decision is to be made. In a sense, it is also valuable

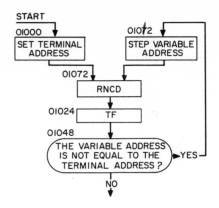

Fig. 28.   Flow chart for terminal address method.

because it forces the programmer to consider seriously the areas in memory which are being used. This is always valuable. We urge all programmers to keep in mind at all times exactly what is happening in the memory of the computer.

A programmer usually works with his program sheet and flow chart side by side. As he reaches each box in the flow chart, he writes, at the top, the address of the instruction which "enters" the box. This makes it much easier to fill in the branch instructions. Notice that in instruction 01084, a glance at the flow chart shows that the program must return to the step box, and that the entering instruction is 01072.

METHOD III.   COUNT CELL

We know that in this illustrative problem there are exactly 100 cards. We set a *count cell* equal to zero and we add *one* to the count cell every time we finish with a card. When the count gets to 100, the job is done. (See Fig. 29.)

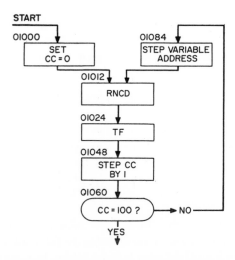

Fig. 29.   Flow chart for count cell method.

```
01000 TFM   16   19502   00̄000        Sets cc  (19500-19502)  to  000.
01012 RN    36   14000   00500
01024 SF    32   14001   00000
01036 TF    26  (17̄004)  14005
10148 AM    11   19502   0000̄1
01060 CM    14   19502   001̄00
01072 BI    46  {01108}  01200        BE
01084 AM    11   01042   0000̄5
01096 B     49   01012   00000
01108   •     •      •       •
```

This is our first illustration of the use of a number in a cell to control a program. When this is done, the memory cell (or area) is said to exercise an *executive* or *control* function over the program. This count cell (which actually includes, for this problem, *three* memory cells) is an executive cell. We shall see others throughout this book.

EXERCISES

1 Whenever a BI 46 command is used, it may be possible to save one (or more) steps by using a BNI 47 command, and vice versa. In all three methods, see what the change would have been if BI had been changed to BNI, or BNI had been changed to BI. This is not an easy exercise, but it is a valuable one for the programmer.

2 In Method II, we set the terminal address in 19995-19999, then compared the contents of this address with the variable address. We can eliminate the first step by using a CM (Compare Immediate) instruction instead of a C (Compare) command. Rewrite the program to save this step. Notice that the SET box appears to be eliminated when this is done. Actually, it is not eliminated; it is implicit in the Immediate command.

3 In Method III, we preset the count cell to zero before reading in the cards. We could have preset the count cell to *one*, meaning that the first card was about to be read in. How would this have altered the program?

14.6   BD 43: BRANCH ON DIGIT

In some programs, it is desirable to type the results (for nonmathematicians) without termination flags, without negative flags, with minus signs where appropriate, and without nonsignificant zeros to the left of the decimal point. We have already discussed much of this. We shall now attack the problem of eliminating zeros. To do this, we shall make use of the BD 43 command. The instruction

$$BD\ 43\ 15064\ 18007$$

means, "Look at the numeral in memory cell 18007. If it is *not* a zero, branch to the instruction in 15064. If it *is* a zero, continue to the instruction after this one."

For the purpose of our illustration, we shall assume that there is a three-digit number in 19997-19999 which we wish to type without leading zeros, unless the only digit is zero. We want a neat table of values, like

$$X$$
$$-47$$
$$0$$
$$356$$
$$-3$$
$$\cdot$$

rather than $\overline{0}47$, $\overline{0}00$, $\overline{3}56$, $\overline{0}0\overline{3}$, and so on.

Figure 30 shows some of the designated areas in the memory. Cell 19996 has a record mark; 19992-19995 is a four cell type-out zone; and 19887-19991 is a work cell which will contain the variable address for the eventual type-out instruction.

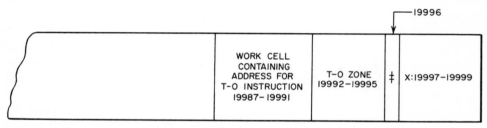

Fig. 30.   Some designated areas in memory.

For reasons which will appear later (in Subsections 14.9 and 14.10), we shall assume that this portion of a program starts away from the main body of the program, with the first instruction at 18000. Before entering this part of the program which we shall call the *type-out subroutine*, we will have cleared the type-out zone to zeros with the instruction

TFM 16 19995 0$\overline{0}$000

and added X into it with the command

A 21 19995 19999

so that the type-out zone contains X in the form $\overline{x}$xxx with a possible negative flag.

Our first instruction will clear the termination flag in 19992. In order to explain the remainder of the program, we must remind you that the *Write* instruction will have to be one of the following:

WN 38 19992 00100

WN 38 19993 00100

WN 38 19994 00100

WN 38 19995 00100

and that the logical decision will depend upon two facts:

1. Whether or not the digit being tested is zero.
2. Whether or not the digit being tested is the last digit.

If it is not the last digit, but is a zero, we shall wish to space once (to make the table "line up"). This is done by varying the "key instruction" or "variable instruction" so that it assumes the proper one of the four aspects shown above.

The flow chart for the program is shown in Fig. 31. In the program (see Fig. 32), we have indicated, by braces ⟨⟩, those addresses which would probably be filled in last, and by parentheses ( ), the variable part of the instruction. In the flow chart, the initial value of this variable address is filled in by an instruction, "Set initial address for testing," and the variable address is modified in the box which has "Step address for testing."

The precise operation of the program is left as an exercise. We may assume, for the present, that the necessity for typing out X arose in the original program at address 06588, that the command at 06600 was "B 49 18000 00000," and that the instruction at 18168 is "B 49 06612."

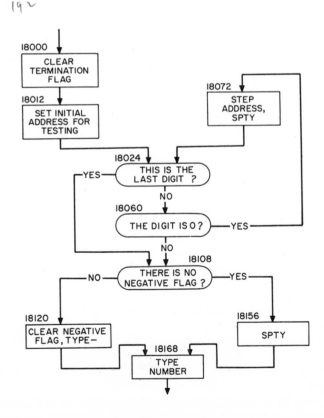

Fig. 31.   Flow chart for type-out subroutine.

EXERCISES

Explain each step of the sample type-out subroutine in Fig. 32.

BOARD .OF EDUCATION OF THE CITY OF NEW YORK

THE BRONX HIGH SCHOOL OF SCIENCE
DR. ALEXANDER TAFFEL, PRINCIPAL

1620 Data Processing System

DEPARTMENT OF MATHEMATICS
DR. I. A. DODES, CHAIRMAN

IBM

PROGRAM INSTRUCTION SHEET

Application: _TYPE-OUT SUBROUTINE_ Date: _10-13-62_ Page: ___ of ___

Routine: _____ Written by: _BERNARD COSELL_

LOCATION	OPERATION MNEM.	NUM.	P 0 1 2 3 4 5 6	Q 7 8 9 10 11	COMMENTS
18000	CF	33	19992	00000	
18012	TFM	16	19991	19992	
18024	CM	14	19991	19995	
18036	BI	46	{18108}	01200	BE
18048	TF	26	18071	19991	
18060	BD	43	{18108}	(00000)	
18072	AM	11	19991	00001	
18084	K	34	00000	00101	SPTY
18096	B	49	18024	0200≠	
18108	BNF	44	{18156}	19995	
18120	CF	33	19995	00000	
18132	WA	39	18105	00100	
18144	B	49	{18168}	00000	
18156	K	34	00000	00101	SPTY
18168	TF	26	18186	19991	
18180	WN	38	(00000)	00100	
18192	B	49	(00000)		(LINKAGE INSTRUCTION)

Fig. 32. Type-out subroutine.

PROJECTS

Write a subroutine, starting at 18000, which will insert decimal points and minus signs, and remove nonsignificant zeros. Assume that you have a number as large as xxxxxxxxxx.xxxxx to begin with. Set up a "whole number" T-O zone and a "decimal" T-O zone. In the latter, leading zeros should not be eliminated.

14.7   OPCODE MODIFICATION

The previous subsection dealt with the modification of an address. The crux of the matter was (and is) the fact that the entire instruction exists as a twelve-digit number in storage. Any part of this number may be modified, provided that it is properly flagged.

To show this, let us attack, once again, the problem of half-adjusting a number when the low-order digit is the one to be dropped. You will remember that in this case (when the number is negative) it is necessary to (*i*) subtract $\overline{0}5$, and (*ii*) replace the flag. The following portion of a program has no great merit. It is merely intended to illustrate the general idea of opcode modification in a simple manner.

ILLUSTRATIVE PROBLEM

In this problem, the number to be rounded is $\overline{x}xxxxxx$ (positive or negative) in memory cells 16001-16007. It is to be rounded to six figures. The flow chart is shown in Fig. 33. As in all programs with variable instructions, it is necessary to *set* the variable instruction so that it will be correct for the next card, or set of cards, to be read in.

01084	TFM	16	{01133}	00011̄
01096	BNF	44	{01132}	16007
01108	AM	11	{01133}	00001̄
01120	SF	32	16006	00000
01132	AM	(1̄1)	16007	00005̄
01144	•	•	•	•

We have placed braces, {}, about the addresses which would probably be left blank by the programmer, the first time around. In other words, he would not know that opcode 11 would be in memory cells 01132-01133 until he reached that instruction. Then he would go back and fill in the blanks.

14.8   DATA MODIFICATION

There are many programs in which some or all of the data are *generated* by the computer rather than read in on cards (or through some other input device).

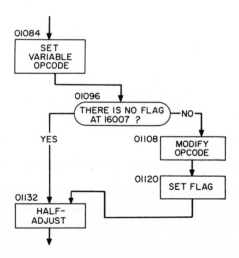

Fig. 33.   Flow chart for opcode modification.

As an illustration, consider the problem to find the sum of all the odd numbers from one to some predetermined *criterion value* or *termination value*, N. The computer is to type the headings, "X" and "SUM," then return the carriage and compute and type the current values of X_i and the sum. A data modification problem is a typical module consisting of a set-compute-logical decision-and-step system.

The flow chart is shown in Fig. 34.

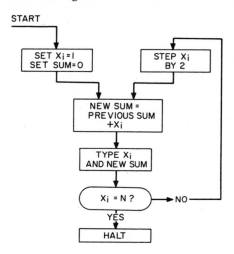

Fig. 34.   Flow chart for sum of odd integers.

EXERCISES

1   Using a terminal value of $N = 99$, write a program to satisfy the flow chart.

2   Write an alternative flow chart and program, using the count cell method.

PROJECTS

1. Using either method developed in the above exercise, add to your program a type-out routine (it will not be necessary to check for negative numbers), and run your program. (If you already have a satisfactory type-out routine which tests negative numbers, not too much time is lost. Be careful about removing cards from a debugged deck. Unfortunately, the variable addresses change.)

2. Write and run a program to compute and punch cards for the first 250 terms in the Fibonacci Sequence, 1, 1, 2, 3, 5, 8, 13, ...

14.9   SUBROUTINES WITH PROGRAMMED LINKAGES

From time to time, you find that the same sort of operation, such as a house-keeping operation, or the computation of square root or a type-out routine, is needed several times during the program. Instead of writing the same steps over and over again, a *subroutine* is written after the main body of the program and a *linkage* is made to get to the subroutine and back again.

For example, suppose that we have a subroutine (like the one in Fig. 32) which is in memory beginning at 18000 and ending with the instruction at 18192. We wish to have the program branch to the subroutine (at 18000), and in 18168 we wish to have the return address in the P-field (18170-18174).

Let us suppose further that we have just completed the instruction at 06744. We then write.

    06756 TFM 16 18174 0̄6780
    06768 B   49 18000 00000
    06780 •   •   •   •

The two instructions form a *linkage* which take the program to the subroutine, each time, and insert the *return address* at the proper place in the subroutine.

A second type of programmed linkage is one in which the return address is always placed in a work cell at a specified position, and the subroutine knows where to look for it. Suppose, for example, that 17995-17999 has been set aside as this work cell, and that in the main program we have the same return address placed there by the instruction

    06756 TFM 16 17999 0̄6780
    06768 B   49 18000 00000
    06780 •   •   •   •

Now the instructions in Fig. 32 are slightly altered. Delete the last three instructions and write the following four instructions:

    18168 TF 26 18186   17999
    18180 B   49 (00000) 00000
    18192 AM 11 19991   0000̄1
    18206 B   49 18024   00000

The first two of these subroutine instructions now form their own linkage back to the main program.

Ordinarily, if you are going to program a linkage, the first of these methods is more satisfactory (since it saves a step), but you will see in the next subsection that there is an automatic device which does the equivalent of the second method.

14.10   BB 42: BRANCH BACK

The Branch and Transmit instruction,

    BT 27 07200 06026

takes the field with the *right address* 06026 and places it at the field with the *right address* 07219. At the same time, it stores in an internal register the *return address*. Then it branches to the instruction at 07200. This amazing command is one of the most compact of all those in the IBM 1620 instructions. Let us say that we have written a program which ends at instruction 17964 and we wish to use a subroutine which begins at 18000. The program instruction sheet would look like this:

```
17964 H      48 00000 00000
17976 NOP    41 00000 00000
17988 NOP    41 00000 00000
18000 CF     32 17999 00000
```

           .   .   .   .   .

           .   .   .   .   .

We designate the area from 17976 through 17999 as the type-out zone, for example. When we wish to type something, we write

04744 BT 27 18000 19999

This takes the field at 19999, places it at 17999, and makes an internal record that the next step in the main portion of the program is at 04756.

How do we get back to the main body of the program? Nothing could be easier. We merely write, at the end of the subroutine,

BB 42 00000 00000

The computer "looks" in the internal register, finds the next address, and returns to that address.

There is also an Immediate command which acts similarly:

BTM 17 18000 12$\overline{3}$45

This places $\overline{3}$45 in memory cells 17997-17999, stores in its internal register the return address (whatever that is), and branches to 18000. The BB command, at the end of the subroutine, returns the program to the proper place.

You may wonder why anyone bothers with programmed linkages when this automatic linkage is available. The reason is that the automatic internal register will save only one return address at a time. We will often have occasion to use a series of loops, one inside the other. In this case, you *must* program the linkage.

EXERCISES

1 What will happen if you forget to place a flag in the Q-field of the BTM 17 command?

2 Rewrite the type-out subroutine so that it makes use of a BT 27 and BB command.

PROJECTS

1. *Numeric fill.* Write a subroutine which will take a positive or negative number (in numeric form) and, by inserting sevens, change it to alphameric form.

2. *Numeric strip.* Write a subroutine which will take a positive or negative number in alphameric form in the memory and, by removing sevens, change it to numeric form. It will be necessary to watch for negative numbers which may not have sevens. For example, a $\overline{3}$ in alphameric form is an L, i.e., 53.

3. Write a program to read in Table I (for which you prepared data cards in Subsection 13.7), type a table with proper spacing and in the usual form (no flags, no nonsignificant zeros, decimal points placed in the proper places, etc.), and, at the end, the total for each column. Use subroutines to do all the house-keeping. Be careful not to put one BT or BTM inside another.

14.11 PROGRAM MODIFICATION

Sometimes it is desired to have a very general program in the machine, but to have this program modified from time to time for special reasons. There are several methods, mentioned in Parts Three and Four, which deal with less elementary problems; but we shall concern ourselves with only two at this point: control by Program Switches, and control by executive cells.

The Program Switches are numbered "1," "2," "3," and "4" on the IBM 1620 console. These Program Switches may be addressed in Q_8 and Q_9, just like the other indicator switches. For example,

$$\text{BI } 46 \; 04756 \; 00200$$

means "Branch to instruction 04756 if Program Switch 2 is *on*, otherwise go to the next instruction."

$$\text{BNI } 47 \; 04756 \; 00400$$

means "Branch to instruction 04756 if Program Switch 4 is *off*, otherwise go to the next instruction."

The load program in Appendix I makes use of Program Switch 1. When Program Switch 1 is "on," the typewriter (slowly) makes a listing of your instructions. When Program Switch 1 is "off," no listing is made and the procedure is much faster. (In a long program, a considerable amount of valuable computer time can be saved by listing your machine language or other program cards on the IBM 407 before going to the computer.)

To illustrate the executive cell control, suppose that a set of mixed IBM cards are to be read into the machine. Each card has a *code number*, from "0" to "6" in cc 76. There is a different subroutine to be used depending upon the code number in the card. The data to be used in the program are in cc 24-26 of the IBM card.

The main body of the program is as follows (see Fig. 35):

01000	RN	36	19001	00500	RNCD into 19001-19080.
01012	TD	25	~(01040)~	19076	Forms variable instruction.
01024	SF	32	19024	00000	Flags the data in cc 24-26.
01036	BT	27	(07000)	19026	(See text.)

In the instruction at 01036, the program will branch to 07000, 07100, 07200, . . . , 07600, depending upon the code number. If the code number is "2," the branch will take place to 07200, the data will go in 07197-17199, and (at the end of the

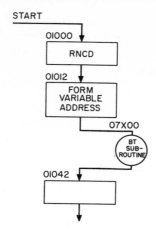

Fig. 35.   Use of subroutines under executive cell control.

subroutine) a BB instruction will bring the program back to instruction 01042.

Another use of the executive cell is in the construction of *alternate* programs. When used this way, the cell is sometimes called an *alternator*.

In order to explain this, we shall propose an illustrative problem and outline its solution.

ILLUSTRATIVE PROBLEM I

A deck of IBM cards has two numbers on each. A = xxx is in cc 1-3, and B = xxx is in cc 4-6. On the first card, we are to find (A + B), then punch A, B, and (A + B) in cc 1-3, 5-7, and 8-11 of a clean card. On the second card, we are to find (A − B), then punch A, B, and (A − B) in cc 1-3, 5-7, and 8-11 of a clean card. Thereafter, the problem alternates as the cards alternate.

Discussion: We shall leave the program steps as an exercise. The flow chart is shown in Fig. 36. First, we set up a work cell in 19995-19999 with $\overline{0}0000$. (The size of the work cell will depend upon the number of cards to be handled.) The executive control cell is the last cell of this work cell, namely, 19999. We read in the card. Now we use the BD 43 command in connection with the executive cell. If it is zero, we compute (A + B) and store it in the proper part of the punch zone. If the executive control cell is a digit *not zero*, then we compute (A − B) and store the result in the proper part of the punch zone (the same part, for this problem). The first card will have a zero, so (A + B) will be computed. After punching the card, we find out if it is the last card. If it is not, we add "5" to the work cell. Now the executive control cell is not zero, and the BD 43 command will cause the program to shift to (A − B). The next time around, the addition of another "5" will cause the executive control cell to revert to zero.

EXERCISES

1   Write the instructions for the above illustrative problem.

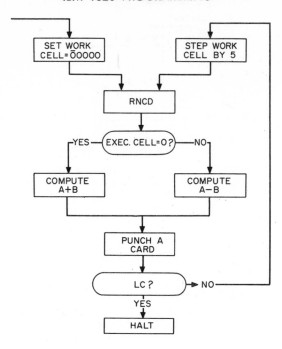

Fig. 36.   Use of BD 43 with executive cell.

2   How would you devise an executive control cell which would cause *five* different programs to take place in sequence?

PROJECTS

No person can call himself a serious programmer unless he has analyzed the load program which he is using. You now have enough information to be able to go through the load program in Appendix I and explain exactly what it does. (Omit cards 5 though 8, and the first 14 cc of card 9, which merely contain addition and multiplication tables.) You are earnestly invited to take the time to do this.

Section 15.   Problems Involving Multiplication and Division

15.1   THE PRODUCT-QUOTIENT AREA

When two numbers are multiplied or divided in a machine language program, the memory cells in 00080 through 00099 are automatically cleared to zero, and the result of the multiplication or division forms in that field. If more places are needed for the result, these must be provided by the program, e.g., by using a TFM or TF command with the required number of zeros. We shall refer to this zone in the memory as the *product-quotient area.*

Unlike the situation in addition and subtraction, the original data is neither destroyed nor replaced when multiplication or division takes place.

15.2   M 23, MULTIPLY, AND MM 13, MULTIPLY IMMEDIATE

The command M 23 10007 12455 multiplies the C(10007) by C(12455), clears spaces 00080-00099, and places the product in the product-quotient zone with the address 00099. A flag for termination is automatically provided at the leftmost digit of the product. If the product is negative, a negative flag is automatically placed at 00099. If the product is to be rounded, the negative flag must be relocated via a BNF 44 decision as shown previously.

The command MM 13 10007 25$\overline{2}$37 multiplies C(10007) by the Q-data, 237. The results are as in the M 23 command. *Bec. the 1st effect of M 23 is to clear 00080 - 00099, one can't expect to require a no. by the command M 23   00095   00099*

ILLUSTRATIVE PROBLEM I

A number of the form ② . ⑫ is in 16001-16014 (with a termination flag), and a number of the form ⑤ . ⑦ is in 15001-15012 (with a termination flag). Multiply, round to the correct accuracy, and store in memory beginning with memory cell 19060.

Solution: (Refer to Subsections 3.1 and 3.2.) The product will be of the form ⑦ . ⑲ , requiring twenty-six memory cells in the product-quotient zone. Twenty cells from 00080 through 00099, are provided automatically. We shall have to clear six more, i.e., from 00074 through 00079. The whole number part of the answer is in 00074 through 00080, and the decimal part of the number is in 00081 through 00099. We symbolize this in the diagram:

$\overline{x}xxxxxx.xxxxxxxxxxxx$

00074   00080   00081   00099

The negative flag, if any, is at 00099 and we wish to round off at 00087 (by the Rule of Accuracy). In the following portion of a program, we assume that the load program has placed $\overline{0}$ in memory cell 00658, and zeros in 00659 through 00682:

05012	TF	26	00079	00663	Clears 00074-00079 to zero.
05024	M	23	16014	15012	
05036	AM	11	00088	000$\overline{0}$5	Half-adjust.
05048	BNF	44	05072	00099	If no flag, skip a step.
05060	SF	32	00087	00000	
05072	TF	26	19073	00087	Transmits rounded number.
05084	•	•	•	•	

EXERCISES

1 A = xx.xxx, B = xx.x, C = x.xxx. These are punched (without decimal points, but with flags) in cc 1-5, 11-13, and 21-24 of an IBM card. Write a program to find A $*$ C $-$ B, round to one decimal place, and punch the results as follows: A (cc 1 ff), B (cc 11 ff), C (cc 21 ff), and the result is (cc 31 ff).

2 Write a program to find $\Sigma(X^2)$ and $(\Sigma X)^2$ for each column of Table I, using the data cards you have already prepared in the exercise of Subsection 13.7.

3 Write a program to generate the data and find

$$\sum_{k\,=\,1}^{k\,=\,99} (-1)^k * k$$

then type k and the sum in two columns, without nonsignificant zeros or flags.

4 Write a program to evaluate a 3×3 determinant, where each entry is of the form xxxxx, and one *column* of entries is on an IBM card.

5 Write a program to multiply two 3×3 matrices, where each entry is of the form xxxxx, and a *column* of entries is on each IBM card.

6 You are given that $y = ax^3 + bx^2 + cx + d$, where a = xxx.xx, b = xx.xx, c = x.xx, and d = xxx.xx. Find and type a table of values for y as x goes from 0 to 1 in intervals of 0.1.

7 A somewhat more efficient procedure is to use *nesting*. This means that the polynomial in (6) is rewritten as

$$y = x(x(ax + b) + c) + d$$

Write the program, using nesting.

PROJECTS

Run the program which you have written. Be sure you have a test program for which you know the correct answers. If you have difficulty, refer to Section 16 on *Debugging*.

15.3 AUTOMATIC DIVISION: LD 28 AND D 29

You will remember that we have assumed no special features on the IBM 1620 except automatic division. (Other special features include indirect addressing, numeric strip and fill, and automatic floating point.) Automatic division requires a *pair* of commands, one to position the dividend, and one to position the divisor.

The LD 28 (*Load Dividend*) command clears 00080-00099 and positions the dividend (the Q-data) in the field with the *right address* given by P. The negative flag, if any, is at 00099.

The D 29 (*Divide*) command positions the divisor (the Q-data) in the field with *right address* given by P, then initiates the division. The quotient is formed in the product-quotient zone with the negative flag, if any, at the proper place in the quotient (on the low-order digit). The quotient is a numeric field and must, therefore, be at least two digits in length. It is advantageous to develop an extra figure in order to facilitate rounding off.

The addresses for positioning the dividend and divisor must be calculated. Two examples are given in the following.

ILLUSTRATIVE PROBLEM I

We wish to divide xx.xx by xx.x and obtain a rounded answer of the form xxx.xx.

The automatic division device operates in such a way that the remainder is as long as the divisor and occupies a field with address 00099. Therefore, since the divisor has three digits, the remainder will also have three digits. It will occupy positions 00097, 00098, and 00099, as shown in the following diagram:

$$\bullet \quad \bullet \quad \bullet \quad 90 \quad 91 \quad 92 \quad 93 \quad 94 \quad 95 \quad 96 \mid 97 \quad 98 \quad 99$$
$$\mid R \quad R \quad R$$

The problem can be slightly rewritten by moving the decimal points so that we have the following requirements:

$$\frac{\text{xxx.x}}{\text{xxx}} = \text{xxx.xxxx}$$

We have made the divisor a whole number, and we have left two extra digits in the result in order to facilitate round-off. The result has *seven* digits, and will, therefore, occupy positions 00090 though 00096. So far, our diagram of the product-quotient zone looks like this:

$$\bullet \quad \bullet \quad \bullet \quad 90 \quad 91 \quad 92 \quad 93 \quad 94 \quad 95 \quad 96 \mid 97 \quad 98 \quad 99$$
$$Q \quad Q \quad Q \quad Q \quad Q \quad Q \quad Q \mid R \quad R \quad R$$

There are two further rules to remember (both being required because of the nature of the Automatic Division procedure):
1. The divisor's leftmost digit is always one position to the right of the quotient's leftmost digit.
2. The leftmost digit of the dividend is at the same position as the rightmost digit of the divisor.

Using these two rules, the diagram of the product-quotient zone is as follows:

$$\bullet \quad \bullet \quad \bullet \quad 90 \quad 91 \quad 92 \quad 93 \quad 94 \quad 95 \quad 96 \quad 97 \quad 98 \quad 99$$
$$Q \quad Q \quad Q \quad Q \quad Q \quad Q \quad Q \quad R \quad R \quad R$$
$$DR \quad DR \quad DR$$
$$DD \quad DD \quad DD \quad DD$$

The divisor is, therefore, in 00091-00093 and the dividend is in 00093-00096.

Using the locations shown in the diagram, we can now write the program. In the following, it is assumed that the divisor is now in 09982-09984, and the dividend is now in 09985-09988, both with high-order flags (and possible negative flags). We want the quotient to be stored in 19001-19005, rounded according to the methods discussed under BNF 44, but not to the final accuracy. (We often keep extra digits in the intermediate stages of a calculation, then scale the final answer.)

$$\begin{array}{c} \bullet \quad \bullet \quad \bullet \quad \bullet \quad \bullet \\ \bullet \quad \bullet \quad \bullet \quad \bullet \quad \bullet \end{array}$$

```
05000 LD    28 00096 09988
05012 D     29 00093 09984
05024 AM    11 00095 00005
05036 BNF   44 05060 00096
05048 SF    32 00094 00000
05060 TF    26 19005 00094
05072  •     •     •      •
```

ILLUSTRATIVE PROBLEM II

We wish to divide xx.xxx by x.xx and obtain an answer with four decimal places after rounding.

In scaling a division, we always allow for the worst possible situation. For example, to accomplish the above, we will analyze the problem as follows:

1. Rewrite the problem with a whole number divisor, i.e., as xxxx.x/xxx.
2. The largest possible numerator is 9999.9, and the smallest possible denominator is 001. Therefore, in the "worst" case, the answer could be 9999.9000 after rounding.
3. To ease the half-adjustment, we shall allow a quotient of the form QQQQ.QQQQQQ (two extra digits).
4. Now the diagram looks like this:

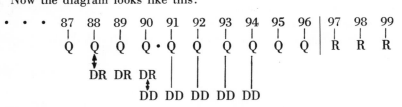

5. The instructions will be:

$$\text{LD } 28 \; 00094 \; Q$$

where Q is the right address of the dividend, and

$$\text{D } 29 \; 00090 \; Q$$

where Q is the right address of the divisor.
6. The round-off will be done at 00095, the transmission of a possible negative flag from 00096 to 00094, and the transmission of the result from 00094.

15.4 LDM 18 AND DM 19

These are Immediate commands. In the usual way, they use the Q-field as *data* rather than as an *address*.

EXERCISES

1 Write a program to find, Mean $= \dfrac{\Sigma X}{N}$ for each column of Table I. Use the data cards prepared for the project of Subsection 13.7.

2 Write a program to find σ^2 (the variance) for each column of Table I. (Refer to Subsection 6.4)

PROJECTS

Run your program for either exercise 1 or 2.

15.5 AN EQUATION PROBLEM

In this and the next subsection, we shall describe rather briefly the technique for *terminating on precision*. This has already been discussed in Subsection 9.4 and the reader is urged to refresh his memory by turning to that text.

We wish to evaluate an algebraic expression to a predetermined amount of precision. In the problem to be illustrated, the computer calculates a quantity, y, iteratively until the error in x is less than some *criterion quantity*, p.

The equation is, for example,

$$y = 2.00075\ x^4 + 4.27668\ x^3 + 3.11493\ x^2 - 1.75443\ x - 7.91258 = 0$$

and we wish to find the smallest positive root correct to six decimal places.

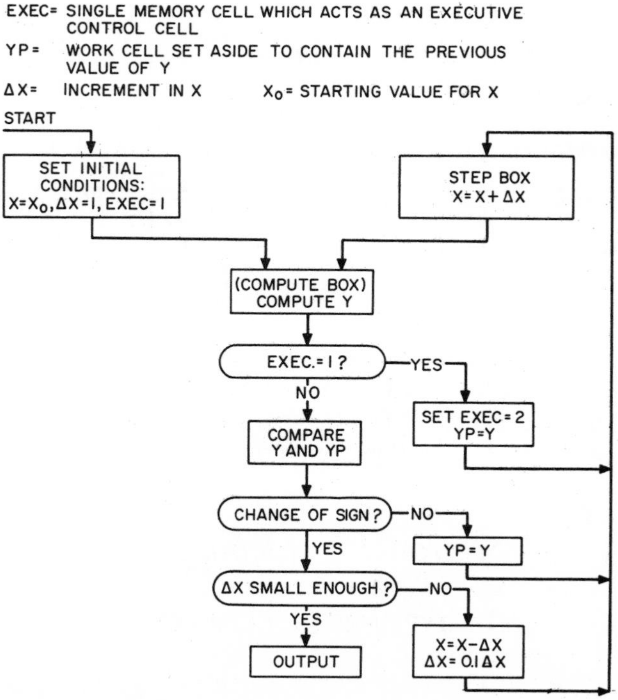

Fig. 37.   Flow chart for solving an equation to a required degree of precision, P.

In other words,

$$p \leqq 5 * 10^{-7}$$

A possible flow chart for this problem is shown in Fig. 37.

We remind you that the statement, $X = X + \Delta X$, means (in computer terminology) "Replace the previous value of X by the value $X + \Delta X$."

We shall not go into the program steps because all this can be done much more easily by the methods of advanced programming included in Parts Three and Four. However, some students find it fun to write the program and run it. Not too many steps are required. The answer comes out almost immediately!

If you intend to write this program, here is a hint. To find the absolute value of a number, transmit a copy to a work cell, then clear the negative flag. (If there is no negative flag, no harm is done.)

15.6   PROBLEMS INVOLVING INFINITE SERIES

We have already discussed (in Part One) the theory for finding the sum of an infinite series to any degree of precision. The easiest kind of series to evaluate is one in which the successive terms alternate, and there is a simple recursive relationship for successive terms. Such a series is

$$\sin x = x - \frac{x^3}{3!} + \frac{x^5}{5!} - \ldots \qquad \text{(valid for all values of x)}$$

EXERCISES

The following exercises refer to the sine series.

1 What is the general term, u_n?

2 What is u_{n+1}?

3 What is the recursion formula which gives u_{n+1} in terms of u_n?

4 Make a flow chart to find sin x, for x in $\left[0, \frac{\pi}{2} \right]$, with error less than 10^{-6}.
The first value of x should be 0 (radians), and the value of x should be incremented by 0.01 radian.

PROJECTS

Write a program based upon your flow chart with the following addition: if Switch 1 is on, the computer will type X and SIN X in a tabular arrangement; if Switch 1 is off, the computer will punch cards with X and SIN X in card columns beginning with cc 1 and cc 20. Run your program.

Section 16. Debugging

16.1   TYPEWRITER CORRECTIONS

As the typewriter lists your program you may find, to your horror, that among the instructions are:

01120 16 23078 00758   Where you wanted 16 13078 00758.
01132 32 A1147 00000   Which you meant to discard.
01144 32 01147 00000   (All right.)

.   .   .   .

.   .   .   .

If you wish, you can make on-the-spot corrections by performing the following after the entire program is loaded:

1. Press INSERT.
2. To correct the first instruction (at 01120) type:

$$15\ 01122\ 00001$$

$$15\ 01129\ 0000\overline{7}$$

(Of course, you do not space these. We have done it to make the instructions easier to read. You may, however, return the carriage after each instruction to make your corrections easier to read. This does no harm.)

3. To eliminate the instruction at 01132, type:

$$41\ 00000\ 00000$$

4. To return to the program, type:

$$49\ 01000\ 00000$$

(if you are using the load program in Appendix I).
5. Now press the R-S button. The computer will make the corrections and immediately start executing your program as amended.

If you make an error while typing the corrections, press RELEASE, RESET, INSERT, and start again on the correction routine.

If there are many corrections, this is a great waste of computer time. Incidentally, the typewriter will not accept more than eight correction instructions on an INSERT, since the INSERT places material into 00000-00099, only.

16.2   THE IBM 1620 CONSOLE

Figure 38 shows the Indicator Displays and Switches on the 1620 Console.

In machine language programs, the PARITY, I-O, and O'FLOW switches are ordinarily set to STOP. This means that if there is an error which *sets* one of these switches, the computer will stop. The type of error is shown in the check lights in line with the switches. A PARITY check may be an internal data transmission error. In this case, you may try running the program again. If there are repeated PARITY or I-O checks, it may be that you are trying to read alphamerically in or out of an even-numbered address. If, however, you are sure that your program is correct,

Fig. 38.   Indicator displays and switches.

try a program which has run previously. If this does not run, call for the customer engineer. There may be a damaged brush. Experience shows, however, that 999 times out of a 1000 the error is in the programming.

If the O'FLOW check light is on, it may mean that you are adding a Q-field with six digits, for example, to a P-field with only five. Look for this kind of error. Also, look for missing flags, especially in Immediate commands. There are also overflow errors connected with division, if the dividend and divisor are not positioned correctly.

16.3   GENERAL DEBUGGING PROCEDURES

In a class situation, you cannot "tie up" the machine. You must gather whatever information you can, then retire to a quiet place and reconsider your program, step-by-step. The following systematic procedure (for machine language programs) should be read in connection with Fig. 38 (Indicator Displays and Switches) and Fig. 39 (Register Display Indicators):

1. Make a note of the check lights, as shown in Fig. 38. At the same time, note the check lights on the READ unit and PUNCH unit of the IBM 1622. If the stop was caused by misreading or mispunching, it may be because of an incorrectly punched card. On the READ side, check to see that your cards are punched

correctly. Be very suspicious of smudges on your program cards. They may indicate a multiple-punch error. On the PUNCH side, check to see that the holes are punched in the correct row and column. If this is the trouble, depress CHECK RESET on the IBM 1622, then INSERT 49 01000 00000, on the typewriter, and start again. Repeated errors may indicate program errors or brush trouble.

There is one other *stop* which occurs that you should know about. The *punch*

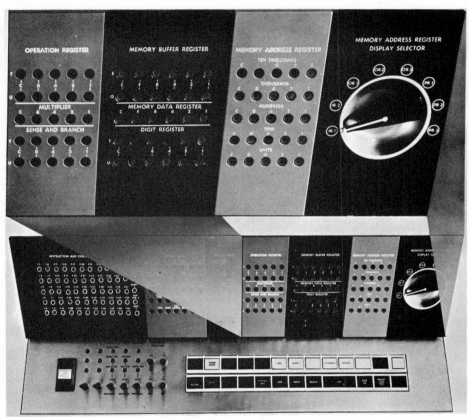

Fig. 39. Register display indicators.

unit throws the little pieces of cardboard into a basket inside the machine. When this is filled, the CHIPS light goes on, and the machine stops. In this case, just empty the basket, press CHECK RESET, and continue.

2. Note the opcode from the OPERATION register (the leftmost register in Fig. 39). The top row is O_0 and the next row is O_1. To translate the lights into an opcode, just add the values as shown in the lights. For example, if the top row has (C,2,1) and the next row has (8), the opcode is 38, or "Write Numerically." This is the opcode for the instruction last executed. Write this down.

3. In the same panel, note the SENSE AND BRANCH register. This tells you the Q_8 and Q_9 address of the branch instruction, i.e., the address of the switch being

operated.

4. Depress RESET, then turn the Memory Address Register Display Selector (MARDS) to position IR-1. Now depress the DISPLAY key on the console. The Memory Address Register (MAR) now tells you the address of the *next* instruction, i.e., the instruction after the one which caused the computer to stop. To find out which instruction caused the trouble, just subtract 12. Write this down.

5. Using the same procedure, turn the MARDS to position IR-2. MAR will show you the address being saved by a BT 27 or BTM 17 command. Write this down.

6. Using the same procedure, turn the MARDS to position OR-1. This tells you the Q-field of the instruction last executed. Write this down.

7. Using the same procedure, turn the MARDS to position OR-2. This tells you the P-field of the instruction last executed. Write this down.

(By this time, you have enough information to tell *where* and sometimes *why* the stop occurred. However, there are two more items in the procedure which are of great importance.)

8. Before running a program, you should at least know the *left addresses* of each sum cell and work cell, and (even better) the place in storage where the designated areas begin. Dump this designated area either on the typewriter (35xxxxx00100) or on cards (35xxxxx00400). The card dump is, of course, much faster and should always be used if (*i*) there is a great deal to be dumped, and (*ii*) you have a machine which will list your cards, such as the IBM 407.

9. Lastly, it is wise to dump that part of your program which was not executed (starting at the address given in IR-1 minus 12). Sometimes an error destroys part of your program.

16.4   SOME FINAL REMARKS

Part Two has dealt in detail with machine language programming. In general, complex programs are *not* done in machine language. There is just too much chance for error, and it takes too long to program and debug.

However, your time has not been wasted. If you have mastered the simple programs thus far, Parts Three and Four should be quite easy. Besides, all debugging must be done in machine language, basically, so all was not lost.

We wish you good luck!

PART THREE

The Symbolic Programming System (SPS)

Interpretive Programs

It is rare, indeed, that any programmer (no matter how adroit) will have his program "go through" on the very first try. In fact, such an occurrence is sufficient excuse for exclamations of surprise and outcries of joy!

There are five major areas of error which will be mentioned presently. As programs become longer and more complex, these errors seem to increase in number exponentially, wasting the valuable time of the programmer and the computing machine.

Some of these errors can be avoided or eliminated by writing the program *symbolically*, allowing the machine to interpret the symbols into numbers, and to punch out the machine language cards for the programmer. There are many kinds of interpretive programs which compile and assemble the final program. This book will discuss two of them: the *Symbolic Programming System* (SPS), and the *Formula Translation System* (FORTRAN).

The first of these is very much like machine language and is probably the most efficient way to write a program in terms of machine time and space. The second of these, discussed in Part Four, is the most efficient in terms of programming time, but not in terms of machine time and space.

Part Three contains a general introduction to SPS, a detailed discussion of a sample program involving some arithmetic and logic with input and output, a sample program involving matrix and vector operations, and statistical and iterative programs involving *floating point* operations and subroutines.

Section 17. An Introduction to SPS

17.1   FIVE PROBLEMS OF PROGRAMMING

As you know by this time, most programs, if not all, are made up of parts, each of which usually has a form somewhat like that shown in Fig. 40. In this figure, HK stands for *housekeeping,* such as placing and removing flags, record marks, nonsignificant zeros, and so on.

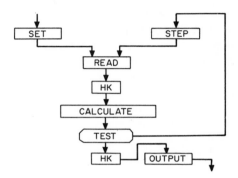

Fig. 40.   A module in a flow chart for SPS.

The five problems which seem to bring about the most errors are: (*i*) addressing, (*ii*) stepping, (*iii*) branch instructions, (*iv*) housekeeping, and (*v*) scaling. The first four of these are handled easily by ordinary SPS, and the last by Floating Point SPS.

17.2   PROCESSING AN SPS PROGRAM

The SPS compiler is called a *two-pass processor.* The order of events is as follows:

1. The program is written in symbolic language, SPS. The resulting deck of cards is called the *source program.* In general, the source deck consists of two different "kinds" of cards: first, *instructions* to be translated from symbolic language to machine language; and second, *area designations* which remove the necessity for doing all the arithmetic needed in a straight machine language program. The very first card is usually a *comment card* which identifies the program for your file of source decks. The second card tells the machine where to place the first instruction (memory cell 00402 or any even-numbered memory cell above this one).

2. *Pass I.* The SPS processor is *loaded.* This deck "tells" the machine how to translate your program.

3. The source program is *read* into the machine. The machine now reads the source

program, card by card, computes the number of spaces needed for instructions, and identifies each designated area with an address (left, right, or left-plus-one). This identification within the machine is called a *table of equivalences*.

4. *Pass II.* The source program is read into the machine a second time. The machine (under switch control) now translates the symbolic instructions into machine language instructions. If the switches are set to prepare punched cards, a deck of cards with machine language instructions will ensue. This resultant deck is called the *object program*. It contains a load program (with arithmetic tables) and your translated instructions.

5. The object program is now loaded into the machine to execute your instructions.

The expression "two-pass" refers to the number of passes for the source program, and not to the total number of passes through the machine. As can be seen, many passes are needed before the program is executed. However, the saving in programming time more than compensates for the added machine time.

In writing a source program, the instructions and area designations are usually written simultaneously on separate sheets. Each area designation is made at the moment when this designation becomes necessary. (We shall explain this fully.)

The writing of instructions is easy and uncomplicated. For pedagogical reasons, we shall start with area designations. Figure 41 shows an SPS card designed to make the checking of a program easy.

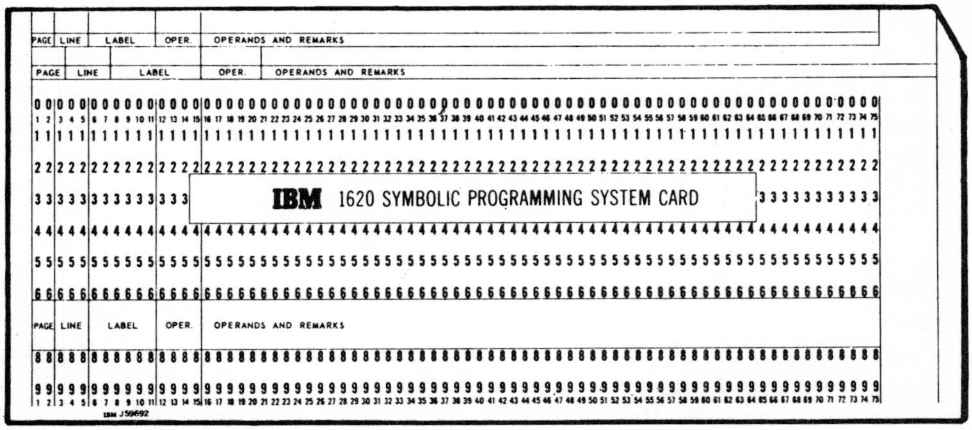

Fig. 41. SPS card.

17.3 PROBLEM OF ADDRESSING

One of the sources of difficulty and error is the fact that arithmetic areas are addressed at the *right* end, transfer areas sometimes at the *right* end (as in TF 26) and sometimes at the *left* end (as in TR 31), and alphameric areas are addressed at the *left-end-plus-one* with the left end in an even location. A second source of difficulty is the housekeeping associated with termination and negative *flags*.

The following subsections will dispose of this problem.

17.4   RIGHT ADDRESS AREAS: DS, DC, DNB

Suppose that you wish to set aside an area nine places long for ΣX and another four places wide for N. You might, in a machine language program, decide to reserve 19991-19999 for ΣX and 19987-19990 for N. The address of ΣX would be 19999, and the address of N would be 19990, so far as arithmetic operations and TF 26 were concerned. If you wished to print or punch these, the addresses would be 19991 for ΣX and 19987 for N. It is quite easy to become a little careless and write a digit incorrectly on your input program cards, and it is quite difficult to find this kind of error.

In SPS, this addressing is done a little differently. Figure 42 shows the coding sheet for an SPS program. The numbers (from 1 to 75) represent the card columns of your input card. Card columns 1 and 2 are at the top right after the words "Page No.," cc 3-5 are under the "Line" column, cc 6-11 are under the "Label" column, cc 12-15 are under the "Operation" column, and cc 16-75 are under the "Operands and Remarks" column.

In Fig. 42, the numbers in cc 1-2 show that this is programming page number 7 and that there are 8 pages of program in all. This is the first page of programming devoted to *area designation*. It is customary to punch a heading card as, e.g.

07010*AREA DESIGNATIONS

to head this part of your program deck. The asterisk (*) in cc 6 informs the SPS Processor Deck (about which we shall have much more to say, later) that this is *not* part of the program. In other words, this card is here for your convenience.

Card 07020 is typed as follows:

07020SUMXbbDSbb9

where the b's stand for blank spaces. The effect of this area designation is to set aside nine spaces somewhere in the machine, the *right* address of which is represented by the symbol SUMX. Whenever you wish to refer to this sum cell for arithmetic, you may write SUMX in place of the actual numerical address. The Processor Deck usually assigns the address and ordinarily you do not care where it is.

The next designation,

07030NbbbbbDSbb4

sets aside four more spaces with the *right* address, N.

The letters DS stand for *Define Symbol* and it is very important that you understand what has happened: the machine has set up a *table of equivalences* in which SUMX = a five-digit number, i.e., an address, and N = a five-digit number, i.e., an address, and that in the first case it has assigned this address to the right end of nine spaces, and in the second case to the right end of four spaces in memory.

IBM

BOARD OF EDUCATION OF THE CITY OF NEW YORK

THE BRONX HIGH SCHOOL OF SCIENCE
DR. ALEXANDER TAFFEL, PRINCIPAL

1620 Symbolic Programming System
Coding Sheet

DEPARTMENT OF MATHEMATICS
DR. I. A. DODES, CHAIRMAN

Program SAMPLE CODING SHEET

Programmed by I. A. DODES

Date 10-15-62

Page No. 107 of 8, 1/2

LINE	LABEL	OPERATION	OPERANDS & REMARKS
01.0	*AREA DESIGNATIONS.		
02.0	SUMX	DS	9
03.0	N	DS	4
04.0	SUMXX	DS	5,,19999
05.0	A	DS	3,N+3
06.0	B	DS	,,SUMX-12
07.0	CARD	DS	80
08.0	CONST	DC	3,1
09.0	K2	DC	2,1
10.0	NEG	DC	5,-812
11.0	RM	DC	1,@
12.0	ZERO	DC	50,0
13.0	AGAIN	DC	50,,A+1000
14.0		DC	1,@,,THIS IS A RECORD MARK
15.0			
16.0		DNB	40,,CARD+40
17.0			
18.0			
19.0			
20.0			

Fig. 42. Right-addressed areas.

To be specific, suppose that just before instruction 07010 the machine has reached memory cell 09508 in the translation of your program into machine language. The machine "looks at" instruction 07010, "sees" the asterisk in cc 6 and disregards this card. Then it "looks at" instruction 07020, "sees" that nine spaces are needed, sets aside 09509 to 09517, and "writes down" in its table of equivalences that whenever you write SUMX, it will "read" 09517.

Sometimes, for one reason or another, the programmer does want the reserved spaces in a specific place. If so, he may indicate this as shown on line 07040. Here, the computer assigns 19999 to SUMXX and disregards the first operand, 5. In fact, the first operand might just as well be omitted whenever the address is assigned. You may think of SUMXX as an area from 19995 to 19999 but, in fact, whenever you assign an address, the computer uses only the assigned number.

If the 19999 had not been written into the program, the assignment of areas would have been

09509-09517   SUMX

09518-09521   N

and SUMXX would have had 09522-09526 reserved, with the address of SUMXX equal to 09526.

Instruction 07050 asks for a reservation of three spaces with the address at $(N + 3)$. Since $N = 09521$, in this example, this means that 09522 to 09524 is set aside for A, with $A = 09524$. If $(N + 3)$ had been left off this instruction, in this specific case, the very same spaces would have been assigned. The machine assigns addresses sequentially except when a contrary instruction is given; in this case, the last address assigned *by the machine* was 09521 $(= N)$, so that it would have gone to 09522-09524 anyhow.

Instruction 07060 does not ask for a reservation of any spaces at all. It merely assigns B to the address $(SUMX - 12)$. Since $SUMX = 09517$, $B = 09505$. Whenever the programmer writes address "B" the machine will translate it as 09505.

Instruction 07070 asks for neither a reservation of space nor an address. The machine now "looks" for the last address assigned by it. That was in 07030 where 09521 was assigned to N *by the machine* (not by the programmer). The same address is now assigned to *CARD*. This is occasionally useful to a programmer, as in the following example.

CARD   DS

DS   80

where eighty spaces have been set aside *after* the space designated as CARD. If you have actually read an IBM card into these eighty spaces (we shall take that up later), then CARD + 1 will stand for cc 1, CARD + 25 will stand for cc 25, and so on. On the other hand, if the instruction is

IBMCD DS 80

then the first card column is IBMCD−79, since the symbol IBMCD, is the *right* address of the eighty spaces set aside.

We now turn to the DC command which *defines a constant* with a termination flag at the left end.

In Fig. 42, card 07090 assembles a three-place constant in the next available three spaces after the last ones assigned by the machine. The constant is $\overline{0}01$, and CONST is the address of the right end of the constant—which is very convenient for arithmetic work. In the same way, K2 is the right address of $\overline{0}1$, and NEG is the right address of $\overline{0}081\overline{2}$.

It is important to note that there are *no flags* in an SPS program. The termination flag is put in by the DC command, and the negative flag is put in by a minus sign. If a flag is typed in the program, it will *not* be assembled properly because the processor reads in alphamerically.

Similarly, a record mark cannot be written into an SPS program. Instead, the SPS processor reads an "at sign" as a record mark. Instruction 07120 places a record mark at the address symbolically represented by RM. Instruction 07130 assembles fifty zeros with a termination flag at the left end. The address of the right end is "ZERO." Up to fifty spaces may be reserved in a single DC command. (There is no limit, except the capacity of the machine, for a DS command.)

Instruction 07140 also assembles fifty zeros with a termination flag at the left end. The address at the right end is "AGAIN." The missing operand is translated as a zero. In this case, there is a *third* operand which, since A was set equal to 09524, is equal to 10524. This directs the machine to reserve the fifty spaces up to (and including) 10524 for fifty zeros. The first of these spaces is evidently 10475. To summarize, instruction 07140 places a $\overline{0}$ in 10475, then 49 more zeros, and identifies the symbol "AGAIN" with the address 10524.

Instruction 07150 has *four* operands. The first gives the length of the field $(= 1)$. The second gives the content of the field (a record mark in SPS notation). The third is missing, and the machine assigns the location to the next one after the ZERO address. The fourth operand is called the *Remarks operand*. It is disregarded by the machine and is sometimes typed on a card to remind the programmer about something. In this case, however, it serves no purpose.

Lastly, we mention the DNB command which designates the right address of a set of *numeric blanks* (up to fifty). In instruction 07170, the DNB command will "clean" the forty positions starting at CARD + 1 and ending at CARD + 40. If it is necessary to clean eighty positions, a second command,

$$\text{DNB } 40,\text{CARD} + 80$$

will complete the job.

A good method for providing a clean numeric area for card punching is a set of three instructions as follows:

CLEAN DS

DNB 40

DNB 40

At the conclusion of the compiling, an eighty-cell clean area will have been formed. In this case, CLEAN + 1 corresponds to cc 1, and CLEAN + 80 corresponds to cc 80.

To summarize these three commands,

$$\text{LABEL DS} \quad \text{L,A,R}$$

$$\text{LABEL DC} \quad \text{L,N,A,R,}$$

$$\text{LABEL DNB L,A}$$

1. In each case, the *first* operand is the number of spaces to be reserved.
2. In the DC command, the *second* operand is the actual constant with high-order zeros omitted and a minus sign inserted if necessary.
3. In each case, A is the operand which gives the *right* address of the area designated. The "LABEL" is equivalent to this address.
4. The remaining operand, R, is for remarks, if desired. In any command which has remarks, missing operands must be indicated by commas as shown in card 07150 of Fig. 42, where the address operand was omitted.
5. In DC and DS, if the first operands are omitted, they are interpreted as zeros; if the address operand is omitted in any of these, the next consecutive address is assigned by the machine.

EXERCISES

Assume that the machine has just finished assigning memory cell 15167. What would be the effect of the following series of commands?

```
HARRY  DS   12,,12000
JOHN   DS   38,19035,FOR THE PRODUCT OF X AND (AX + B)
TOM    DS   ,HARRY,DICK
DICK   DC   6
SAM    DC   5,−23,TOM + 15, DICK − 7
RM     DC   2,@
       DC   5,−0
       DNB 10,HARRY + JOHN − DICK
```

17.5   LEFT ADDRESS AREAS

You know from your machine language programs that information is read in and out of the IBM 1620 from left to right. It is convenient, then, to have I-O (input-output) information in positions with the labels at the proper place. However, this is not essential. The left addresses can always be calculated if the length and the right addresses are known.

Areas can be designated at their left addresses as shown in Fig. 43. Assuming that the last address designated was 14000, the commands are as follows:

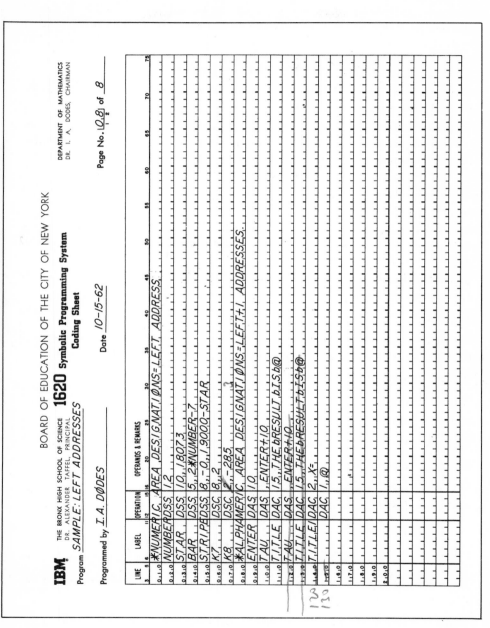

Fig. 43. Left-addressed areas.

08010 is a *comment card*, and is disregarded.

08020 sets aside 14001-14012, and NUMBER = 14001.
Remember that the machine does *not* really set aside 14001 to 14012. It merely specifies NUMBER = 14001 and completely disregards the length operand. However, it is convenient to consider this area as set aside. We shall maintain this polite fiction throughout our discussion.
08030 sets aside 18073-18082, and STAR = 18073.

08040 computes $2*\text{NUMBER}-7=2(14001)-7=27995$, then sets aside 27995-27999, with BAR = 27995.

(Unfortunately, the basic machine has only 20,000 memory cells numbered from 00000 to 19999, so that the resulting location will not exist on the basic machine. However, the location exists on the IBM 1620 with an extra module and this illustrates the fact that the basic machine will compile a program for a larger machine.)

08050 sets aside eight spaces, from 00000 to 00007, with STRIPE = $0000\bar{0}$, and regards "19000 − STAR" as a "Remark."

08060 defines a *special constant*, 00000002. The last spaces reserved *by the machine* were 14001-14012. Consequently, this number is placed in 14013-14020, and K7 = 14013. No flags are set.

08070 defines 00 in 14021-14022. K8 = 14021. The fourth operand, −285, is regarded as a "Remark."

EXERCISES

Assume that the machine has assigned memory cell 10007 at the last position. What would be the effect of the following series of commands?

P38	DSS 17
	DSS 3,47,15228
IQ200	DSS 5,3*P38−29
ALPHA	DSC 9,,P38−1,P38+1
BETA	DSC ,ALPHA
GAMMA	DSC 4,−378
DELTA	DSC 2,3,18045

17.6   LEFT-PLUS-ONE ADDRESS AREAS

We shall continue with the commands in Fig. 43. The last area assigned by the machine was 14021-14022 (for instruction 08070).

08080 is a *comment card*, disregarded by the machine.

08090 defines an *alphameric symbol* with 2 * 10 memory locations beginning at the next *even* number, 14024, and ending at 14043. ENTER = 14025, i.e., the left-plus-one address. DAS means *Define Alphameric Symbol.*

08100 reserves no spaces but sets TAU = 14035.

08110 reserves 2 * 15 memory locations, beginning at the next available even number, 14044 and ending at 14073. The content of the first *pairs* of memory cells is as follows:

14044-5	$\bar{6}3$	(= T)
14046-7	48	(= H)
14048-9	45	(= E)
14050-1	00	(= b)

DAC means *Define Alphameric Constant.* In this case, TITLE is defined as 14045, the address of the odd part of the T in THE.

08120 reserves 2 * 2 memory locations, 14074-14077, containing $(\bar{6},7)$ (3,3). TITLE⚹ = 14075.

08130 reserves 2 * 1 locations, 14078-14079, and places an alphameric record mark in these spaces.

EXERCISES

If the last location assigned by the machine was 16000, what is the effect of the following series of commands?

```
RHO    DAS  10
RM     DC   1,@
ZETA   DAC  8,IFbXb=b@
PHI    DAC  10,THENbYb=b@
```

17.7 STORING ADDRESSES, DSA

We have already identified the following locations: NUMBER = 14001, TITLE = 14045, and ENTER = 14025. The command

LIST DSA NUMBER,TITLE,ENTER, . . .

will list up to ten addresses. If the next available address is 19000, then the DSA (*Define Symbolic Address*) command will store these addresses as follows:

19000-19004	$\bar{1}4001$
19005-19009	$\bar{1}4045$
19010-19014	$\bar{1}4025$

LIST is the address of the first address stored, i.e., LIST = 19004 (the *right* address).
The addresses to be stored may be numerical or symbolic.

17.8   PROBLEM OF STEPPING, BRANCHING, AND HOUSEKEEPING

We have disposed of the problem of *addressing* by specifying addresses symbolically in the most convenient fashion for our purposes, i.e., arithmetic, numeric I-O or alphameric I-O.

The second problem we mentioned was that of *stepping*. To a certain extent, we have almost solved this problem as well. In the usual case, we have a count cell, for example, which we may designate as N. To step this, we merely need add 1 to N. After the stepping operations, we *branch* to some predetermined instruction.

We shall solve branching and housekeeping by investigating the symbolic form of an instruction.

17.9   SYMBOLIC INSTRUCTION

A complete symbolic instruction may have as many as six parts: a *label* in cc 6-11, an *opcode* in cc 12-15, and four *operands* in cc 16-75. In addition, the first five columns ordinarily have the page and line number of the instruction. In preparing program cards for SPS, including area designation commands, it is convenient to provide the following drum card for the IBM 026 keypunch:

blank	in cc 1
+ (or &)	in cc 2-5
1	in cc 6
A	in cc 7-11
1	in cc 12
A	in cc 13-75
skip-minus	in cc 76
+ (or &)	in cc 77-80

With this drum program on, and all three switches of the keypunch on, the first five digits will be numeric, and all the others alphameric. If any field, e.g., the LABEL field, is not needed, a touch on the SKIP button will carry the IBM card to the next field.

We shall discuss the opcodes first, then the other parts of the symbolic instructions.

17.10   SYMBOLIC OPCODE

You already have extensive experience with the opcodes A 21, AM 11, S 22, and so on. In SPS, only the mnemonic is written—not the machine language opcode. The processor deck reads the mnemonic and translates it into the machine language equivalent (see Table IV).

Table IV.   SYMBOLIC OPCODES

TYPE	OPERATION CODE		OPERATION
	Mnemonic	Machine	
Arithmetic	A	21	Add
	AM	11	Add (Immediate)
	S	22	Subtract
	SM	12	Subtract (Immediate)
	C	24	Compare
	CM	14	Compare (Immediate)
	M	23	Multiply
	MM	13	Multiply (Immediate)
Internal Data	TD	25	Transmit Digit
Transmission	TDM	15	Transmit Digit (Immediate)
	TF	26	Transmit Field
	TFM	16	Transmit Field (Immediate)
	TR	31	Transmit Record
Branch	B	49	Branch
	BNF	44	Branch No Flag
	BNR	45	Branch No Record Mark
	BD	43	Branch on Digit
	*BI	46	Branch Indicator
	*BNI	47	Branch No Indicator
	BT	27	Branch and Transmit
	BTM	17	Branch and Transmit (Immediate)
	BB	42	Branch Back
Input Output	*RN	36	Read Numerically
	*WN	38	Write Numerically
	*DN	35	Dump Numerically
	*RA	37	Read Alphamerically
	*WA	39	Write Alphamerically
Miscellaneous	*K	34	Control
	SF	32	Set Flag
	CF	33	Clear Flag
	H	48	Halt
	NOP	41	No Operation

*Mmemonic codes which require modifiers in the Q operand.

17.11   P AND Q FIELDS

Ordinarily, the P and Q fields in SPS are given in symbolic form, as follows:

1.
$$\text{A   X,Y}$$

This adds the contents of the area addressed as Y to the contents of the area addressed as X, and replaces the latter by the sum.

2.
$$\text{AM   X,Y}$$

In all *immediate* instructions, a flag is automatically placed at Q_7 unless there is another instruction (in the flag *operand*, to be explained in Sub-section 17.12) to the contrary. In this instruction, the *address* of Y is added to the *contents* of X.

3.   M   X,Y

This multiplies the contents of Y by the contents of X, with the result in the product area (80-99). Except in floating point SPS (discussed at the end of Part Three), products and quotients are dealt with precisely as in ordinary machine language programs.

4.   TD   X+1,RM

If RM is the address of a numeric record mark, this instruction places the record mark at the position with the address (X+1). *This is the only way to place a record mark by a programmed instruction.* If an alphameric record mark is needed, the command, TF OMEGA+2*N,ARM will place it, where N is the length of the alphameric OMEGA field, and ARM is the address of an alphameric record mark.

Table V lists the so-called *unique mnemonics*, which may be used in place of the mnemonics requiring a modifier. Modifiers for these mnemonics are supplied by the processor.

Table V.   UNIQUE MNEMONICS TO REPLACE MNEMONICS REQUIRING MODIFIERS

MNEMONICS Equivalent	Unique	OPERATION	UNIT REFERENCED
	BH	Branch High	High-positive indicator
	BP	Branch Positive	High-positive indicator
	BE	Branch Equal	Equal-zero indicator
	BZ	Branch Zero	Equal-zero indicator
BI	BV	Branch Overflow	Overflow indicator
	BA	Branch Any	ANY latch
	BNL	Branch Not Low	High-positive/equal-zero indicator
	BNN	Branch Not Negative	High-positive/equal-zero indicator
	BC1	Branch Console Switch 1 ON	Program Switch 1
	BC2	Branch Console Switch 2 ON	Program Switch 2
	BC3	Branch Console Switch 3 ON	Program Switch 3
	BC4	Branch Console Switch 4 ON	Program Switch 4
	BNH	Branch Not High	High-positive indicator
	BNP	Branch Not Positive	High-positive indicator
	BNE	Branch Not Equal	Equal-zero indicator
	BNZ	Branch Not Zero	Equal-zero indicator
	BNV	Branch No Overflow	Overflow indicator
	BNA	Branch Not Any	ANY latch
	BL	Branch Low	High-positive/equal-zero indicator

BNI	BN	Branch Negative	High-positive/equal-zero indicator
	BNC1	Branch Console Switch 1 OFF	Program Switch 1
	BNC2	Branch Console Switch 2 OFF	Program Switch 2
	BNC3	Branch Console Switch 3 OFF	Program Switch 3
	BNC4	Branch Console Switch 4 OFF	Program Switch 4
RN	RNTY	Read Numerically	Typewriter
	RNPT	Read Numerically	Paper Tape
	RNCD	Read Alphamerically *numerically*	Card Reader
WN	WNTY	Write Numerically	Typewriter
	WNPT	Write Numerically	Paper Tape
	WNCD	Write Numerically	Card Punch
DN	DNTY	Dump Numerically	Typewriter
	DNPT	Dump Numerically	Paper Tape
	DNCD	Dump Numerically	Card Punch
RA	RATY	Read Alphamerically	Typewriter
	RAPT	Read Alphamerically	Paper Tape
	RACD	Read Numerically *alphamerically*	Card Reader
WA	WATY	Write Alphamerically	Typewriter
	WAPT	Write Alphamerically	Paper Tape
	WACD	Write Alphamerically	Card Punch
K	TBTY	Tabulate	Typewriter
	RCTY	Return Carriage	Typewriter
	SPTY	Space	Typewriter

These unique mnemonics greatly simplify the problems of reading in and out, housekeeping and branching. We shall illustrate only the first of these, at the moment:

1. An area has been designated by the command

> CARD DSS 80

and we wish to read a card into this area. The instruction is

> RNCD CARD

2. We wish to type the number in cc 25-27. The instructions are

> TD   CARD+27,RM
>
> WNTY CARD+24

Remember that CARD is the address of cc 1, and therefore the number is actually in CARD+24 to CARD+26.

3. We have designated an area by the command

> A   DS   2

and we wish to read a two-digit number into A. The instruction is

> RNTY A − 1

After this instruction, the IBM 1620 prepares itself to receive a number via the typewriter. We must enter it in some such form as $\overline{0}8$ in order to satisfy the instruction, then press the R-S button.

17.12 FLAG OPERAND

The third operand of the symbolic instruction specifies where the flags are to be placed within an instruction. The positions in the instruction are numbered in the usual fashion,

$$O_0O_1 \quad P_2P_3P_4P_5P_6 \quad Q_7Q_8Q_9Q_{10}Q_{11}$$

from 0 to 11. If more than one flag is desired in the instruction, then a sequence of numbers in *ascending* order is given as the flag operand:

1.   TFM SUM1,SUM2 which becomes $16199987\overline{1}9890$

where SUM1 = 19987 and SUM 2 = 19890. This instruction places the *address* of SUM2 as the *contents* of SUM1. No flag operand is needed because this is an immediate instruction with the flag at Q_7.

2.   TFM SUM1,8,9 which becomes $161998700\overline{0}08$

This places 008 in SUM1.

3.   H   SUM1,SUM2,01234567891011 which becomes $\overline{4}\overline{8}\overline{1}\overline{9}\overline{9}\overline{8}\overline{7}\overline{1}\overline{9}\overline{8}\overline{9}\overline{0}$

Since the P and Q fields of a HALT instruction are not used for anything, these spaces may be filled with numbers for other purposes in the program.

17.13 REMARKS OPERAND

The *fourth* operand of a symbolic non-floating instruction may be used for clarifying remarks. The fourth operand is not, of course, processed by the machine.

The student should note that missing operands *except for the last one not used* must be represented by commas. This is shown in the following:

1.   AM SUM1,,,VARIABLE INSTRUCTION

This assembles as $111998700\overline{0}000$.

2.   TF ,SUM2,,TRANSFER TO ZERO

This assembles as $260000\overline{0}19890$.

3.   AM SUM1

This is the same as (1). The commas are not needed because there are no operands missing *between* other operands.

17.14   PROBLEM OF BRANCHING

We are almost ready to dispose of the problem of branching. *First*, we note that we can define the O_0 position by a label in cc 6-11, just as we defined area designations. For example, if we write

STEP AM N,1,10

this may assemble as

$$(08164) \quad 11150200000\bar{1}$$

where N = 15020 and STEP = 08164. In a later command, we may write

BD STEP, SUM1+5

which assembles as

$$43 \quad 08164 \quad 19992$$

and, if the digit in 19992 is not zero, the program will branch to instruction 08164.

Note that arithmetic is allowed in operands to the extent of A ° B ° C ° D where ° may be +, −, or *.

Second, a branch can be based upon a so-called *asterisk notation*. In any instruction card, an asterisk can have any of three meanings: (*i*) it can represent a comment, if the asterisk is in cc 6, (*ii*) it can represent a multiplication if it is between two numbers, as shown above, and (*iii*) it can represent the O_0 address of the same instruction, as shown in the following instructions:

1.   B *+24

This means "Branch to the instruction the address of which is twenty-four more than the address of the present instruction."

2.   BD *+36, *−1

This means, "If there is a digit in Q_{11} of the previous instruction, branch to the instruction the address of which is thirty-six more than the address of the present instruction."

The asterisk is also used to *set* variable instructions

1. $\begin{cases} \text{TFM} \;\; *+35,\text{SUM1} \\ \text{TF} \;\;\;\; *+18,\text{TABLE}+5 \\ \text{A} \end{cases}$

If the machine address of the first instruction is 09736, and the address of TABLE is 14488, this will assemble as

$$(09736) \quad 16 \quad 09771 \quad \bar{1}9987$$
$$(09748) \quad 26 \quad 09766 \quad 14493$$
$$(09760) \quad 21 \quad 00000 \quad 00000$$

When the program is actually run, the first two instructions will "set" the third instruction as follows, assuming that TABLE+5 contains $\overline{1}$7827:

$$(09760)\ 21\ \overline{1}7827\ \overline{1}9987$$

17.15 PROCESSOR CONTROL CODES

The first card of a program, except for possible comment cards, is a **DORG** command which *defines the origin*, i.e., the O_0 address of the first program instruction. A comfortable starting point is 1000, but may be any even number from 402 up. The very last card (after the area designations) is a **DEND** command which *defines the end*. If the first instruction is labelled descriptively, e.g., START, and if the last card is DENDSTART, the program will be ready to begin at the first instruction. Otherwise, the program has to be started by a typewriter unconditional branch command.

The following is an example of a (fictitious) program and its translation into machine language by the SPS processor.

```
END OF PASSI
01010* PROGRAM TO DEMONSTRATE VARIOUS TRANSLATIONS.
01020        DORG 5000
01021START  A    3507,2726
01030       A    3507,2726,1
01040       A    3507,2726,10
01050       A    3507,2726,01
01060       SM   3507,2726
01070       SM   3507,2726,8
01080       SM   3507,2726,11
01090       SM   3507,2726,711
01100       SF   12633,40026,7891011,1357
01110       C    2345,12345
01120       CM   2345,12345,8,257
01130       CM   2345,12345,,257
01140       CM   2345,12345,257
01150       H
01160       LD   96,9988
01170       LD   96
01170       LD   ,9988
01190       D    93,9984
01200       D    ,9984
02010       D    93
02020       TD   2733,4186,2345,6789
02030       TDM  2733,4186,2345,6789
02040       TF   2733,4186,2345,6789
02050       TFM  2733,4186,2345,6789
02060       TR   2733,4186,2345,6789
02070       WNTY 5000
```

```
05000
05000 21 03507 02726
05012 2̄1 03507 02726
05024 21 03507 0272̄6
05036 2̄1 03507 02726
05048 12 03507 0̄2726
05060 12 03507 02̄726
05072 12 03507 0272̄6
05084 12 03507 0̄272̄6
05096 32 12633 4̄0026̄
05108 24 02345 12345
05120 14 02345 12̄345
05132 14 02345 1̄2345
05144 14 0̄2345 1̄2345
05156 48 00000 00000
05168 28 00096 09988
05180 28 00096 00000
05192 28 00000 09988
05204 29 00093 09984
05216 29 00000 09984
05228 29 00093 00000
05240 25 0̄273̄3 04186
05252 15 0̄273̄3 04186
05264 26 0̄273̄3 04186
05276 16 0̄273̄3 04186
05288 31 0̄273̄3 04186
05300 38 05000 00100
```

```
02080          WATY 6001
02090          RCTY
02100          RCTY 2357,1234,3356
02120MIKE      AM   *+3, *-5,10
02130WENDY     B    MIKE
02140SUSAN     BD   SUSAN+30,WENDY-52
02150HENRY     BE   SUSAN,WENDY
02160          DEND START
```

```
05312 39 06001 00100
05324 34 00000 00102
05336 34 02357 00132
05348 11 05351 05343
05360 49 05348 00000
05372 43 05402 05308
05384 46 05372 01260
05000
```

```
END OF PASSII
05000    START  05348   MIKE   05360   WENDY   05372   SUSAN   05384   HENRY
```

EXERCISES

Translate into machine language the following fictitious program:

```
01010*PROGRAM FOR VARIANCE@
01020          DORG 5000
01030START     RNCD CARD-79
01040          A    N,ONE
01050          SF   CARD-60
01060          A    SUMX,X
01070          M    X,X
01080          A    SUMX2,99
01090          BLC  TOTAL
01100          B    START
01110TOTAL     M    SUMX,SUMX
01120          TF   SUM2X,99
01130          M    SUMX2,N
01140          S    99,SUM2X
01150          TF   NUM,99
01160          M    N,N
01170          TF   N2,99
01180          TF   79,ZERO
01190          LD   89,NUM
01191          D    79,N2
01200          RCTY
01210          TD   N+1,RM
01220          WNTY N-3
02010          TBTY
02020          TD   92,RM
02030          WNTY 71,RM
02031          H
02040*AREA DEFINITIONS
02050N         DC   4,0
02060RM        DC   1,@
02070CARD      DS   80
02080ONE       DC   2,1
02090SUMX      DC   8,0
```

IBM 1620 PROGRAMMING

—020800NE ——— DC — 2,1
—02090SUMX ——— DC ——8,0

(handwritten annotations)
02100X   DS   } CARD—56
02110SUMXL   DC   13,0
02120 SUM2X   DS   16
02130 NUM   DS   17
02140 NL   DS   8
02150 ZERO   DC   10,0

17.16   SUMMARY
02160   DENDSTART

We shall close this general discussion with a list of fourteen steps to follow in writing an SPS program. In section 18, we shall go through the planning and writing of a program step-by-step in order to weave together all these rules which seem so puzzling to the beginner. The following list is for reference.

1. Make a flow chart. (We are using *flow chart* as synonymous with *block diagram.*)
2. Using the flow chart, write the program beginning with a title or cover card, then DORG, then program steps, then AREA DESIGNATIONS, and finally DENDSTART. You will find it convenient to use two sheets simultaneously; one for program steps and one for areas. You will find it useful to split long programs into segments. Label your first program step (after DORG) START.
3. Using simplified data, check your program steps to see that there are no errors in coding or scaling.
4. Check addresses very carefully. Among the things to watch are: (*i*) proper placement of flags for transmission and arithmetic; be sure these are on the high-order (left-most) digits, (*ii*) proper placement of record marks; be sure that @ is used for numeric and 0@ for alphameric material, and (*iii*) read in and write out for alphameric material is always addressed at an odd location; an instruction like

WATY TITLE&2J—1

is suspect because TITLE is probably "odd," and therefore the modified address will be "even," i.e., incorrect for an alphameric output.
5. Punch the cards. List them on an accounting machine and make sure that the opcode starts at cc 12 and operands at cc 16. Check for commas, also. Then check to see that no label was defined as two different things.
6. Clear the machine, using

$31\overline{0}000300002$

which will place flagged zeros throughout the core.
7. Set the check switches as follows: PARITY to "Stop," I-O to "Stop," O'FLOW to "Program." Now *load* the SPS processor with Program Switches 1 and 2 "on," and 3 and 4 "off." Then depress CONSOLE START.
8. *Precompiling (Two Passes).* The SPS Processor Deck was written in such a way that various kinds of things can be done. (Table VI shows all the possibilities.)

We shall recommend certain switch settings for our general purpose.

In precompiling, the console switches are set so that the machine *simulates* compiling but does not actually punch out the machine language instructions. We

Table VI.   OPERATION OF PROGRAM SWITCHES FOR THE PAPER TAPE PROCESSOR AND THE CARD PROCESSOR FOR PASSES I AND II

SWITCH	PASS I		PASS II	
	On	Off	On	Off
1	For the paper tape processor, when input is from the paper tape reader. For the card processor, when input is from the card reader.	When input is from the typewriter.	When on, the entire input statement together with the assembled machine language instruction is typed out.	When off, no typeout of listing.
2	The machine stops after an error message has been typed, so that a corrected statement can be entered at the typewriter.	Processing continues after an error is typed, but the error is adjusted by the processor as indicated under ERROR CORRECTION.	Same as pass I.	Same as pass I.
3		For the card processor, switch must be off.	For the card processor, when the object program is to be in condensed form.	For the card processor, when the object program is to be in uncondensed form.
4	Turn on to correct a typing error made while entering a statement, and depress release and start keys,	then off, and re-enter the entire statement at the typewriter. Should be off when SPS processor is assembling data.	When on, no object program is punched except loader and arithmetic tables. (This switch is used when pre-editing the source program.)	When off, the object program is punched.

recommend that for Pass I, only Program Switch 1 be "on"; and for Pass II, only Program Switches 3 and 4 be "on." The other Program Switches should be turned off. A few cards will be punched. These are load cards and may be discarded. During the precompiling, fourteen possible errors in coding are discovered and displayed on the console typewriter. The errors are as follows:

ER 1.   A record mark is in the label or opcode field.

ER 2.   For address adjustment, a product greater than ten digits has resulted from a multiplication.

ER 3.   An invalid operation code has been used. (This sometimes happens when a blank card, or a partially punched card, has inadvertently been included in your source program, or when the opcode has been typed in the wrong card columns.)

ER 4.   A dollar sign which is being used as a HEAD indicator is incorrectly positioned in an operand. (We shall not need HEAD-HEADING area designations for our mathematical and scientific programs. Curious readers may refer to the IBM Manual for information about this feature.)

ER 5.   (*i*) The symbolic address contains more than six characters. (*ii*) The actual address contains more than five digits. (*iii*) An undefined symbolic address or an invalid special character such as) or (is used in the operand. ER 5 often occurs when a previous error has caused the machine to refuse to list this designated area. Always check to make sure all your areas have actually been defined and accepted.

ER 6.   A DSA statement has more than ten operands.

ER 7.   A DSB statement has the second operand missing.

ER 8.   (*i*) A DC, DSC, DAC or DNB has a specified length more than 50. (*ii*) A DC, DSC or DAC statement has no constant specified. (*iii*) A DC or DSC has a specified length which is less than the number of digits in the constant itself. (*iv*) A DAC statement has a specified length not equal to the number of characters in the constant itself.

ER 9.   The symbol table is full. If this happens, some of the symbols should be replaced using the asterisk notation.

ER 10.   A label is defined more than once.

ER 11.   An assembled address is greater than five digits.

(*ER 12.*   An invalid special character is used as a head character in a HEAD statement.)

(*ER 13.*   A HEAD statement operand contains more than one character.)

ER 14.   An invalid special character is used in a label. The eight invalid special characters are: b) (+$*—,. An all-numeric label is also invalid at this time (for the 1963 processor).

Precompiling involves two passes. For *Pass I*, only Program Switch 1 should be "on." The source program is now *read* in (not loaded). Errors are indicated as follows on the typewriter:

TOTAL+0002   ER5

This means that an error such as those listed under ER 5 has been discovered in the second card after the one which has the label, "TOTAL." For *Pass II*, only Program Switches 3 and 4 should be "on." The source program is *read* in again. At the end of Pass II, a *table of equivalences* begins to appear on the typewriter. The typing can be stopped by turning Program Switch 4 "on."

9. *Desk Debugging.*   Using the typewritten list of errors, examine your listing and correct your source program cards.

10. *Uncondensed Compilation (Two Passes).*   Before starting the actual processing, (*i*) clear the IBM 1622 by depressing the NON-PROCESS RUN-OUT key on *both* sides ("Read" and "Punch"), then (*ii*) fill the punch hopper carefully with blank cards, twelve-edge forward. For *Pass I*, only Program Switches 1 and 2 should be "on." *Read* the source program in. If there is still an error, the compiling will stop before an incorrect card is punched. The correction can be entered by the typewriter. When the R-S key is depressed, the compiling will continue. (If a mistake is made in typing, turn Program Switch 4 "on," depress R-S key, turn Program Switch 4 "off," then retype and depress the R-S key.) At the end of the first pass, the typewriter displays "END OF PASS I." For *Pass II*, only Program Switch 2 should be "on." Replace the source deck in the read hopper. Depress PUNCH START, CONSOLE START, and READER START. Your SPS *object deck* will be formed in the punch output hopper. At the end of the pass, the typewriter will display "END OF PASS II," and will type a table of equivalences.

11. *Third Pass: Condensed Compilation (One Pass).*   For actual running of a program, remove the uncondensed object program, turn on Program Switch 3, replace the source deck in the read hopper, depress PUNCH START, CONSOLE START, and READER START. This will produce a small condensed deck with five machine language instructions per card. The table of equivalences may be inhibited by turning on Program Switch 4.

12. List the *uncondensed* deck on the IBM 407. The result is a display, side-by-side, of the SPS instructions and the machine language instructions. This listing is very useful for debugging. If there is only a small error in the program, you may locate the proper card either in the condensed or uncondensed deck and make the change. If the change is made in the uncondensed deck (this is usually easier), a *condenser* program is available to make a corrected condensed deck.

13. If *subroutines* are required for your program, the message "LOAD SUBROU-TINES" is typed instead of "END OF PASS II" (see step 10). Place the subroutines deck in the read hopper, depress CONSOLE START and READER START. If the subroutines are for variable length, the message "ENTER MANTISSA LENGTH" is typed and the machine halts. You enter the (two-digit) mantissa on the typewriter, e.g., $\bar{0}7$, $\bar{4}5$, then depress the R-S key. The proper subroutines are then compiled in your object deck. On the third pass, these may be condensed, as in step 11.

14. Every program should be tested with data for which the answer is known. **Various** general debugging devices are discussed in Subsection 18.6. A specific debugging device using the SAVE key is explained in Subsection 21.3.

Following, is a *summary* of the operations at the console:

1. Clear the machine with 31̄0000300002.
2. Set the check switches to "Stop" except for the O'FLOW switch.
3. Load the Precompiler with Program Switches 1 and 2 "on," and switches 3 and 4 "off." For *Pass I*, have Program Switch 1 "on," and switches 2, 3, and 4 "off." For *Pass II*, have Program Switches 3 and 4 "on," and switches 1 and 2 "off."
4. Load the Compiler with Program Switches 1 and 2 "on," switches 3 and 4 "off." For *Pass I*, Program Switches 1 and 2 "on," switches 3 and 4 "off." For *Pass II*, Program Switch 2 "on," switches 1, 3, and 4 "off." (This results in the uncondensed deck.) For *Pass III*, Program Switches 2 and 3 "on," switches 1 and 4 "off." (This results in the condensed deck.)
5. List the *uncondensed deck* on the IBM 407. The wiring of the board is discussed in the IBM SPS Manual.

Section 18. A Sample Program

18.1 PROBLEM

In order to introduce you to the various operations of SPS, we shall propose the following fictitious problem which involves the various arithmetic and logical commands.

You are given data of the form A = xxxx (no flag) in cc 22-25 of an IBM card, and B = xxxxx (no flag) in cc 72-76 of the same IBM card. You are to insert into memory C = $\bar{x}$xx (positive or negative) via the console typewriter. Now you wish to calculate

$$\frac{(A + 1) * (B + A)}{C}$$

if A > 50, and

$$\frac{(A - 1) * (B + A)}{C}$$

if A ≤ 50.

The output is to be as follows: We are to have headings Y, N, A, B, C, and Result. For this program, Y = $\bar{9}$99. For various values of A, B, and C, the value of N is to progress by one beginning with N = 1. The values of A, B, C, and Result are to be *typed* without flags, but with plus and minus signs in the proper places, nonsignificant leading zeros removed, and decimal points inserted. However, if there are no significant figures before the decimal point, we wish to have 00 typed.

In addition, if Program Switch 1 is "on," we wish to punch a card with Y, N, A, B, C, and Result in the usual machine fashion (with flags, but without plus, minus signs and decimal points) except that we want the *absolute value* of the Result.

18.2   FLOW CHART

The flow chart for this strange program is shown in Fig. 44. It is straightforward in every respect, having the form of one set-and-step module and some housekeeping. The "boxes" have been numbered to facilitate discussion.

18.3   CODING

The first two pages of the coding for this program are shown in Fig. 45 (a and b). You will find it convenient to use *two* pads for writing symbolic programs: one for the *instructions*, and another for the *area designations*. From time to time, you will find that you have omitted an instruction. This is inserted as shown (for instruction 01181) at the bottom of the sheet. The number of the instruction, 01181, means: page 01, line 18, insertion 1.

In coding symbolic programs, be very suspicious of *immediate commands*, such as

AM   SUM1,A

This means "Add the *address* of A to the *contents* of Sum 1."

In this sample program, "box numbers" have been used both as comments (preceded by an *) and as instruction labels.

18.4   TYPE-OUT SUBROUTINE

It has already been mentioned that many programs involve the repetition of the same instructions over and over again, often with different data. A great deal of time and space can be saved by making use of the BT ("Branch and Transmit") and BTM ("Branch and Transmit Immediate") commands. A command like

BT   SQRT,A

takes the *contents* of A, places it in the spaces just before SQRT (i.e., at SQRT−1, and continuing to SQRT−2, etc., until the termination flag is reached for the contents of A), branches to the SQRT subroutine, accomplishes it, then branches back (BB) to the instruction following the BT command.

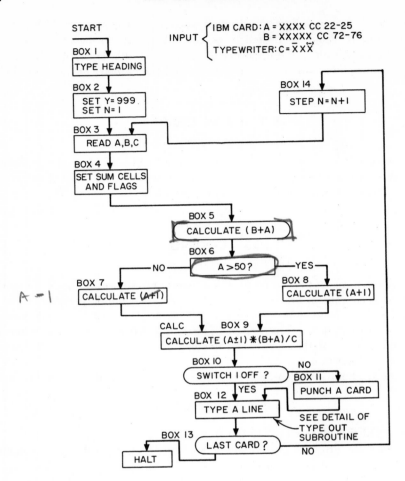

Fig. 44.　Flow chart for sample program in SPS.

It is obvious that anything just before the SQRT subroutine will be "wiped out" by the contents of A. If A, by some chance, does not have a termination flag, the entire contents of the memory will be spoiled. The moral is that space must be provided for the contents of A, and that the contents of A must have a termination flag. The space is most easily provided by a *No Operation* (NOP) command, as follows:

```
        NOP
SQRT    SM      *-1,1,10,SUBTRACTS 1 FROM A
                •
                •
        BB
```

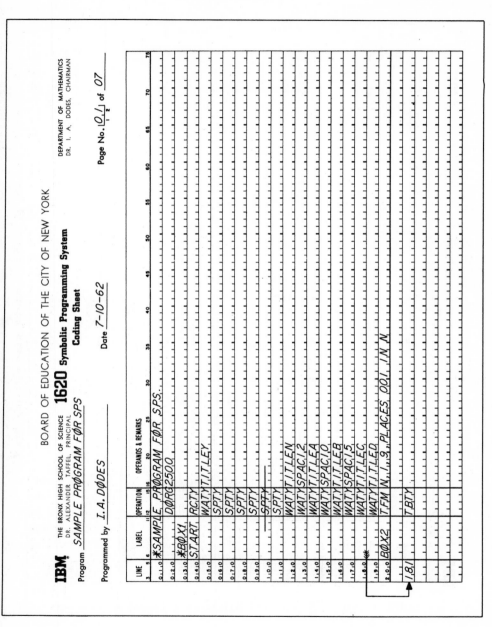

Fig. 45a. First page of instructions for the Sample SPS Program.

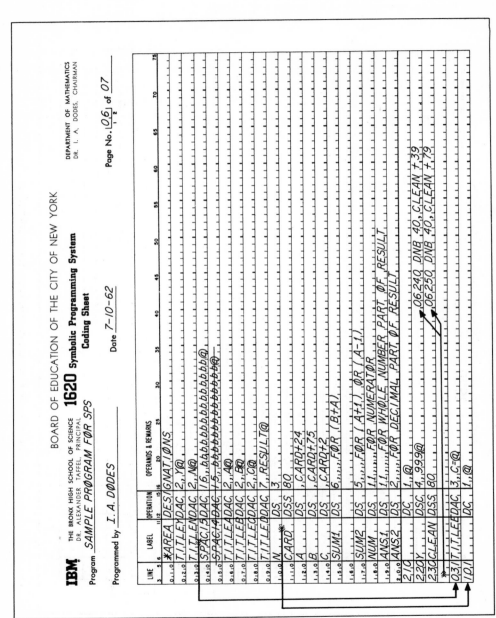

Fig. 45b. First page of area designations for the Sample SPS Program.

If more space is needed, more NOP commands may be used.

The BTM command, like all immediate commands, automatically places a termination flag at Q_7 unless there is a flag operand. Thus,

$$\text{BTM} \qquad \text{SQRT,A,9}$$

takes the last three digits of the address of A, with a flag at the first of the three digits (from left to right) and places these three digits in SQRT−1, SQRT−2, and SQRT−3. The flag is at SQRT−3.

The flow chart for a simple Type-Out subroutine is shown in Fig. 46. This is purposely left imperfect in order to provide some exercise for the reader in problem 7 at the end of this section.

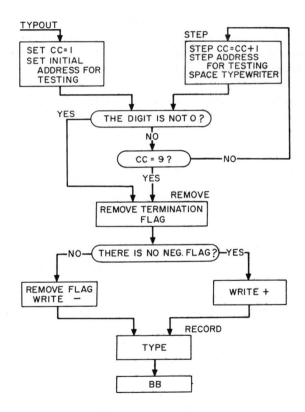

Fig. 46   Detail of type-out subroutine.

18.5   MACHINE LANGUAGE INSTRUCTIONS

After the flow chart has been made, and the cards cut, the cards should be listed on an IBM 407. This will protect the programmer against certain obvious errors such as the writing of commands in the wrong card columns, misspellings (such as ATM for BTM), and other gross errors. This listing should be compared *very* carefully with the original program.

Then a sample set of data should be prepared with all intermediate results calculated by hand or on a desk calculator. It cannot be overemphasized that the programmer will save a tremendous amount of time if this is done very carefully.

The next step is to "walk through" the flow chart with your preliminary data and note what is supposed to happen. The more you know about your program before you go on the machine, the easier it will be to detect your inevitable errors.

Now you are almost ready to have the IBM 1620 compile your program. Before you actually do this, rearrange your *area designations* in the following order:

alphameric output first

constants

constant work cells, if any

variable work cells or sum cells, if any

The reason for this is that you will inevitably have to debug your program, and it is usually not necessary to debug the alphameric or constant part. (We shall have much more to say about this, later.)

The listing for the debugged *sample program* follows. It will repay careful study. The output for three test cases is shown at the end of the sample program.

```
01010*SAMPLE PROGRAM FOR SPS.
01020         DORG 2500
                                              02500
01030*BOX1
01040START   RCTY
                                              02500 34 00000 00102
01050        WATY TITLEY
                                              02512 39 03785 00100
01060        SPTY
                                              02524 34 00000 00101
01070        SPTY
                                              02536 34 00000 00101
01080        SPTY
                                              02548 34 00000 00101
01090        SPTY
                                              02560 34 00000 00101
01100        SPTY
                                              02572 34 00000 00101
01120        WATY TITLEN
                                              02584 39 03789 00100
01130        WATY SPAC12
                                              02596 39 03847 00100
01140        WATY TITLEA
                                              02608 39 03793 00100
01150        WATY SPAC10
                                              02620 39 03825 00100
01160        WATY TITLEB
                                              02632 39 03797 00100
01170        WATY SPAC15
                                              02644 39 03873 00100
01180        WATY TITLEC
                                              02656 39 03801 00100
01181        TBTY
                                              02668 34 00000 00108
01190        WATY TITLED
                                              02680 39 03805 00100
01200BOX2    TFM  N,1,9,PLACES 001 IN N
                                              02692 16 04101 00001
02010BOX3    RNCD CARD,,,PLACES 1 IN CARD+21 TO 24, B IN CARD+71 TO 75
                                              02704 36 03904 00500
02011        TBTY
                                              02716 34 00000 00108
02012        WATY TITLEE
                                              02728 39 03819 00100
```

```
02020        RNTY  CARD,,,PLACES C IN CARD TO CARD+2
                                          02740 36 03904 00100
02030*BOX4
02040        SF    A-3
                                          02752 32 03925 00000
02050        SF    B-4
                                          02764 32 03975 00000
02060        TF    SUM1,ZEROS,,SUM1 WILL EQUAL (B+A) EVENTUALLY.
                                          02776 26 04108 04082
02070        TFM   SUM2
                                          02788 16 04113 0̄0000
02080*BOX5
02090        A     SUM1,A
                                          02800 21 04108 03928
02100        A     SUM1,B,,FORMS (B+A)
                                          02812 21 04108 03979
02110        A     SUM2,A,,FORMS A IN SUM2
                                          02824 21 04113 03928
02120*BOX6
02130        CM    A,50,10,CALCULATES (A-50) INTERNALLY
                                          02836 14 03928 0005̄0
02140        BP    BOX8
                                          02848 46 02884 01100
02150*BOX7
02160        SM    SUM2,1,10,FORMS (A-1)
                                          02860 12 04113 0000̄1
02170        B     CALC
                                          02872 49 02896 00000
02190BOX8    AM    SUM2,1,10,FORMS (A+1)
                                          02884 11 04113 0000̄1
02190*BOX9
02200CALC    M     SUM1,SUM2
                                          02896 23 04108 04113
03010        TF    NUM,99
                                          02908 26 04124 00099
03020        LD    95,NUM
                                          02920 28 00095 04124
03030        D     85,C
                                          02932 29 00085 03906

03040        AM    95,5,10,FOR HALF-ADJUSTING
                                          02944 11 00095 0000̄5
03050        BNF   ADJ,95,,CHECK FOR FLAG AT 00096
                                          02956 44 02980 00095
03060        SF    94,,,ANSWER IS IN 00082 TO 00094
                                          02968 32 00094 00000
03070ADJ     TF    ANS1,92,,PLACES WHOLE NUMBER PART IN ANS1
                                          02980 26 04137 00092
03080        SF    93
                                          02992 32 00093 00000
03090        TF    ANS2,94,,PLACES DECIMAL PART IN ANS2
                                          03004 26 04139 00094
03100        CF    93
                                          03016 33 00093 00000
03110        CF    ANS2-1
                                          03028 33 04138 00000
03120*BOX10
03130        BNC1  BOX12,,,IF SW 1 IS OFF, BRANCH TO BOX 12 (SKIP PUNCHING)
                                          03040 47 03148 00100
03140*BOX11
03141        SF    Y
                                          03052 32 04095 00000
03150        TF    CLEAN+2,Y+2,,PLACES Y IN CC 1 TO 3
                                          03064 26 03986 04097
03160        TF    CLEAN+8,N,,PLACES N IN CC 7,8,9.
                                          03076 26 03992 04101
03170        TF    CLEAN+14,A,,PLACES A IN CC 12 TO 15
                                          03088 26 03998 03928
03180        TF    CLEAN+22,B,,PLACES B IN CC 19 TO 23
                                          03100 26 04006 03979
03190        TF    CLEAN+28,C,,PLACES C IN CC 27 TO 29
                                          03112 26 04012 03906
03200        TF    CLEAN+52,94,,PLACES ANSWER IN CC 41 TO 53
                                          03124 26 04036 00094
03210        WNCD  CLEAN
                                          03136 38 03984 00400
04010BOX12   RCTY
                                          03148 34 00000 00102
04020        WNTY  Y
                                          03160 38 04095 00100
04030        SPTY
                                          03172 34 00000 00101
```

04040	SPTY		03184	34 00000 00101
04041	WNTY	N-2	03196	38 04099 00100
04042	SPTY		03208	34 00000 00101
04043	SPTY		03220	34 00000 00101
04050	TF	TYPOUT-1,TWELVZ,,CLEANS SPACE BELOW TYPOUT SUBROUTINE	03232	26 03531 04094
04060	BT	TYPOUT,A	03244	27 03532 03928
04070	SPTY		03256	34 00000 00101
04071	SPTY		03268	34 00000 00101
04072	TF	TYPOUT-1,TWELVZ,,CLEANS SPACE BELOW TYPOUT SUBROUTINE	03280	26 03531 04094
04080	BT	TYPOUT,B	03292	27 03532 03979
04090	SPTY		03304	34 00000 00101
04091	SPTY		03316	34 00000 00101
04091	TF	TYPOUT-1,TWELVZ,,CLEANS SPACE BELOW TYPOUT SUBROUTINE	03328	26 03531 04094
04100	BT	TYPOUT,C	03340	27 03532 03906
04101	SPTY		03352	34 00000 00101
04110	SPTY		03364	34 00000 00101
04111	TF	TYPOUT-1,TWELVZ,,CLEANS SPACE BELOW TYPOUT SUBROUTINE	03376	26 03531 04094
04112	BNF	*+24,96	03388	44 03412 00096
04113	SF	ANS1	03400	32 04137 00000
04120	BT	TYPOUT,ANS1	03412	27 03532 04137
04130	WATY	DOT	03424	39 04073 00100
04140	WNTY	ANS2-1	03436	38 04138 00100
04150*BOX13				
04160	BLC	END	03448	46 03496 00900
04170*BOX14				
04180	AM	N,1,10	03460	11 04101 00001̄
04181	TBTY		03472	34 00000 00108
04190	B	BOX3	03484	49 02704 00000
04200END	H		03496	48 00000 00000
04210	B	START	03508	49 02500 00000
05010	NOP		03520	41 00000 00000
05020TYPOUT	TFM	CC,1,10	03532	16 04126 00001̄
05030	TFM	*+23,TYPOUT-11	03544	16 03567 0̄3521
05040T1	BD	REMOVE,,,CURRENT ADDRESS BEING TESTED IS IN T1+11	03556	43 03592 00000
05050	CM	CC,10,10	03568	14 04126 0001̄0
05060	BNE	STEP	03580	47 03736 01200
05070REMOVE	TF	*+18,T1+11	03592	26 03610 03567
05080	CF		03604	33 00000 00000
05090	BNF	RECORD-12,TYPOUT-1	03616	44 03664 03531
05100	CF	TYPOUT-1	03628	33 03531 00000
05110	WATY	DASH	03640	39 04065 00100
05120	B	RECORD	03652	49 03676 00000

```
05130        WATY PLUS
                                                      03664 39 04069 00100
05140RECORD  TD   TYPOUT,RM,,DESTROYS THE FIRST DIGIT OF OPCODE 16
                                                      03676 25 03532 04076
05150        TF   *+18,T1+11
                                                      03688 26 03706 03567
05160        WNTY
                                                      03700 38 00000 00100
05170        TDM  TYPOUT,1,,REPLACES THE 1 IN OPCODE 16
                                                      03712 15 03532 00001
05180        BB
                                                      03724 42 00000 00000
05190STEP    AM   CC,1,10
                                                      03736 11 04126 00001
05200        AM   T1+11,1
                                                      03748 11 03567 00001
05210        SPTY
                                                      03760 34 00000 00101
05220        B    T1
                                                      03772 49 03556 00000
06010*AREA DESIGNATIONS
06020TITLEY  DAC  2,Y@
                                                      03785 00002
06030TITLEN  DAC  2,N@
                                                      03789 00002
06060TITLEA  DAC  2,A@
                                                      03793 00002
06070TITLEB  DAC  2,B@
                                                      03797 00002
06080TITLEC  DAC  2,C@
                                                      03801 00002
06090TITLED  DAC  7,RESULT@
                                                      03805 00007
06031TITLEE  DAC  3,C=@
                                                      03819 00003
07051SPAC10  DAC  11,          @
                                                      03825 00011
07052SPAC12  DAC  13,            @
                                                      03847 00013
06040SPAC15  DAC  16,               @
                                                      03873 00016
06110CARD    DSS  80
                                                      03904 00080

06120A       DS   ,CARD+24
                                                      03928 00000
06130B       DS   ,CARD+75
                                                      03979 00000
06140C       DS   ,CARD+2
                                                      03906 00000
06230CLEAN   DSS  80
                                                      03984 00080
06240        DNB  40,CLEAN+39
                                                      04023 00040
06250        DNB  40,CLEAN+79
                                                      04063 00040
07020DASH    DAC  2,-@
                                                      04065 00002
07030PLUS    DAC  2,+@
                                                      04069 00002
07050DOT     DAC  2,.@
                                                      04073 00002
07040RM      DC   1,@
                                                      04076 00001
06160ZEROS   DC   6,0
                                                      04082 00006
06161TWELVZ  DC   12,0
                                                      04094 00012
06220Y       DSC  4,999@
                                                      04095 00004
06100N       DS   3
                                                      04101 00003
06101        DC   1,@
                                                      04102 00001
06150SUM1    DS   6,,,FOR (B+A)
                                                      04108 00006
06170SUM2    DS   5,,,FOR (A+1) OR (A-1)
                                                      04113 00005
06180NUM     DS   11,,,FOR NUMERATOR
                                                      04124 00011
07010CC      DS   2
                                                      04126 00002
06190ANS1    DS   11,,,FOR WHOLE NUMBER PART OF RESULT
                                                      04137 00011
```

```
06200ANS2    DS    2,,,FOR DECIMAL PART OF RESULT
                                                    04139 00002
06210        DC    1,@
                                                    04140 00001
07060        DEND START
                                                    02500
```

```
END OF PASSII
02500   START    02692  BOX2     02704  BOX3    02884  BOX8     02896  CALC
02980   ADJ      03148  BOX12    03496  END     03532  *TYPOUT  03556  T1
03592  *REMOVE   03676 *RECORD   03736  STEP    03785 *TITLEY   03789 *TITLEN
03793  *TITLEA   03797 *TITLEB   03801 *TITLEC  03805 *TITLED   03819 *TITLEE
03825  *SPAC10   03847 *SPAC12   03873 *SPAC15  03904  CARD     03928  A
03979   B        03906  C        03984  CLEAN   04065  DASH     04069  PLUS
04073   DOT      04076  RM       04082  ZEROS   04094 *TWELVZ   04095  Y
04101   N        04108  SUM1     04113  SUM2    04124  NUM      04126  CC
04137   ANS1     04139  ANS2
```

THE TYPEWRITTEN OUTPUT IS AS FOLLOWS FOR THREE DATA CARDS.

```
Y     N        A        B         C        RESULT      C=246RS
999  001    +1234    +56789    +246    +291294.33   C=315RS
999  002    +34      +56789    +315    +5952.89     C=323RS
999  003    +00      +00       -323    +00.00
```

18.6   DEBUGGING

We have already mentioned that the processor deck will do *some* of the work of debugging for you. In other words, many of the *coding* errors are discovered by the processor while your machine language deck is being compiled. However, there are many other kinds of errors which do not show up in compiling, such as *logical errors*. Before getting off the machine, you will want to know as much about the state of the program as possible.

First, you should know where the program stopped. This can be found by reading OP and MAR on the console. OP tells you what operation (e.g., 21, 49, 16, etc.) is in the OPERATION REGISTER.

Now suppose that the operation being executed is (05012) 26 15000 07033 and the next instruction is (05024) 21 12278 13461.

Then "26" will be in the OPERATION REGISTER and if MAR is displayed, IR-1 will contain 05024, OR-1 will contain the part of the Q-address on which the machine is working, and OR-2 will contain the part of the P-address on which the machine is working. By displaying MAR, you can tell where the program ran into trouble.

We have already mentioned that the *area designations* should be arranged so that the variable sum and work cells are at the end. If these are followed by a record mark (DC 1,@), then, instead of a "dump" you may use a "38" command which is somewhat more convenient. Suppose, for example, that your symbol table tells you that your first work cell, SUM1, has the address 18859. Suppose this is a nine-digit area. Then it begins at 18851. The command, 38 18851 00100, will write all the sum cells up to the record mark, wherever it is.

If you have reason to expect troubles in a rather complex program, you may insert HALT cards (use a different color) at various places. When the machine stops, you may dump out (or write out) the variable sum cells, then press START to continue the program. In doing this, be very careful to avoid the error of disturbing a computed address. For example,

$$(05000) \quad \text{TF} \; *+18,*-1$$
$$(05012) \quad \text{B}$$

will assemble as

$$26 \quad 05018 \quad 04999$$
$$49 \quad 00000 \quad 00000$$

and in the program, the second of these instructions will contain

$$49 \quad \overline{0}0500 \quad 00000$$

if $\overline{0}0500$ is in 04995-04999.

However, if a HALT instruction is inserted, we have

$$(05000) \quad \text{TF} \; *+18,*-1$$
$$(05012) \quad \text{H}$$
$$(05024) \quad \text{B}$$

and the program will assemble as

$$26 \quad 05018 \quad 04999$$
$$48 \quad 00000 \quad 00000$$
$$49 \quad 00000 \quad 00000$$

and, when run, will become

$$48 \quad \overline{0}0500 \quad 00000$$
$$49 \quad 00000 \quad 00000$$

so that when you press START there will be a CHECK STOP or some other unexpected result.

After debugging, the HALT cards can be removed and the source deck processed to a condensed deck without the intermediate listing.

Occasionally, the error is a small one and involves something like a typographical error, as, for example, 36 10001 00400 instead of 37 10001 00400. This may be corrected by the following procedure:

1. Calculate the address of the incorrect digit. (If, for example, the illustrative instruction starts at 05000, the incorrect digit is in 05001.)
2. Press STOP, RESET, and INSERT. This prepares the typewriter to receive an instruction.
3. Type 15CCCCC0010049RRRRR, where CCCCC is the address of the incorrect cell, and RRRRR is the return address. (In the illustrative problem, CCCCC = 05001.)

4. Press the R-S key on the typewriter. This releases the typewriter, and starts the one-step correction program, then returns to the main program.

Another method for checking a program is a systematic method called "Bus-Stop." In this system, the following cards are inserted at appropriate intervals (wherever trouble may be expected, or wherever intermediate results are available which may indicate whether your program is working properly):

```
        TFM      ADRESS,*-12
        B        BUSTOP
```

This is called a *linkage*. At the end of your program (but before the Area Designation) write the *subroutine:*

```
BUSTOP  RCTY
        WNTY     ,ADRESS-4
        SPTY
        WNTY     SUM1-4
        TF       *+30,ADRESS
        AM       *+18,36,10
        B
```

Somewhere in your Area Designations, include

```
    ADRESS  DS       5
            DC       1,@
```

and, at the end of the section where your sum cells and work cells are located, add a card which has

```
        DC       1,@
```

Wherever you have the linkage cards, the program will halt (pause), branch to the Bus-Stop subroutine, type the address of the instruction just completed, space once, type the contents of your sum cells and work cells, then branch to the next instruction in the regular program. The linkage cards may be moved from place to place (you may make many sets and insert them in your source deck all at once) and, after your program is debugged, you may remove them and reassemble the program.

In using this Bus-Stop subroutine, be very careful to avoid disturbing computed addresses. In particular, look for computations involving the asterisk (*).

EXERCISES

1 How could steps 01060-01100 be avoided?
2 If 06110 had been "DS 80" how would this alter steps 06120 and 02010?
3 What would be the result if 02090 had been AM SUM1,A?
4 Explain the calculation of the addresses of 03020 through 03070.
5 If the Result, instead of its absolute value, had been wanted on the card, what additional steps would have been needed in Box 11?

6 In the output, if a blank space had been wanted in place of a $+$, what change would have been needed in the Type-Out subroutine?

7 Rewrite the Type-Out subroutine to (i) allow only *one* zero before the decimal point instead of two, and (ii) to accept numbers with up to twenty-four digits.

PROJECTS

Write a square root subroutine to be used for any number up to ten digits in length.

Section 19. Matrix Operations

19.1 VECTORS AND MATRICES

We shall mention here only that a vector is an n-dimensional number of the form $(a_1, a_2, a_3, \ldots, a_n)$ and that it may be horizontal (a *row* vector) or vertical (a *column* vector).*

A matrix may be regarded as an even more general m $\times$ n (m by n) dimensional number. It may also be considered as a collection of row or column vectors.

We cannot go into an explanation of operations with vectors and matrices. We mention only that under certain conditions they may be added, subtracted, and multiplied. There are different kinds of multiplication, e.g., scalar and matrix. There is no division, but there is the analog of a reciprocal. The operation of finding the reciprocal of a matrix or vector is called *inversion*.

Operations with matrices are tremendously important in all branches of science and mathematics. As examples, we cite the use of matrices in operations research, in calculations of probability, e.g., Markov Chains, and in transformation theory, e.g., in atomic physics and the Theory of Relativity.

19.2 PROGRAMMING PROBLEM

Assuming that you have "brushed up" on matrix operations, in particular, matrix multiplication, we note that the major problem in programming a machine to work with matrices is the problem of finding the entries when we want them! In other words, suppose we have matrix A with (up to) 25 x 25 rows and columns, and matrix B with (up to) 25 x 25 rows and columns. We wish, at some point, to multiply the elements of the 17th row of A by the elements of the 25th column of B in serial order, in order to find the entry in the 17th row and 25th column of the product matrix, C. (We are, of course, assuming that these are conformable matrices.) Where are these entries stored in memory?

---

*The reader is referred to Dodes, I.A. and Greitzer, S. L., *op. cit.*, for further information on vectors and matrices.

Well, first we remark that matrices are always read in by *columns.* It is most convenient to type the IBM cards in such a way that all the matrices to be read in are in the column-wise sequence, i.e., $a_{11}, a_{21}, a_{31}, \ldots, a_{n1}$ and $b_{11}, b_{21}, \ldots, b_{n1}$. In general, this may be one element to a card or more. Reading the matrices into the memory requires a program. We shall illustrate this.

How do we set aside spaces in memory? We could, of course, write

$$A11 \quad DS \ (length)$$
$$A21 \quad DS \ (length)$$
$$\bullet$$
$$\bullet$$
$$A2525 \ DS \ (length)$$
$$B11 \quad DS \ (length)$$
$$\bullet$$
$$\bullet$$
$$B2525 \ DS \ (length)$$

but this would require, even for this rather simple example, typing $625 * 2 = 1250$ IBM cards.

Instead, we make use of a command designed for matrix area designations:

$$A \quad DSB \quad (length), (number \ of \ elements)$$

where A is the *label*, DSB means "Define Symbolic Block," and the numbers in parentheses give, respectively, the length to be set aside for each element and the number of elements. For example,

$$MATRIX \ DSB \ 7,38$$

will set aside $7 * 38 = 266$ spaces in memory for the block called "MATRIX." Let us suppose that this block of spaces starts with memory cell 15001 and ends at 15266. Then, 15001 through 15007 will be set aside for the first element $(= a_{11})$ and 15260 through 15266 will be set aside for the last element $(= a_{mn})$. *The address of MATRIX is the address of the very first element.* To get the address of the second element, we would merely write $MATRIX + 7$. To get the address of the 15th element, we would write $MATRIX + 7 * (15 - 1)$.

19.3   TEST PROBLEM

In order to explore this important topic, we shall assume that we have, on IBM cards, elements of the form $\overline{x}xx$ in column-wise order, for matrices A and B. We wish to find the elements of the product matrix $C = AB$. In particular, we shall take

$$A = \begin{bmatrix} 3 & 1 & 2 \\ -1 & 2 & 3 \\ 2 & -5 & 7 \end{bmatrix} \qquad B = \begin{bmatrix} -2 & 4 & 1 \\ 3 & -1 & 2 \\ 4 & 1 & 3 \end{bmatrix}$$

for which the answer is

$$C = \begin{bmatrix} 5 & 13 & 11 \\ 20 & -3 & 12 \\ 9 & 20 & 13 \end{bmatrix}$$

19.4 ANALYSIS OF THE MATRIX PROBLEM

Given:

$$\begin{bmatrix} a_{11}\ a_{12}\ a_{13}\ \ldots \\ a_{21} \\ \bullet \\ \bullet \\ \bullet \end{bmatrix} , \begin{bmatrix} b_{11}\ b_{12}\ b_{13}\ \ldots \\ b_{21} \\ \bullet \\ \bullet \\ \bullet \end{bmatrix}$$

Each element is in the form $\bar{x}xx$. Read in by columns, one column per card (up to 25 elements per column).

Output: Typewritten, one row at a time, as a row vector:

$$(c_1, c_2, c_3 \ldots)$$

Detail:

Addresses:

$a_{11} : A$	$a_{21} : A + 3$	$a_{31} : A + 6\ldots$
$a_{12} : A + 75$	$a_{22} : (A + 3) + 75$	$a_{32} : (A + 6) + 75\ldots$
$a_{13} : A + 2(75)$	$a_{23} : (A + 3) + 2(75),\ldots$	b_{31} :
$b_{11} : B$	$b_{21} : B + 3, b_{31} : B + 6\ldots$	
$b_{12} : B + 75$, etc.		

Formation of products:

First level $a_{11}b_{11} + a_{12}b_{21} + a_{13}b_{31} + \ldots \quad = c_1$
$\qquad\qquad\quad a_{11}b_{12} + a_{12}b_{22} + a_{13}b_{32} + \ldots \quad = c_2$
$\qquad\qquad\quad a_{11}b_{13} + a_{12}b_{23} + a_{13}b_{33} + \ldots \quad = c_3$

$I = 1$
$K = 1, 2, 3, \ldots$
$J = 1, 2, 3, \ldots$

Second level $a_{21}b_{11} + a_{22}b_{21} + a_{23}b_{31} + \ldots \quad = c_1$
$\qquad\qquad\quad a_{21}b_{12} + a_{22}b_{22} + a_{23}b_{32} + \ldots \quad = c_2$
$\qquad\qquad\quad a_{21}b_{13} + a_{22}b_{23} + a_{23}b_{33} + \ldots \quad = c_3$

$I = 2$
$K = 1, 2, 3, \ldots$
$J = 1, 2, 3, \ldots$

Third level

$$a_{31}b_{11} + a_{32}b_{21} + a_{33}b_{31} + \ldots \quad = c_1$$
$$a_{31}b_{12} + a_{32}b_{22} + a_{33}b_{32} + \ldots \quad = c_2$$
etc.

$$\left. \begin{array}{l} I = 3 \\ K = 1, 2, 3, \ldots \\ J = 1, 2, 3, \ldots \end{array} \right\}$$

19.5 READING IN THE MATRICES

The flow chart for the read-in is shown in Fig. 47. The program is constructed in such a way that the terminal values of i, j, and k for a_{ij} and b_{jk} are typed into memory cells called IT, JT, and KT. In the test program, these were typed in as IT = $\bar{0}3$, JT = $\bar{0}3$ and KT = $\bar{0}3$. Since there is a card for each column (in the test progam), JT is also equal to the total number of cards to be read in for each matrix. In the detail flow chart, this was designated as CCT (total card count). In addition, a variable card count cell (CC) was designated for comparison with CCT.

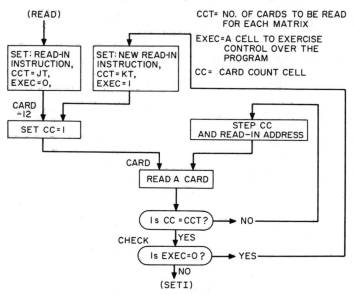

Fig. 47. Detail of flow chart for matrix multiplication (SPS).

We know that there are two read-ins. To control this, we established an *executive control cell* which we called EXEC. This was set as 0 for the first time and then stepped to 1. After reading in the second matrix, the machine checks the state of EXEC. If EXEC is not zero, it "understands" that the read-in has been accomplished, and branches to the main body of the program.

Each column has to be read into a different locatable part of the memory. This means that there is a *variable instruction* to be set and stepped.

The technique of this read-in is so typical of advanced programming that the flow chart and actual steps will repay careful study. The actual steps are from 01130 to 02050 in the listing.

19.6   PROGRAM FOR MATRIX MULTIPLICATION

The flow chart (Fig. 48) and listing for matrix multiplication follow. At the bottom of the listing is the input as requested by the machine, and the output which, as you see, is correct. This program will operate for matrices up to 25 x 25 with entries of the form $\bar{x}xx$. Note that the area designations have been rearranged and numbered in cc 1-2. This was done by typing the original cards without page and line numbers, then rearranging them and typing the numbers on the cards. Cards 20 and 21 were unnecessary in this program.

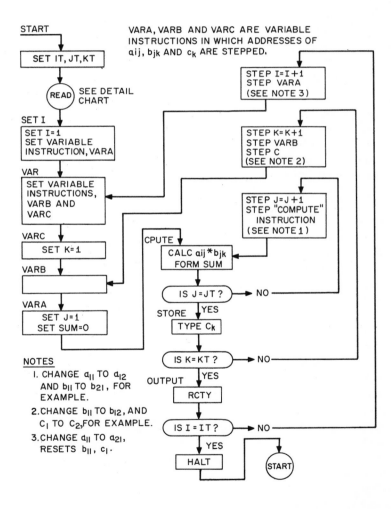

Fig. 48.   Flow chart: matrix multiplication (SPS).

```
END OF PASS1
01010*PROGRAM TO MULTIPLY TWO MATRICES, UP TO 25 X 25 EACH.
01020         DORG 2500                              02500
01030START  RCTY                                     02500 34 00000 00102
01040       WATY TITLE1                              02512 39 03197 00100
01050       RNTY IT-1                                02524 36 07049 00100
01060       RCTY                                     02536 34 00000 00102
01070       WATY TITLE2                              02548 39 03227 00100
01080       RNTY JT-1                                02560 36 07051 00100
01090       RCTY                                     02572 34 00000 00102
01100       WATY TITLE3                              02584 39 03257 00100
01110       RNTY KT-1                               .02596 36 07053 00100
01111       RCTY                                     02608 34 00000 00102
01120*READ IN THE TWO MATRICES.
01130        TFM  CARD+6,A-2                         02620 16 02674 0̄3286
01140        TF   CCT,JT                             02632 26 07040 07052
01150        TDM  EXEC,0                             02644 15 07036 00000
01160        TFM  CC,1,10                            02656 16 07038 0000̄1
01170CARD    RNCD                                    02668 36 00000 00500
01180        C    CCT,CC                             02680 24 07040 07038
01190        BE   CHECK                              02692 46 02740 01200
01200        AM   CC,1,10                            02704 11 07038 0000̄1
01210        AM   CARD+6,75,10                       02716 11 02674 0007̄5
01220        B    CARD                               02728 49 02668 00000
02010CHECK   BD   SET1,EXEC                          02740 43 02800 07036
02020        TDM  EXEC,1                             02752 15 07036 00001
02030        TFM  CARD+6,B-2                         02764 16 02674 0̄5161
02040        TF   CCT,KT                             02776 26 07040 07054
02050        B    CARD-12                            02788 49 02656 00000
02060SET1    TFM  I,1,10                             02800 16 07056 0000̄1
02070        TFM  VARA+11,A                          02812 16 02871 0̄3288
02080VAR     TFM  VARB+11,B                          02824 16 02859 0̄5163
02110VARC    TFM  K,1,10,SETS K = 1                  02836 16 07060 0000̄1
02120VARB    TFM  CPUTE+11,B                         02848 16 02907 0̄5163
02130VARA    TFM  CPUTE+6,A,,PLACES ADDRESS OF A(11) IN P6 OF CPUTE
                                                     02860 16 02902 0̄3288
02140        TFM  J,1,10                             02872 16 07058 0000̄1
02150        TF   SUM,ZEROS                          02884 26 07068 07048
02160CPUTE   M    0,0,,ADDRESSES ARE INSERTED FROM VARB AND VARA
                                                     02896 23 00000 00000
02170        A    SUM,99                             02908 21 07068 00099
02180        C    JT,J                               02920 24 07052 07058
02190        BE   STORE                              02932 46 02992 01200
02200        AM   J,1,10                             02944 11 07058 0000̄1
02210        AM   CPUTE+6,75,10,CHANGES A(11) TO A(12)
                                                     02956 11 02902 0007̄5
02220        AM   CPUTE+11,3,10,CHANGES B(11) TO B(21)
                                                     02968 11 02907 0000̄3
02230        B    CPUTE                              02980 49 02896 00000
03010STORE   WNTY SUM-7
```

```
03011        TBTY
                                              03004 34 00000 00108
03020     C   KT,K
                                              03016 24 07054 07060

03030     BE  OUTPUT
                                              03028 46 03076 01200
03040     AM  K,1,10
                                              03040 11 07060 00001
03050     AM  VARB+11,75,10,CHANGES B(11) TO B(12) IN VARB
                                              03052 11 02859 00075
03070     B   VARB
                                              03064 49 02848 00000
030800OUTPUT RCTY
                                              03076 34 00000 00102
03090     RCTY
                                              03088 34 00000 00102
03150     C   IT,I
                                              03100 24 07050 07056
03160     BE  END
                                              03112 46 03160 01200
03170     AM  I,1,10
                                              03124 11 07056 00001
03180     AM  VARA+11,3,10,CHANGES A(11) TO A(21) IN VARA
                                              03136 11 02871 00003
03190     B   VAR,,,RESETS B TO B(11), C TO C(1)
                                              03148 49 02824 00000
03200END   H
                                              03160 48 00000 00000
03210     RCTY
                                              03172 34 00000 00102
03220     B   START
                                              03184 49 02500 00000
04010*AREA DESIGNATIONS
1     TITLE1 DAC  15,TYPE IT AS XX.@
                                              03197 00015
2     TITLE2 DAC  15,TYPE JT AS XX.@
                                              03227 00015
3     TITLE3 DAC  15,TYPE KT AS XX.@
                                              03257 00015
4     A      DSB  3,625,,A=ADDRESS OF A(11)
                                              03288 00003 00625
5     B      DSB  3,625,,B=ADDRESS OF B(11)
                                              05163 00003 00625
7     EXEC   DS   1
                                              07036 00001
8     CC     DS   2
                                              07038 00002
9     CCT    DS   2
                                              07040 00002
10    ZEROS  DC   8,0
                                              07048 00008
12    IT     DS   2
                                              07050 00002
13    JT     DS   2
                                              07052 00002
14    KT     DS   2
                                              07054 00002
15    I      DS   2
                                              07056 00002
16    J      DS   2
                                              07058 00002
17    K      DS   2
                                              07060 00002
18    SUM    DS   8
                                              07068 00008
19    RM     DC   1,@
                                              07069 00001
20           DC   2,-0,401
                                              00401 00002
21           DAC  1,0
                                              07071 00001
22           DEND START
                                              02500
END OF PASSII
02500    START    02668    CARD     02740    CHECK    02800    SETI     02824    VAR
02836    VARC     02848    VARB     02860    VARA     02896    CPUTE    02992    STORE
03076    *OUTPUT  03160    END      03197    *TITLE1  03227    *TITLE2  03257    *TITLE3
03288    A        05163    B        07036    EXEC     07038    CC       07040    CCT
07048    ZEROS    07050    IT       07052    JT       07054    KT       07056    I
07058    J        07060    K        07068    SUM      07069    RM
```

THE FOLLOWING SHOWS THE OUTPUT OF THIS PROGRAM

```
TYPE IT AS XX.0̄3RS
TYPE JT AS XX.0̄3RS
TYPE KT AS XX.0̄3RS

0̄0000005    0̄0000013    0̄0000011

0̄0000020    0̄0000003̄    0̄0000012

0̄0000009    0̄0000020    0̄0000013
```

EXERCISES

1 Write a program to add two vectors. Each vector has up to twenty-five components on a series of cards. Each component is of nine-digit length and there are six on a card.

2 Write a program to multiply two vectors with input as in exercise 1 (row vector * column vector).

3 Write a program to add two matrices.

4 Alter the demonstration program to multiply two matrices with input as in exercise 1.

5 Write a program to find the determinant of a (square) matrix.

6 Write a program to invert a matrix (difficult!).

PROJECTS

Prepare and run the program as written. They are in order of increasing difficulty and number 6 is quite hard.

Section 20. Introduction to Floating Point

20.1   PURPOSE OF FLOATING POINT

Up to this point, we have treated every datum as though it were a whole number. In other words, we have had to calculate the position of the decimal points (if any) and insert them in the proper places after the machine finished its work.

This is still a perfectly satisfactory (if troublesome) procedure and *fixed point* calculations, as they are known, are used for a tremendous variety of applications.

However, if the programmer can spare some extra space in the memory, and if he is satisfied with up to forty-five significant figures, he may let the machine do all the scaling.

As an added bonus, *floating point* operations not only treat each datum as a number with a decimal point, but also provide a great number of subroutines which have been thoroughly debugged. These are in a supplementary deck called the *variable-length subroutines deck.* We shall have more to say about them in Subsection 20.5. For the present, we merely mention the order of operations in working with floating point:

1. The SPS processor deck is loaded.

2. The source deck (your program) is read in twice: once to set memory spaces for designated areas, and a second time to compile the machine language instructions.

3. The variable length subroutines deck is read in. As soon as the first card is read, the console typewriter requests the number of significant digits desired. The programmer now types any number from $\overline{0}2$ to $\overline{4}5$. Every number in the floating-point program, as written, and the input and output has the same number of significant figures, so far as the machine is concerned.

4. The deck may be condensed in the usual fashion.

20.2   FLOATING-POINT NUMBERS

Every floating-point number has two parts: a *characteristic* (which gives the power of 10) and a *mantissa* which gives the significant figures in the number. In the following, we shall assume that the programmer has elected to use *five* significant figures. In other words, in answer to the typewriter query, he has typed $\overline{0}5$. The three columns below show various numbers in "ordinary" notation, in "scientific" notation, and in SPS floating point notation:

Ordinary	*Scientific*	*SPS*
1234.5	1.2345×10^3	$\overline{1}2345\overline{0}4$
−123.45	-1.2345×10^2	$\overline{1}234\overline{5}\overline{0}3$
1.2345	1.2345×10^0	$\overline{1}2345\overline{0}1$
−0.12345	-1.2345×10^{-1}	$\overline{1}234\overline{5}\overline{0}0$
0	0	$\overline{0}0000\overline{9}\overline{9}$
−0.00012345	-1.2345×10^{-4}	$\overline{1}234\overline{5}\overline{0}3$

Except for the floating-point zero which, as you can see, has a special form, floating-point numbers are always in the form $\overline{MMM} \ldots \overline{CC}$, where the M's stand for the mantissa and the C's for the characteristic. Except for the floating-point zero, any number in "ordinary" notation can be converted to SPS floating point by moving the decimal point to the left of the first non-zero digit, then multiplying by the proper power of ten. In other words, −123.4567 is treated as −0.1234567 x 10³ and is written as $\overline{1}23456\overline{7}\overline{0}3$; and 0.0000001234 is treated as 0.1234 x 10⁻⁶ and is written as $\overline{1}234\overline{0}\overline{6}$. Notice that the mantissa and characteristic have separate termination and negative flags.

Input and output floating-point data are written and handled as shown above. However, programmed floating-point constants must be handled a little differently because, if you remember, the SPS processor reads your program in alphamerically. In other words, you cannot read in flags, as such.

If you need constants in your area designations, such as TENTH = 0.1, FLZERO = 0, and CONST = −5 x 10⁻¹⁰, they are entered as follows (assuming that you have selected three-digit floating point):

	DC	3,100
TENTH	DC	2,0
	DC	3,0
FLZERO	DC	2,−99
	DC	3,−500
CONST	DC	2,−09

Each *pair* of the area designations forms a floating-point program constant. Notice that the label is on the *characteristic*, and that the order of these area designations is important. These three constants will assemble as $\overline{1000}0$, $\overline{0009}9$, and $\overline{5000}9$.

We mention at this point that remarks and flag operands are not permitted in floating-point commands of any kind. This includes both area designations and instructions.

20.3   FLOATING-POINT COMMANDS

We shall limit ourselves to four arithmetic operations, one transmission, and one branch and transmit floating-point instruction. There are others, will not be needed in our mathematical and scientific work.

Fixed-Point Command		*Floating-Point Command*	
A	P,Q	FA	P′,Q′
S	P,Q	FS	P′,Q′
M	P,Q	FM	P′,Q′
LD and D		FD	P′,Q′
TF		TFLS	
BT		BTFS	

Instead of the fixed-point commands in the first column, we use the floating-point commands in the second column. When the processor reads these commands, it eventually compiles, with your program, a set of *linkage* instructions and a subroutine which performs the indicated operation. For our purpose, as programmers, we are less interested in the details of the linkage than in the actual location of the operands. We shall use the fact that the addresses of P′ and Q′ are, respectively, in LABEL + 23 and LABEL + 28, where "LABEL" is the actual or symbolic address of the floating-point arithmetic command.

In all arithmetic commands, the *contents* of Q′ are operated on by the *contents* of P′ *and the result is placed in P′*. This is different from the fixed point situation in multiplication and division, where the result is found in 80-99.

Floating-point instructions are called *macro-instructions* because each command stands for an entire set of machine language or fixed-point instructions.

It should be remembered that in the arithmetic floating-point operations the contents of P′ are destroyed. If it is necessary to save them, a work cell should be set aside, as in the following:

$$\text{TFLS   PROD,X}$$
$$\text{FM   PROD,Y}$$

Now X is undamaged, Y is undamaged, and X * Y is in PROD.

20.4   VARIABLE FLOATING-POINT INSTRUCTIONS

If there is a variable floating-point instruction to be set and stepped, it can be done as follows:

```
          TFM   VARA+23,A
          TFM   VARA+28,B
VARA FA   A,B
            •

            •

          AM    VARA+23,5,10
          AM    VARA+28,7,10
          B     VARA
```

The first two steps place the *address* of A in the P' part of instruction VARA and the *address* of B in the Q' part. The two AM instructions step the A-address in P' by 5 and the B-address in Q' by 7.

20.5   FLOATING-POINT SUBROUTINES

In all the following subroutines (supplied by IBM), the contents of B are acted upon, and the result is placed in A:

Floating Point Subroutine	*Result*
FSQR A,B	$\sqrt{B}$ in A
FSIN A,B	sin B in A
FCOS A,B	cos B in A
FATN A,B	Arctan B in A
FEX A,B	e^B in A
FEXT A,B	10^B in A
FLN A,B	ln B ($= \log_e B$) in A
FLOG A,B	log B ($= \log_{10} B$) in A

In general, the result of a floating-point subroutine is in doubt in the last digit (which is unrounded). However, in a series of such subroutines, the errors may conceivably build up. We shall return to this in Subsection 20.7.

20.6   SUBROUTINE ERROR MESSAGES

We have already indicated that several types of *coding* errors are announced during the original processing of your source program into an object program. We mentioned that logical errors are not, of course, found and that a careful dumping routine may uncover these errors.

Where subroutines are used, however, this is not always sufficiently complete to enable you to debug your program. The difficulty may, unfortunately, occur while the machine is executing a subroutine and it takes a great deal of desk work to find out what went wrong. A dump-out is not enough.

Under the circumstances, the IBM subroutines deck has, built in, a set of error messages which are typed (under certain conditions) when something goes wrong within a subroutine, as follows:

Error Codes (Floating-Point Subroutines)

01   FA or FS, Exponent Overflow. (This means that the result is $\geq 10^{99}$.)

02   FA or FS, Exponent Underflow. (This means that the result $< 10^{-99}$.)

03   FM, Exponent Overflow.

04   FM, Exponent Underflow.

05   FD, Exponent Overflow.

06   FD, Exponent Underflow.

07   FD, Division by Zero.

08   FSQR, Square Root of a Negative Number.

09   FSIN or FCOS, Input argument too great.

10   FSIN or FCOS, Input argument too small.

11   FEX or FEXT, Exponent Overflow.

12   FEX or FEXT, Exponent Underflow.

13   FLN or FLOG, Input argument is Zero.

14   FLN or FLOG, Input argument is Negative.

The message is typed in the form RRRRROOEC, where RRRRR is the *return address to the main program* and EC is the *error code*.

In general, the machine will accept and process numbers with characteristics between 10^{-99} and 10^{+99}. There are three important exceptions:

1. In the *sine* and *cosine* subroutines, the argument (for angles, the number of radians) is limited to the range $[10 ** (-8), 10 ** (+8)]$. For example, do not expect the machine to calculate sin $(3 * 10^{-9})$.

2. In the exponential subroutines, the quantity to be considered must be between e^{-228} and e^{+228}. The problems involving 10^x and, in general, a^x, are converted into the *e* form, so that you must know the natural exponential equivalent in considering this limitation. For example, for the machine to calculate A ** B, it calculates $e^{B \ln A}$ (where ln is the natural logarithm, $\log_e A$) and you must be sure that

$|B \ln A|$ is < 228.

3. For the calculation of logarithms, the arguments must be positive (as you might expect, since the logarithm of 0 is undefined, and the logarithm of a negative number is a complex number).

For the first two limitations, the boundaries are set by the subroutines merely because it was convenient for the programmer who wrote the package. If you need greater precision than this (which occasionally happens), you may write a special set of instructions to accomplish your purpose.

In some of the cases where an error message is generated, pressing the START key causes the program to continue with some alternative; but we shall not exercise this option for our mathematical and scientific programming. Instead, we shall insert under *Area Designations*, third card from the end, the following command whenever we use floating-point SPS:

$$DC\ 2,-0,401$$

This stores a $\bar{0}$ in cell 401 and instructs the machine to HALT whenever one of these errors occurs. (This may seem strange. What happens is that after an error the machine "looks" in memory cell 00401 for instructions.)

20.7   MISSING DIGITS

We have already mentioned that once the programmer has selected the variable length of mantissa desired, all input and output must be of that length. However, it may happen, during the course of a program, that some of the significant digits are lost. For example, in finding the *standard deviation*, σ, of a distribution of scores, the formula $\sigma = L/N$, is used, where $L^2 = N\ \Sigma(X^2) - (\Sigma X)^2$. Each of the two terms in the right member may have 16 significant digits and the difference may very well have none! What shall the machine do?

Since the machine is, so to speak, committed to 16 significant digits in the example chosen, it must fill in the spaces with something! At this point, it is instructed to seek the programmer's choice for "fill-in." The programmer places his chosen digit in the card just before the last card of the program:

$$DAC\ 1,0$$

which means that the machine should fill in with zeros, and

$$DAC\ 1,9$$

which means that the machine should fill in with nines.

If the program is assembled *twice*, once with the first of these and the second time with the second of these, the difference in output will inform the reader which of the output figures are "accidental." We shall illustrate this in the sample program.

For the present, remember that the last *three* cards in the two source programs should be:

DC   2,−0,401   DC   2,−0,401

DAC 1,0   DAC 1,9

DENDSTART   DENDSTART

20.8   STATISTICAL PROGRAM

Following is a floating-point program to find M and σ for two distributions of data (the flow chart is shown in Fig. 49). Note the following:

1. Each macro-instruction is typed as its primary linkage.
2. Variable instructions are set (01170 to 01200) and stepped (02070 to 02100) as previously explained.
3. Floating-point zero is designated as ZEROF in *two* commands.
4. On page 181, the result of two runs, one with DAC 1,0 and one with DAC 1,9 is shown. Notice that the last four digits of σ_1 are not significant.

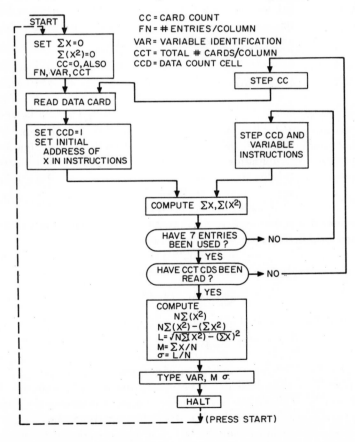

Fig. 49.   Flow chart: m and σ in variable floating-point SPS.

5. A dump-out of the memory (from SUMX) is displayed.

Sample Program for M and σ in Variable Floating-Point SPS

1. *Input Instructions.* The *first* card has the total number of entries/column in cc 1-9 (in the sample, 13) as a floating-point number ($\overline{1}3000000\overline{2}$), the variable number in cc 10-12 in fixed point (in the sample, $\overline{0}01$ and $\overline{0}02$), and the number of cards per column in cc 13-15 in fixed point (in the sample, $\overline{0}02$).

The rest of the cards contain data in floating-point notation, seven per card, in card columns beginning 1, 11, 21, 31, 41, 51, 61. The card number is in 78-80.

2. *Data.*

Variable 1		Variable 2	
X_1	Floating	X_2	Floating
501.99	$\overline{5}0199000\overline{3}$	1.815	$\overline{1}8150000\overline{1}$
493.37	$\overline{4}9337000\overline{3}$	0.698	$\overline{6}9800000\overline{0}$
545.06	$\overline{5}4506000\overline{3}$	−0.474	$\overline{4}7400000\overline{0}$
566.59	$\overline{5}6659000\overline{3}$	−1.637	$\overline{1}6370000\overline{1}$
540.75	$\overline{5}4075000\overline{3}$	−2.386	$\overline{2}3860000\overline{1}$
648.43	$\overline{6}4843000\overline{3}$	−0.815	$\overline{8}1500000\overline{0}$
467.53	$\overline{4}6753000\overline{3}$	0.298	$\overline{2}9800000\overline{0}$
652.73	$\overline{6}5273000\overline{3}$	−0.774	$\overline{7}7400000\overline{0}$
575.21	$\overline{5}7521000\overline{3}$	−2.086	$\overline{2}0860000\overline{1}$
605.36	$\overline{6}0536000\overline{3}$	0.991	$\overline{9}9100000\overline{0}$
562.28	$\overline{5}6228000\overline{3}$	−0.537	$\overline{5}3700000\overline{0}$
428.77	$\overline{4}2877000\overline{3}$	−1.268	$\overline{1}2680000\overline{1}$
536.44	$\overline{5}3644000\overline{3}$	−0.822	$\overline{8}2200000\overline{0}$

In each case, a floating-point zero ($0000000\overline{99}$) was placed in cc 61-69 of the second card in order to make seven entries per card.

```
END OF PASSI
01010*PROGRAM FOR M AND SIGMA. FIRST CARD HAS FL PT N IN CC 1-9,
01020*VARIABLE NO. IN FX PT IN CC 10-12, NO. OF CDS IN CC 13-15
01030          DORG 2500
                                        02500
01031START     RCTY
                                        02500 34 00000 00102
01040          WATY SPACE
                                        02512 39 03335 00100
01050          WATY TITLE1
                                        02524 39 03357 00100
01060          WATY SPACE
                                        02536 39 03335 00100
01070          WATY TITLE2
                                        02548 39 03365 00100
01080          WATY SPACE
                                        02560 39 03335 00100
01090          WATY TITLE3
                                        02572 39 03383 00100
01100BEGIN     TFLS SUMX,ZEROF
                                        02584 16 03749 02607  ⎫ THIS IS A
                                        02596 49 03718 00000  ⎬ TYPICAL
                                        02603 00005 03402     ⎪ LINKAGE
                                        02608 00005 03412     ⎭
01110          TFLS SUMXX,ZEROF
```

```
01120        RNCD  IBMCD

01130        TFM   CC,0,9

01140        AM    CC,1,10

01150READ    RNCD  DATA

01160        TFM   CCD,1,10

01170        TFM   A1+28,X

01180        TFM   A2+23,X

01190        TFM   A2+28,X

01200        TFM   A3+28,X

02010A1      FA    SUMX,X



02020A2      FM    X,X



02030A3      FA    SUMXX,X



02040        CM    CCD,7,10

02050        BE    TERM

02060        AM    CCD,1,10

02070        AM    A1+28,10,10

02080        AM    A2+23,10,10

02090        AM    A2+28,10,10

02100        AM    A3+28,10,10

02110        B     A1

02120TERM    C     CC,IBMCD+14

02130        BNE   READ-12

02140        TFLS  SSUMX,SUMX



02150        FM    SSUMX,SSUMX





02160        TFLS  NSXX,SUMXX



02170        FM    NSXX,FN



02180        FS    NSXX,SSUMX



02190        FSQR  L,NSXX
```

```
02614 16 03749 02637
02626 49 03718 00000
02633 00005 03421
02638 00005 03412

02644 36 03422 00500

02656 16 03504 00000

02668 11 03504 00001

02680 36 03505 00500

02692 16 03586 00001

02704 16 02780 03513

02716 16 02805 03513

02728 16 02810 03513

02740 16 02840 03513

02752 16 03749 02775
02764 49 03638 00000
02771 00005 03402
02776 00005 03513

02782 16 03749 02805
02794 49 03658 00000
02801 00005 03513
02806 00005 03513

02812 16 03749 02835
02824 49 03638 00000
02831 00005 03421
02836 00005 03513

02842 14 03586 00007

02854 46 02938 01200

02866 11 03586 00001

02878 11 02780 00010

02890 11 02805 00010

02902 11 02810 00010

02914 11 02840 00010

02926 49 02752 00000

02938 24 03504 03436

02950 47 02668 01200

02962 16 03749 02985
02974 49 03718 00000
02981 00005 03595
02986 00005 03402

02992 16 03749 03015
03004 49 03658 00000
03011 00005 03595
03016 00005 03595

03022 16 03749 03045
03034 49 03718 00000
03041 00005 03604
03046 00005 03421

03052 16 03749 03075
03064 49 03658 00000
03071 00005 03604
03076 00005 03430

03082 16 03749 03105
03094 49 03618 00000
03101 00005 03604
03106 00005 03595

03112 16 03749 03135
03124 49 03698 00000
03131 00005 03613
03136 00005 03604
```

```
02200        FD    L,FN
                                            03142  16  03749  Ō3165
                                            03154  49  03678  00000
                                            03161  00005      Ō3613
                                            03166  00005      Ō3430
03010        FD    SUMX,FN
                                            03172  16  03749  Ō3195
                                            03184  49  03678  00000
                                            03191  00005      Ō3402
                                            03196  00005      Ō3430
03020        RCTY
                                            03202  34  00000  00102
03030        WATY  SPACE
                                            03214  39  03335  00100
03040        TD    IBMCD+12,RM
                                            03226  25  03434  03614
03050        WNTY  IBMCD+9
                                            03238  38  03431  00100
03060        WATY  SPACE
                                            03250  39  03335  00100
03070        WNTY  SUMX-8
                                            03262  38  03394  00100
03080        WATY  SPACE
                                            03274  39  03335  00100
03090        WNTY  L-8
                                            03286  38  03605  00100
03100        H
                                            03298  48  00000  00000
03101        RCTY
                                            03310  34  00000  00102
03110        B     BEGIN
                                            03322  49  02584  00000
04010*AREA DESIGNATIONS.
04020SPACE   DAC   11,
                                            03335  00011
04030TITLE1  DAC   4,VAR@
                                            03357  00004
04040TITLE2  DAC   9,MEAN
                                            03365  00009
04050TITLE3  DAC   6,SIGMA@
                                            03383  00006
04060SUMX    DS    9
                                            03402  00009
04070        DC    1,@
                                            03403  00001
04080        DC    7,0
                                            03410  00007
04090ZEROF   DC    2,-99
                                            03412  00002
04100SUMXX   DS    9
                                            03421  00009
04110IBMCD   DSS   80
                                            03422  00080
04120CC      DS    3
                                            03504  00003
04130DATA    DSS   80
                                            03505  00080
04140CCD     DS    2
                                            03586  00002
04150X       DS    ,DATA + 8
                                            03513  00000
04160SSUMX   DS    9
                                            03595  00009
04170NSXX    DS    9
                                            03604  00009
04180FN      DS    ,IBMCD+3
                                            03430  00000
04190L       DS    9
                                            03613  00009
04200RM      DC    1,@
                                            03614  00001
05010        DC    2,-0,401
                                            00401  00002
05020        DAC   1,0
05030        DEND  START
                                            03617  00001
LOAD SUBROUTINES
                                            02500
ENTER MANTISSA LENGTH Ō7RS
                                            03618  16  04140  Ō4874
                                            03630  49  03738  0
                                            03638  16  04140  Ō4894
                                            03650  49  03738  0
                                            03658  16  04140  Ō5594
                                            03670  49  03738  0
                                            03678  16  04140  Ō5790
                                            03690  49  03738  0
                                            03698  16  04140  Ō6038
                                            03710  49  03842  0
                                            03718  16  04140  Ō6698
                                            03730  49  03842  0
```

EXERCISES

Using Table I, write programs for the following, using floating-point notation and subroutines:

1 Arithmetic Means.
2 Standard Error of the Standard Deviation and of the Mean.
3 Skewness of each column.
4 Kurtosis of each column.
5 Pearson r between columns.
6 Partial correlation coefficients for three columns.
7 Chi-square for the entire table on some hypothesis.

PROJECTS

Prepare and run one of these programs.

Section 21. An Iterative Floating-Point Program

21.1   SOLVING ITERATIVE PROBLEMS

We have mentioned several times that digital computers are indispensable in modern life because they make it possible to solve two general categories of problems: (i) where the mass of data is overwhelmingly great (as in statistical problems), and (ii) where the number of arithmetical trials is overwhelmingly great (as in the solution of equations and the preparation of tables of constants). We have already illustrated the solution of a statistical problem. We now mention that the solution of all kinds of equations, polynomial, irrational, simultaneous, differential and integral, is easily accomplished by a digital computer once the basic program has been debugged.

The chief difference between the two types of problems is that in a statistical problem (including many matrix problems), the task involves a useful way of getting the information into the machine in locatable form. In the iterative type of problem, the task involves a useful way of establishing a criterion so that the machine will know when to stop trying solutions.

21.2   ILLUSTRATIVE ITERATIVE PROBLEM

To illustrate the solution of an iterative problem, we seek a solution, correct to $3*10^{-10}$, of the equation

$$x \log x - k = 0$$

where k is a constant to be typed into the machine.

The flow chart is shown in Fig. 50. In this program, we are using FT as a

Cont. from 181

```
END OF PASS11
02500    START    02584    BEGIN    02680    READ     02752    A1       02782    A2
02812    A3       02938    TERM     03335    SPACE    03357    *TITLE1  03365    *TITLE2
03383    *TITLE3  03402    SUMX     03412    ZEROF    03421    SUMXX    03422    IBMCD
03504    CC       03505    DATA     03586    CCD      03513    X        03595    SSUMX
03604    NSXX     03430    FN       03613    L        03614    RM
```

THE FOLLOWING IS THE OUTPUT FOR A DAC 1,0 CARD PRECEDING <u>DENDSTART</u>

VAR	MEAN	SIGMA
001	548039203	630116902
002	538230700	T17244901

THE FOLLOWING IS THE OUTPUT FOR A DAC 1,9 CARD PRECEDING <u>DENDSTART</u>.

VAR	MEAN	SIGMA
001	548039203	630121502
002	538230700	T17244901

A DUMP OF THE MEMORY STARTING AT 03394 LOOKS LIKE THIS:

```
350339400100
538230700‡000000099216362902T30000002002‡02000000000000000000000000000000000000
0000000000000000000000000000000025990760000435139601098208100002883690000T60782401
0675684000000000009900000099020007489580002232313703T17244901‡079160414004874490 3
7389160414004894490373891604140055944903738916041400579049037389160414006038490 3
```

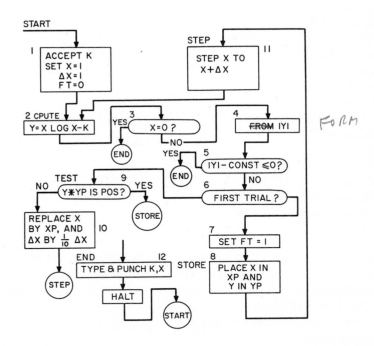

Fig. 50.   Flow chart: X log X — K = Y = 0.

"first trial" executive cell, and XP and YP as "previous values" of X and Y, i.e., values already tested. An alternative procedure, left for the student as an exercise, is to set YP = 0 at the beginning. Then the use of an executive control cell can be avoided.

In planning this program, we first calculate a few values in order to check intermediate results:

X	LOG X	X LOG X	Y
1	0.00000	0.00000	−1.20000
2	0.30103	0.60206	−0.59794
3	0.47712	1.43136	+0.23136

where K was taken as $+1.2$.

Note that the sign of Y changes as X goes from X = 2 to X = 3, so that the root of the equation is between 2 and 3, for this value of K.

Now we are ready to proceed.

In Box 1, we plan to accept a value of K from the typewriter (as a floating-point constant), and since we want the answer correct to $3 * 10^{-10}$, we shall type it in as a ten-place floating-point number, in this case $\overline{1}2000000000\overline{0}1$. We shall request ten places from the variable subroutines deck. In Box 1, we also set X and ΔX (both as ten-place floating-point numbers).

Box 2 has the actual computation of Y which, as we already know, is the easiest part of computing.

If Y = 0, we are finished and have an exact answer, so we branch to the end. This would happen, for example, if X = 1, and K = 0.

If Y is not 0, we wish to know when to terminate our calculation. You may remember that in Subsection 9.4 we proved (Example 1) that the error in x is given by:

$$0 \leqslant E \leqslant \frac{|y|}{1.69315}$$

If we now make $|Y| \leqslant 5 * 10^{-10}$, the error will be $\leqslant 3 * 10^{-10}$. Therefore, we set CONST = $5 * 10^{-10}$ and compare this to the absolute value of Y. This merely involves placing Y in another work cell (in this case, ABS) and removing the flag, if any. Notice that

$$|Y| \leqslant \text{CONST} \qquad \Longleftrightarrow \qquad |Y| - \text{CONST} \leqslant 0$$

In practice, we perform the floating subtraction (instruction 01150) and branch if the result is not positive (instruction 01160). Notice that a *Compare* cannot be used with floating-point numbers; a simple Compare would merely operate on the two characteristics, since that is where the termination flags are first met. However, as in the case of any arithmetic operation, the positive, zero, or negative result is enough to set the console indicators, so that the *branch* command can follow the arithmetic command directly.

If the difference is not positive, we are finished and can branch to the end. If, however, the difference is positive, we have not, as yet, reached the end and must continue with our trials.

What we do now depends on what has happened to Y when we went from X to $(X + \Delta X)$, and that, in turn, depends upon whether this is the first time around. If it *is* the first time around, we have no previous value of Y. We merely store the present value (Box 8) and branch to STEP (Box 11). If it is *not* the first time around, then we have previous values of X and Y. We now compare the signs of Y and YP to see whether they have changed (Box 9). This is most easily done by multiplying them (instructions 02020 and 02030) and examining the product (instruction 02040). If Y and YP are different in sign, then the product will be negative. If Y and YP are the same in sign, the product will be positive (we know $Y \neq 0$.) If they are the same, we merely wish to branch to STEP and increment X again. If they are different, however, we have incremented X by too much. We now go to Box 10 where we replace X by the previous value, XP, and change the increment, ΔX, to one-tenth of its previous value.

Another suitable plan of attack is to step Δx until Δx is equal to one-tenth of the desired precision, and until y changes sign. This will give one more place than desired, and the proper result can be obtained by half-adjusting. In this problem, if x were desired to the nearest billionth by this method, we would step Δx until it was proceeding in intervals of 10^{-10}, and would type the answer when the sign had changed and the result half-adjusted. This method of attack is illustrated in the problem of Part Four, (Subsection 24.1).

21.3   PROGRAM FOR X LOG X − K = 0

Following is the program for x log x − k = 0:

```
31000030000 2RS

SPS PROCESSOR  FOR 1620/1710 CARD I/O SYSTEM,DATED 1/1/1962

END OF PASSI

01010*PROGRAM TO SOLVE X LOG X - K = 0
01020        DORG 2500
                                    02500
01030START   RCTY
                                    02500 34 00000 00102
01040        WATY TITLE1
                                    02512 39 03233 00100
01050        RNTY K-11
                                    02524 36 03457 00100
01060        TFLS X,ONE
                                    02536 16 03637 02559  ⎫ THIS IS A
                                    02548 49 03606 00000  ⎬ TYPICAL
                                    02555 00005    03455  ⎭ LINKAGE
                                    02560 00005    03403
01070        TFLS DELTAX,ONE
                                    02566 16 03637 02589
                                    02578 49 03606 00000
                                    02585 00005    03520
                                    02590 00005    03403
01080        TDM  FT,0
                                    02596 15 03522 00000
01090CPUTE   FLOG Y,X
                                    02608 16 03637 02631
                                    02620 49 03586 00000
                                    02627 00005    03481
                                    02632 00005    03455
01100        FM   Y,X
                                    02638 16 03637 02661
                                    02650 49 03566 00000
                                    02657 00005    03481
                                    02662 00005    03455
```

```
01110       FS    Y,K
                                          02668 16 03637 0̄2691
                                          02680 49 03526 00000
                                          02687 00005    0̄3481
                                          02692 00005    0̄3468
01120       BE    END
                                          02698 46 03004 01200
01130       TFLS ABS,Y
                                          02710 16 03637 0̄2733
                                          02722 49 03606 00000
                                          02729 00005    0̄3494
                                          02734 00005    0̄3481
01140       CF    ABS-2,,,REMOVES FLAG IF PRESENT
                                          02740 33 03492 00000
01150       FS    ABS,CONST
                                          02752 16 03637 0̄2775
                                          02764 49 03526 00000
                                          02771 00005    0̄3494
                                          02776 00005    0̄3416
01160       BNP  END
                                          02782 47 03004 01100
01190       BD    TEST,FT
                                          02794 43 02830 03522
01200       TDM  FT,1
                                          02806 15 03522 00001
02010       B     STORE
                                          02818 49 03160 00000
02020TEST   TFLS PROD,YP
                                          02830 16 03637 0̄2853
                                          02842 49 03606 00000
                                          02849 00005    0̄3507
                                          02854 00005    0̄3442
02030       FM    PROD,Y
                                          02860 16 03637 0̄2883
                                          02872 49 03566 00000
                                          02879 00005    0̄3507
                                          02884 00005    0̄3481
02040       BP    STORE
                                          02890 46 03160 01100
02050       TFLS X,XP
                                          02902 16 03637 0̄2925
                                          02914 49 03606 00000
                                          02921 00005    0̄3455
                                          02926 00005    0̄3429
02060       FM    DELTAX,TENTH
                                          02932 16 03637 0̄2955
                                          02944 49 03566 00000
                                          02951 00005    0̄3520
                                          02956 00005    0̄3390
02070STEP   FA    X,DELTAX
                                          02962 16 03637 0̄2985
                                          02974 49 03546 00000
                                          02981 00005    0̄3455
                                          02986 00005    0̄3520
02080       B     CPUTE
                                          02992 49 02608 00000
02090END    TFLS IBMCD+11,K
                                          03004 16 03637 0̄3027
                                          03016 49 03606 00000
                                          03023 00005    0̄3309
                                          03028 00005    0̄3468
02100       TFLS IBMCD+25,X
                                          03034 16 03637 0̄3057
                                          03046 49 03606 00000
                                          03053 00005    0̄3323
                                          03058 00005    0̄3455
02110       WNCD IBMCD
                                          03064 38 03298 00400
02120       RCTY
                                          03076 34 00000 00102
02130       WNTY K-11
                                          03088 38 03457 00100
02140       SPTY
                                          03100 34 00000 00101
02150       SPTY
                                          03112 34 00000 00101
02160       WNTY X-11
                                          03124 38 03444 00100
02170       H
                                          03136 48 00000 00000
02180       B     START
                                          03148 49 02500 00000
02190STORE  TFLS XP,X
                                          03160 16 03637 0̄3183
                                          03172 49 03606 00000
                                          03179 00005    0̄3429
                                          03184 00005    0̄3455
```

```
02200          TFLS YP,Y
                                                    03190 16 03637 03213
                                                    03202 49 03606 00000
                                                    03209 00005      03442
02210      B      STEP                              03214 00005      03481

03010*AREA DESIGNATIONS                             03220 49 02962 00000
03020TITLE1 DAC  33,TYPE K AS 10 PLACE FL PT NUMBER.@
1     IBMCD  DSS  80                                03233 00033
2            DNB  40,IBMCD+39                       03298 00080
3            DNB  40,IBMCD+79                       03337 00040
4            DC   1,@                               03377 00040
5            DC   10,1000000000                     03378 00001
6     TENTH  DC   2,-0                              03388 00010
7            DC   1,@                               03390 00002
8            DC   10,1000000000                     03391 00001
9     ONE    DC   2,1                               03401 00010
10           DC   1,@                               03403 00002
11           DC   10,5000000000                     03404 00001
12    CONST  DC   2,-9                              03414 00010
13           DC   1,@                               03416 00002
14    XP     DS   12                                03417 00001
15           DC   1,@                               03429 00012
16    YP     DS   12                                03430 00001
17           DC   1,@                               03442 00012
18    X      DS   12                                03443 00001
19           DC   1,@                               03455 00012
20    K      DS   12                                03456 00001
21           DC   1,@                               03468 00012
22    Y      DS   12                                03469 00001
23           DC   1,@                               03481 00012
                                                    03482 00001

24    ABS    DS   12,,,TO FORM ABS VALUE OF Y
25           DC   1,@                               03494 00012
26    PROD   DS   12,,,TO FORM Y * YP               03495 00001
27           DC   1,@                               03507 00012
28    DELTAX DS   12                                03508 00001
29           DC   1,@                               03520 00012
30    FT     DS   1                                 03521 00001
31           DC   1,@                               03522 00001
32           DC   2,-0,401                          03523 00001
33           DAC  1,0                               00401 00002
34           DEND START                             03525 00001
                                                    02500
LOAD SUBROUTINES
ENTER MANTISSA LENGTH TOPS
```

```
                                            03598 49 03730 0
                                            03606 16 04028 07072
                                            03618 49 03730 0
      END OF PASSII
      02500  START    02608  CPUTE   02830  TEST   02962  STEP    03004  END
      03160  STORE    03233 *TITLE1  03298  IBMCD  03390  TENTH   03403  ONE
      03416  CONST    03429  XP      03442  YP     03455  X       03468  K
      03481  Y        03494  ABS     03507  PROD   03520 *DELTAX  03522  FT
```

The following shows some of the intermediate dumpouts of the type used in debugging the program. To obtain these intermediate dumpouts, press the SIE (Single Instruction Execute) button. Then the SAVE button, then the INSERT button. Then type the dump instruction followed by a 42 command. When you have enough dumped, press RELEASE. This causes the machine to return to the program. The following shows four "dumps." Notice how the use of *record marks* helps to locate designated areas.

TYPE K AS 10 PLACE FL PT NUMBER.T2000000000‾1

```
   35033790010042  ( DUMP COMMAND)
T0000000000‾0‡T0000000000‾1‡500000000009‡260000000001‡T21069296000‡270000000001‡T2
0000000001‡T21069296000‡21069295500‡2483736353‾0T‡T0000000000‾0‡1‡70160402804‾7624
90362601604028‾04782490362601604028‾054824903626
```

```
   35033790010042  ( DUMP COMMAND)
T0000000000‾0‡T0000000000‾1‡500000000009‡274020000001‡389046000003‡274030000001‡T2
0000000001‡389046000003‡389045500003‡T852843246‾06‡T0000000000‾3‡1‡70160402804‾7624
90362601604028‾04782490362601604028‾054824903626‾0160
```

```
   35033790010042  ( DUMP COMMAND)
T0000000000‾0‡T0000000000‾1‡500000000009‡274064000001‡531700000005‡274065000001‡T2
0000000001‡531700000005‡531650000005‡7464536300T‾0‡T0000000000‾4‡1‡70160402804‾7624
90362601604028‾04782490362601604028‾054824903626‾0
```

```
   35033790010042  ( DUMP COMMAND)
T0000000000‾0‡T0000000000‾1‡500000000009‡274064600001‡840000000007‡274064601001‡T2
0000000001‡300000000008‡250000000008‡252000000015‡T0000000007‡1‡70160402804‾7624
90362601604028‾04782490362601604028‾054824903626‾016040
```

THE FOLLOWING IS THE TYPEWRITTEN OUTPUT. WHEN K=12, X= 2.740646097
   TO THE REQUIRED PRECISION.

T2000000000‾1 274064609701

21.4 DEBUGGING AN ITERATIVE PROGRAM

In order to assist in debugging an iterative program, it is, as has been mentioned, quite important to know something about the intermediate results. In the illustrative example, the constants and sum cells (see pages 187 and 188) were separated by record marks in order to make the numerical dump-out easy to read.

Some intermediate dump-outs are shown on pages 187 and 188. The address for the beginning of the dump was that of the left end of TENTH. (We didn't need this, but it illustrates the advantage of separating designated areas by record marks.) Reading any one of the dump-outs from left to right, we have, then, TENTH, ONE,

CONST, XP, YP, X, K, Y, ABS, PROD, DELTAX, and FT. The material at the end, $\overline{7}01604028. \ldots$, is part of the subroutines package and does not concern us. Notice how Y gets smaller and smaller.

The answer is at the bottom of the listing.

According to the program, another value of K could be tested by merely pressing the START button.

EXERCISES

1 Write a program to multiply two matrices, with the components in floating point. If you run this program, be sure to check for significance by altering the end card.

2 Write a program to generate a table for

$$\frac{m}{m_0} = \frac{1}{\sqrt{1 - (v^2/c^2)}}$$

where $c = 3 * 10^{10}$ cm/sec, and v varies from 10 cm/sec to 10^9 cm/sec, with $v_{i+1} = 10 * v_i$.

3 Write a program to generate a table for sin x, with x varying from 0° to 45° in intervals of 0.1°. Do not, of course, use the floating-point subroutine. Use a Maclaurin Series (which is alternating, for this case) and terminate with an error less than 10^{-9}. Remember that the argument must be converted to radians.

4 Write a program to generate a table for arcsin x, with x varying from 0 to 1. Use a Maclaurin Series with Remainder.

5 Write a program to solve an equation of the form $Ax^3 + Bx^2 + Cx + D = 0$, with x correct to the nearest 10^{-6}, given that x is between x_1 and x_2 (the initial trial value to be typed on the console typewriter). For testing, you may use $5x^3 + 2x^2 - 15x - 6 = 0$, for which the answer is approximately 1.73.*

6 Write a program to solve $Ax + B \cos x + C = 0$ to the nearest millionth, given that x is between x_1 and x_2 (the initial trial value to be typed on the console typewriter). For testing, you may use $3x - \cos x - 1 = 0$, for which one answer is approximately 0.61.

7 Write a program to solve a pair of simultaneous equations of the form:

$$\begin{cases} f(x,y) = 0 \\ g(x,y) = 0 \end{cases}$$

to the nearest millionth. To do this, you rewrite the equations as

$$\begin{cases} x = F(x,y) \\ y = G(x,y) \end{cases}$$

You make a fairly good estimate of x and y from a graph (enter this in the machine as x_0, y_0 via the typewriter) then calculate

$$\begin{cases} x_1 = F(x_0, y_0) \\ y_1 = G(x_0, y_0) \end{cases}$$

You continue, substituting new values of x and y, until

$$|x_n - x_{n-1}| \leqslant 10^{-6} \quad \text{and} \quad |y_n - y_{n-1}| \leqslant 10^{-6}$$

This method does not always work, unfortunately, and a full discussion can be found in advanced books on *Numerical Analysis*.

8   Using Simpson's Rule, write a program to prepare a table of "areas under the normal curve" in intervals from $z = 0$ to $z = z_n$, where z_n varies from 0.1 to 2.0. You may check by looking up a table of such areas. Hasting's Rule is a better method for numerical integration.*

9   Using Hasting's Approximation,** write a program to generate the Gamma function of $(1 + x)$, $\Gamma (1 + x)$.

PROJECTS

Prepare the cards and run one of the above programs.

* footnote P. 193

PART FOUR

FORTRAN
With Format

Advantages and Limitations

The purpose of FORTRAN (FORmula TRANslation) is to make it very easy for a mathematician or a scientist to solve numerical problems requiring one or more formulas. For example, if in a problem it is necessary to find

$$E(k) = \int_0^{\pi/2} \sqrt{1 - k^2 \sin^2 \theta \; d\theta}$$

for $0 \leqslant k \; 1$, this may be done quickly and efficiently by using

$$E*(k) = \{1 + a_1 p + \ldots + a_4 p^4\} + \{b_1 p + \ldots + b_4 p^4\} \ln (1/p)$$

where $p = (1 - k^2)$ and the a's and b's are constants.*** The error is less than $1.5 * 10^{-8}$.

Other problems are, similarly, preceded by numerical analysis. We cannot go deeply into this phase of the problem in this book. We merely mention that *series* are extremely important in the preparation of a problem for computation. Both the *point* type (e.g., Taylor Series) and the *interval* type (e.g., Fourier Series) are important, and in either case it is essential that the error term be known.

In any case, we shall assume that the problem has been developed to a point where the mathematician or scientist knows exactly what he wants the machine to do and the only remaining problem is how to get the machine to do it.

You already know that SPS has tremendous power and you may wonder why FORTRAN is needed. Actually, it is not needed—but it has some great advantages. These advantages are as follows:

1. It is extremely easy to program. In contrast to machine language which has individual instructions, and SPS which has only a few macro-instructions, FORTRAN has almost exclusively macro-instructions. As a matter of fact, the formula illustrated above can be evaluated almost as it stands with the addition

---

*Error formulas for integrals are beyond the scope of this book on computing. An excellent discussion, for those competent in the calculus, can be found in Hildebrand, *op. cit.*, Chapter 8, and in similar works.

**See, Hastings, Cecil, Jr., *Approximations for Digital Computers*, Princeton University Press, p. 158.

***Hastings, Cecil, Jr., *op. cit.*, p. 175.

of read-in and print-out instructions. A single instruction in FORTRAN may, in some cases, be translated by the processor and subroutines decks into *hundreds* of machine language instructions!

2. There is little or no need for housekeeping. You need worry neither about flags nor about scaling. All of this is taken care of by the processor.

3. The programs are *upward compatible* provided the programs are written properly. Thus, a 1620 FORTRAN program can be inserted into an IBM 7090 without change.

4. A *Precompiler Deck* enables the programmer to correct typing errors before compiling the source program into an object program.

5. A built-in *Tracer* enables the programmer to check for logical errors.

6. Whereas SPS is a two-pass processor, FORTRAN assembles the object program in a single pass.

There are also some limitations on FORTRAN. These limitations are as follows:

1. There is less control over the output format. In both machine language and SPS, there is complete control over format.

2. There is no limitation, except the capacity of the memory, on the precision of a result in machine language. In SPS, the limit is 45 digits. In FORTRAN for the basic 20K machine, the limit is eight digits, and the eighth is not always accurate (because of round-off problems). We should mention that this limitation is relaxed in machines with larger capacity, so that this is a limitation imposed by the size of the memory rather than by the program itself.

3. The FORTRAN processor takes a great deal of room in memory, approximately half the basic machine. This makes it impossible to work with large matrices, for example, on the basic machine. Again, this is a limitation of the size of the memory, rather than the FORTRAN program.

4. Although FORTRAN is one-pass, it is quite lengthy and the processor must be reloaded for each program. The SPS processor, once loaded, can be used for any number of compilations.

To summarize very briefly, SPS is the ideal program for economy of machine time and space, whereas FORTRAN is the ideal program for economy of programming time provided that the problem can be fitted into the memory.

Section 22. Reading Data In and Out

22.1 INTRODUCTORY REMARKS

Even the simplest type of program usually consists of "program modules" somewhat like those shown in Fig. 51.

The instructions for a FORTRAN program are most conveniently key-punched on specially printed cards such as the one shown in Fig. 52. Card columns 1 through 5 in that figure are reserved for (*i*) Cbb, which introduces a "comment card," or (*ii*) a *statement number*, which (for the IBM 1620) may be any number from 1 to 9999 *except 999*. The statement numbers correspond to the memory cell addresses of the

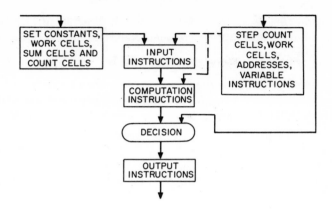

Fig. 51.   Program module for FORTRAN.

instructions which they precede. As in the case of SPS *labels,* instructions may or may not be identified by statement numbers.

Card column 6 is used for another purpose in larger computers and we shall, therefore, usually skip this column.

Card columns 7 through 72 are used for the actual instruction, which is *always* symbolic.

For convenience, the following key-punch drum card may be used:

cc 1	b (blank)
cc 2-6	+ (or ampersand)
cc 7	1
cc 8-72	A

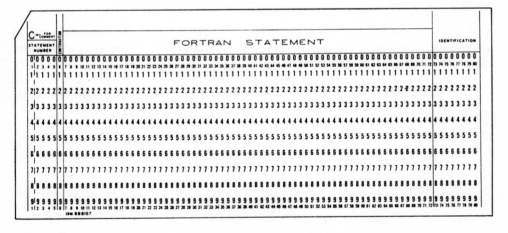

Fig. 52.   A FORTRAN IBM card.

cc 73   — (on the skip-minus key)

cc 74-80   + (or ampersand)

All three control switches on the keypunch should be "on."

22.2   INPUT COMMANDS AND OUTPUT COMMANDS

In FORTRAN, each input or output command consists of a *pair* of statements. One member of the pair of statements is an instruction which "tells" the machine whether to read a card ("READ"), punch a card ("PUNCH"), or use the typewriter ("ACCEPT" for input, "TYPE" or "PRINT" for output). The other member of the pair of statements is a *specification* or "FORMAT" statement, which informs the machine concerning the *form* in which the input exists or the output is desired.

As an example, the following *pair* of statements:

$$\left\{ \begin{array}{ll} & \text{READ 37, SUMX} \\ 37 & \text{FORMAT (F10.0)} \end{array} \right.$$

commands the machine to read a card, specifies that the information is in the first ten card columns (we shall explain this in detail presently), and designates this input as SUMX.

The following *pair* of statements:

$$\left\{ \begin{array}{ll} & \text{PUNCH 5267, SIGMA} \\ 5267 & \text{FORMAT (F10.3)} \end{array} \right.$$

commands the machine to punch a card, designates the output as SIGMA, and specifies that the output, in this case, is in cc 1-10, with a decimal point in cc 7 (we shall explain this, too).

All input and output is alphameric and is converted internally without any need for housekeeping on the part of the programmer.

In the discussion which follows, we have simplified the procedure somewhat by omitting a great many alternative methods for specifying input and output requirements. The method to be explained is just as good as any other and is quite satisfactory for mathematical and scientific work. The alternative methods may, however, be needed if the programmer is using data prepared by someone else. In that case, reference should be made to the current IBM FORTRAN Manual.

22.3   FIXED-POINT INPUT (Iw)

In all FORMAT specification statements, w stands for the actual number of spaces required, i.e., the number of card columns or the number of typewriter spaces. For *input* of fixed-point numbers (integers) in the IBM 1620, a maximum of *four digits and a sign* may be entered with a FORMAT statement. The input of the fixed-point number, −4378, requires a FORMAT statement like

576   FORMAT(I5)

where the 5 in I5 means that −4378 requires either five card columns or five typewriter spaces. The input of a single digit, like "7," requires a FORMAT statement like

1923   FORMAT (I1)

FORMAT statements are *always* numbered and are usually placed at the *end* of the program (like "Area Designations" in SPS).

If there are excess digits in the input of a fixed-point number, the *high-order* digits (but not the sign) will be truncated. For example, the number −1234567, read in with a FORMAT(I8) statement, will appear in memory as $\overline{456}\overline{7}$.

Any fixed-point number can be given a *name* consisting of (up to) five letters or numbers beginning with I, J, K, L, M or N. These names are called *fixed-point variables*. Some typical fixed-point variables are: I, ISUM, K2408, LOAN, MASS7, etc.

22.4   FLOATING-POINT INPUT (Ew.d)

For numbers with decimal points there are *two* kinds of floating-point specification statements. These are called *E-mode* and *F-mode*.

E-mode is an exponential notation and is useful mainly for numbers which are very small or very large, i.e., the kind of number for which scientific notation is usually employed. The w in the specification statement refers, again, to the actual number of spaces required, i.e., card columns or typewriter spaces. The d is ignored by the processor as long as there is a decimal point in the input data, and we may write a 0 or any other number there. We shall always write floating-point numbers with decimal points and this will greatly simplify the small problem of input specification.

Here are some examples of input data and their FORMAT specifications:

Data	*Specification (statement numbers omitted)*
$-1.2345E5$ $(= -1.2345 * 10^5)$	FORMAT(E9.0)
$235.789E{-}27$ $(= 235.789 * 10^{-27})$	FORMAT(E11.0)
$3.025734567E{-}37$ $(= 3.025734567 * 10^{-37})$	FORMAT(E15.0)

In the last case, only eight significant digits will be stored (as $30257345\overline{3}\overline{6}$).

Any floating-point constant can be given a name consisting of (up to) five letters or numbers beginning with any letter other than I, J, K, L, M, or N. Some typical floating-point variables are: A, ZN, SUM3, TOTAL.

22.5 FLOATING-POINT INPUT (Fw.d)

F-mode is the most convenient mode for input of numbers of ordinary size. The w in the specification statement stands, once again, for the actual number of spaces required. The d is ignored by the processor provided that there is a decimal point in the input datum.

Here are some examples of input data and their F-mode specifications:

Data	*Specification (statement numbers omitted)*
−23.778	FORMAT(F7.0)
0.000012345678	FORMAT(F14.0)
−12345.678999	FORMAT(F13.0)

In the last case, the low-order 999 will be truncated.

Floating-point constants in F-mode may be named exactly like those in E-mode.

22.6 INPUT SPACES

If an input card has the following data:

cc 1-10	blanks (or information to be disregarded)
cc 11-17	−3.1416
cc 18-19	blanks
cc 20-29	1234.5E−27

this may be read into memory with the single FORMAT statement

    65   FORMAT(10XF7.0,2XE10.0)

where the 10X and 2X stand for spaces to be skipped. Commas must always follow I, E, and F specifications (except for the one before a right parenthesis) but may be omitted for the spacing specification.

22.7 READ-IN INSTRUCTIONS

We shall use two read-in instructions in FORTRAN. The first is

READ n, list

where n refers to the statement number of the appropriate FORMAT specification, and *list* refers to the names (variables) to be applied to the data being read in. The READ instruction means that a *card* is to be read.

The second read-in instruction is

ACCEPT n, list

which means that the data are to be read from the typewriter.

EXAMPLES

1. An IBM card has 754.26 in cc 1-6, 89 in cc 9-10, 3.72E—42 in cc 13-20, and unwanted material in 21-49. Read this into memory.

READ 1, A, I, B

1   FORMAT(F6.0,2X,I2,2X,E8.0)

Note that the *list* refers only to numerical data and that it must have the same order as the data on the card.

2. Read into memory from the typewriter 2.75E3, 28, and 448.67, where two spaces are left between the typed numbers.

ACCEPT 2, SUM1, IT, ZNUM

2   FORMAT(E6.0,2X,I2,2X,F6.0)

22.8 FIXED-POINT OUTPUT (Iw)

Again the *w* stands for the total number of spaces needed *except that the sign* (+ .or −) is included. This means that no fixed-point number with more than four digits can be typed out or punched out in a FORTRAN program for the IBM 1620. The following examples show how the (I4) specification will cause the numbers in memory to be typed or punched:

Numbers in Memory	Output
7	bb+7
0	bb+0
−29	b−29
−146	−146
2146	+146
−2146	−146

22.9 FLOATING-POINT OUTPUT (Ew.d)

The *w* gives the number of spaces required and the *d tells how many digits are to follow the decimal point.* Remember that the memory has the numbers in SPS floating point and that is why you must indicate your choice.

As in the case of (Iw) a space *must* be provided for the sign in front of the number. In addition, spaces must be provided for E±xx at the end and for a decimal point where it is needed. This means that six spaces are needed for the number before you even begin to calculate the number of decimal places.

A variety of possibilities exist but we recommend that when the output is in

E-mode you use the FORMAT specification E14.8. This gives you all eight decimal places right after the decimal point and avoids possible truncation of an answer. (Remember that FORTRAN for the basic 20K machine has only eight-place floating point so that you will get all that you can from this specification.) If you use E14.7, the result will be in scientific notation, and this is also quite satisfactory.

The following examples show what happens to various numbers in memory when they are typed or punched with the specification (E10.3):

Number in Memory	Output
−.008	−8.000E−03
.472	+4.720E−01
.000000000006	+6.000E−12
−10.0468	−1.004E+01
1234567.8	+1.234E+06

In the last case, after deducting six spaces for housekeeping arrangements, there were only four spaces left for digits.

22.10 FLOATING-POINT OUTPUT (Fw.d)

Again, the w refer to the number of spaces required, including one for the sign and one for the decimal point; and d refers to the number of figures to follow the decimal point.

This gives the "prettiest" output, but can be used only when you have a fair idea of the nature of the output. The following examples show what happens to various numbers in memory when they are typed or punched with specification (F7.3):

Numbers in Memory	Output
28.601	+28.601
−6.4	b−6.400
−.8	bb−.800
4.721	b+4.721
2.48721	b+2.487

If the number in memory is larger than the amount specified by w, the answer will automatically be typed or punched in (E14.8) format, with an error message on the console typewriter.

22.11 ALPHAMERIC OUTPUT (wH)

Any alphameric material up to 49 characters and spaces may be typed or punched with the use of a Hollerith specification. For example,

9123   FORMAT(23HbPARTIALbCORRELATIONS.b)

will, under a suitable "Write" command, type or punch PARTIAL CORRELATIONS. with the spaces and the period as required.

22.12   OUTPUT CONTROL

Spaces may be provided on the typewriter or on cards by a (wX) specification. A slash (/) within a FORMAT statement causes the typewriter carriage to return (RCTY) except when the slash is part of an H-command.

Except for numerical specifications (I, E, and F), commas may or may not be used within the FORMAT statement, as you please.

22.13   READ-OUT INSTRUCTIONS

The two read-out instructions for the IBM 1620 are TYPE n, list and PUNCH n, list where, as before, *n* refers to the statement number of the FORMAT specification statement, and *list* refers to the names of the variables to be typed or punched. (PRINT is interpreted as TYPE by the compiler.)

EXAMPLES

We have in memory J = 23, SUMX = $\overline{2}143658\overline{7}03$, and ZMEAN = $\overline{8}765432\overline{12}3$. We wish to type the following two lines:

$$J = (+23)$$
$$\text{THE SUM OF X} = 214.36587 \text{ AND M} = \overline{8}765432\overline{12}3$$

Actually, we cannot accomplish this exact form of output. We shall have to be satisfied with a compromise:

$$J = (+23)$$
$$\text{THE SUM OF X} = +214.36587 \text{ AND M} = +.87654321E{-}23$$

The command and the specification are:

$$\text{TYPE 756, J, SUMX, ZMEAN}$$

756 FORMAT (3HJ=(I3,1H)/15HTHE SUM OF X = F10.3,9H AND M = E14.8)

This FORMAT specification will run from cc 7 to cc 66. At times, it is necessary to have a few extra spaces for the specification statement. The IBM 1620 will read it correctly even if it is started in an earlier column, but it must not project beyond cc 72.

Notice how the FORMAT statement inserts the numbers in the order in which they are listed.

22.14   TERMINATING A SIMPLE PROGRAM

For the present, in order to allow you to practice some simple read-in and read-out instructions, we mention that the termination of the instructions may be

PAUSE or STOP. The first of these, PAUSE, is a temporary stop. Upon pushing the START button, the machine will proceed to the next instruction (if there is one—otherwise there will, of course, be a CHECK STOP). The STOP is an unconditional halt. After the FORMAT specifications, an END card *must* be provided.

To summarize, your source program consists of (*i*) instructions in cc 7-72 with or without statement numbers in cc 1-5, (*ii*) usually, PAUSE or STOP at the end of the instructions, (*iii*) FORMAT specifications with statement numbers, and (*iv*) a *last card* with END in cc 7, 8, and 9.

ILLUSTRATIVE PROBLEM

An IBM card has 385 (= A) in cc 4-6, −27.639 (= B) in cc 12-18, 35894. (= C) in cc 27-32, and −6.502E−4 (= D) in cc 35-43. Read these into memory. Then type into memory −27381. (= E). Return the carriage twice, then type the constants as follows: C (in E mode), 10 spaces, D (in F mode). Punch A in card columns beginning with cc 12, then 4 spaces, then B in E mode preceded by the phrase "THE SECOND CONSTANT IS."

The program is typed on FORTRAN cards according to the listing in Fig. 53. (For a real program, we would use separate sheets for the instructions and area designations as we did with SPS, but in this case we shall not bother.)

The sample program below shows the actual machine listing of the program and, at the bottom (under "LOAD DATA"), −27381. RS which is the value of E as typed in, followed by the values of C and D typed in correct format according to the FORMAT instruction (statement number 3). Notice that the decimal point was placed for the type-in and that the R-S button on the console typewriter has to be pressed to release control and restart the sequence of instructions. In the type-out, notice the format of the E14.8 output. As we stated, this is not the prettiest output, but it is certainly the most efficient.

There is one more thing to call to your attention. We mentioned, in the problem, that A = 385, but we had to read it in as IA. We could as equally well have used JA, KA, LA, MA, NA or, in fact, any combination of five letters and numbers beginning with I, J, K, L, M or N. It is very important to read in fixed-point constants by using fixed-point variables, and to read in floating-point constants by using floating-point variables. Often, if a programmer wishes to read in a floating-point number which he thinks of as, say, "log P," he will designate this as "ZLOGP." The "Z" in front makes it a floating-point variable.

IN THE FOLLOWING, THE COMPILED ADDRESSES ARE SHOWN IN A SYMBOL TABLE. ORDINARILY, THIS IS NOT VERY USEFUL. IT IS SHOWN HERE MERELY AS A DEMONSTRATION.

```
     260000200003RS
ENTER SOURCE PROGRAM, PUSH START

08000 C   ILLUSTRATIVE PROBLEM FOR FORTRAN INPUT
08000        READ 1,IA,B,C,D
08060        ACCEPT 2,E
08084        TYPE 3, C,D
08120        PUNCH 4, IA,B
08156        STOP
```

BOARD OF EDUCATION OF THE CITY OF NEW YORK

IBM THE BRONX HIGH SCHOOL OF SCIENCE
DR. ALEXANDER TAFFEL, PRINCIPAL

FORTRAN CODING FORM

DEPARTMENT OF MATHEMATICS
DR. I. A. DODES, CHAIRMAN

Form X28-7327-2
Printed in U.S.A.

Program SAMPLE ØF FØRTRAN CØDING
Coded By I. A. DØDES
Checked By

Identification 73 80

Date 8-1-62
Page 1 of 1

C FOR COMMENT — STATEMENT NUMBER 1 5 — Cont. 6 — 7 FORTRAN STATEMENT 72

```
C    SAMPLE PRØGRAM
      READ 1,IA,B,C,D
      ACCEPT 2,E
      TYPE 3,C,D
      PUNCH 4,IA,B
      STØP
1     FØRMAT(3XI3,5XF7.0,8XF6.0,2XE9.0)
2     FØRMAT(F7.0)
3     FØRMAT(//E14.8,10XF9.7)
4     FØRMAT(11XI4,4X23HTHEbSECØNDbCØNSTANTbISbE14.8)
      END
```

Fig. 53. Coding a simple FORTRAN input-output program.

```
08204 1      FORMAT(3XI3,5XF7.0,8XF6.0,2XE9.0)
08306 2      FORMAT(F7.0)
08328 3      FORMAT(//E14.8,10XF9.7)
08392 4      FORMAT(11XI4,4X23HTHE SECOND CONSTANT IS E14.8)
08516        END

PROG SW 1 ONFOR SYMBOL TABLE, PUSH START
T9999 SIN
T9989 SINF
T9979 COS
T9969 COSF
T9959 ATAN
T9949 ATANF
T9939 EXP
T9929 EXPF
T9919 LOG
T9909 LOGF
T9899 SQRT
T9889 SQRTF
T9879 0001
T9869 0001
T9859 IA
T9849 B
T9839 C
T9829 D
T9819 0002
T9809 0002
T9799 E
T9789 0003
T9779 0003
T9769 0004
T9759 0004

SW 1 OFF TO IGNORE SUBROUTINES, PUSH START

PROCESSING COMPLETE

THE FOLLOWING IS THE TYPE WRITTEN OUTPUT.

LOAD DATA


-27381.RS

+.35894000E+05        -.0006502
STOP
```

It is of some interest that this small program consumed some 300 cards. This is because the processor deck "assumes" that if FORTRAN is being used, certain subroutines will always be needed. They are compiled automatically. How many steps and cards would this little (useless) program require in machine language? in SPS?

The card that is punched is "clean." There is no need for housekeeping at all.

EXERCISES

1 You have -357 in cc 1-4, 257.6448 in cc 15-22, and $-.503378E-7$ in cc 41-51 of an IBM card. Write a program to (i) read these into memory, (ii) punch them out in reverse order with the third given number in F-mode and the second in E-mode, (iii) type the statement "(A)b=b" followed by the first number. (Remember that b stands for a blank space.)

Tell whether each of the following is fixed point, floating point or incorrect.

2	0	3	-77
4	01234	5	9.478
6	3.1416	7	111222.333
8	-0.00000000000012345678	9	3.E72

10	−12.E16	11	3186.E48
12	13.E17	13	14.E−18
14	B	15	RATE
16	N	17	M2444
18	MAIL23	19	2NITE
20	LOAD	21	SAVING
22	B/O	23	TEMP7
24	JOBNO		

Section 23. Generating a Table from a Formula

23.1 PROBLEM IN ATOMIC PHYSICS

D. C. Peaslee's *Elements of Atomic Physics** states that the rate of emission of electrons per square centimenter of surface (j) is given by

$$j = \frac{m \; k^2}{2\pi^2 \; \hbar^3} \; T^2 \; e^{-\epsilon\phi/kT}$$

where m = electron relativistic rest mass, k = Boltzmann's constant $\hbar = \dfrac{h}{2\pi}$, where h is Planck's constant, T is the absolute temperature, ϵ = electronic charge in electrostatic units, ϕ = the thermionic work function for the metal.

We start by looking up the numerical values of some of these:

m = $9.1085 * 10^{-28}$ grams

k   = $1.38042 * 10^{-16}$ erg/degree

π = 3.1415927

h   = $6.6252 * 10^{-27}$ erg-sec

ϕ = something between 4.5 and 4.7 in various experiments for nickel. For the purpose of this program we shall arbitrarily take it as 4.685 with the remark that this is not the only mistake we shall be making.

ϵ = $4.80288 * 10^{-10}$ esu

(All of the above can be found in any standard handbook with physical and chemical constants.)

We start in the usual fashion by making a flow chart as in Fig. 54.

The plan is clearly to generate a table showing the variation of j with T for a given value of ϕ read in via the console typewriter. This appears to be an extremely

---

*D. C. Peaslee, *Elements of Atomic Physics*, Prentice-Hall, p. 356.

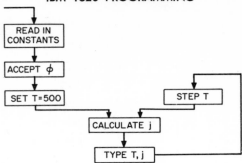

Fig. 54   Preliminary flow chart for the electron gas problem.

simple program with no "frills"—not even a termination instruction.

The (incorrect) program is shown in Fig. 55. The first card is a *comment card*, identified as such by the C in cc 1 and the two blank spaces following the C. The processor disregards comment cards, of course.

The second card is an instruction to read in five constants in the format given by the instruction with statement number 101.

The third card is an instruction to type something according to the instruction with statement number 102. At this point in the program, we expect the typewriter to print "RATE OF EMISSION OF ELECTRONS." We invite you to find the obvious error in the FORMAT statement.

The fourth card has the typewriter type a heading. You will find the error here, too, we trust. There are other errors which we shall consider later.

The fifth card instructs the typewriter to accept a value of ϕ as written on the typewriter.

We skip over cards 6, 7, and 8 which involve the arithmetic. We shall discuss arithmetic instructions presently.

Card 9 is an instruction to type the result.

We shall pause now for several subsections to discuss arithmetic instructions and the simplest branch instruction.

23.2   EQUALS SIGN

In FORTRAN language, the equals ($=$) sign may be interpreted as *is replaced by*. Here are some examples:

X = X + 0.1 means X is replaced by X + 0.1

Y = Y + DELTA means Y is replaced by Y + DELTA

where X, Y, and DELTA are floating-point quantities which have been previously defined.

The "equation" is therefore an equivalence which is set up, the *left* member being the identification of the new quantity.

$$X = A + B$$

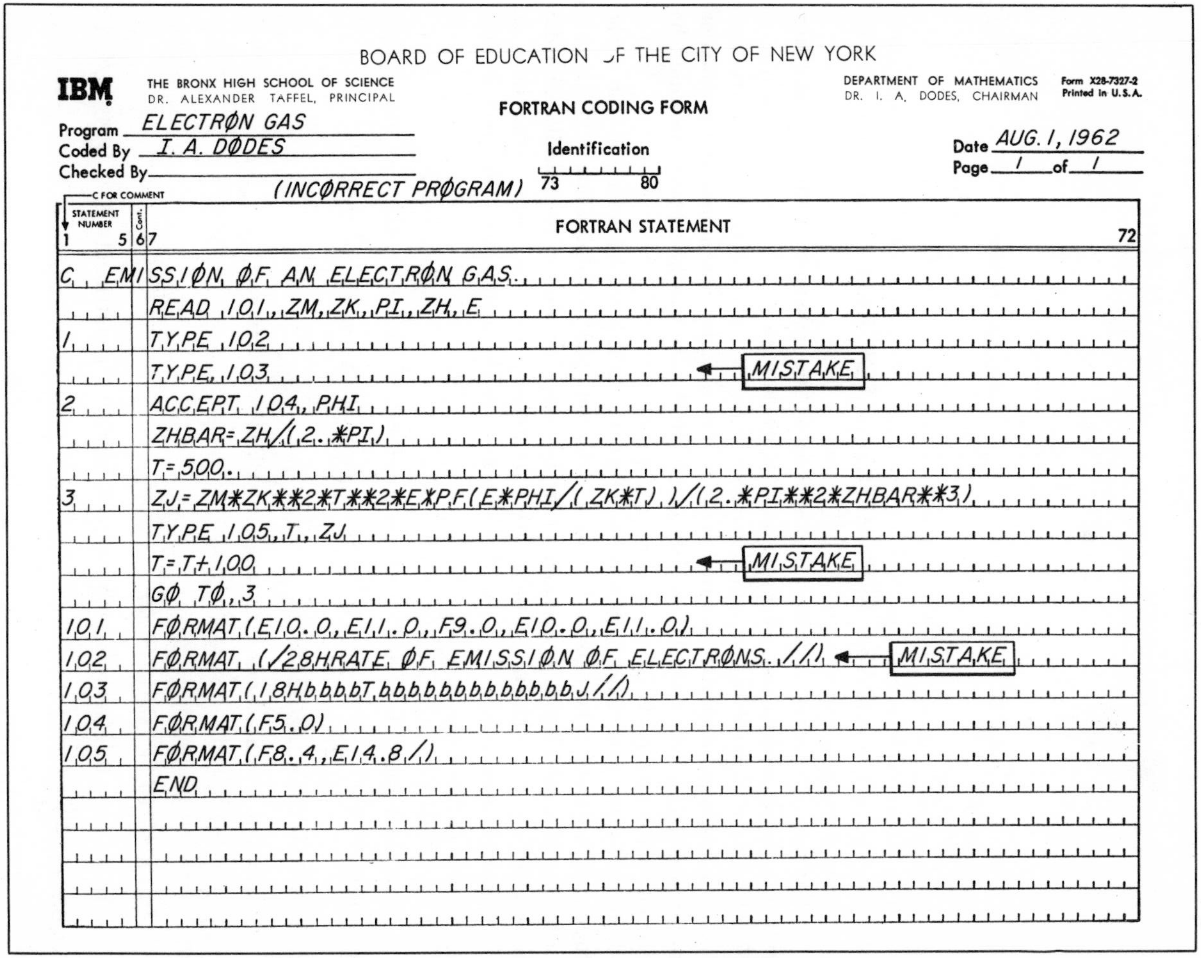

IBM

BOARD OF EDUCATION OF THE CITY OF NEW YORK

THE BRONX HIGH SCHOOL OF SCIENCE
DR. ALEXANDER TAFFEL, PRINCIPAL

DEPARTMENT OF MATHEMATICS
DR. I. A. DODES, CHAIRMAN

Form X28-7327-2
Printed in U.S.A.

FORTRAN CODING FORM

Program ELECTRON GAS
Coded By I. A. DODES
Checked By _____ (INCORRECT PROGRAM)

Date AUG. 1, 1962
Page 1 of 1

Identification
73   80

STATEMENT NUMBER 1 5	C FOR COMMENT 3 6 7	FORTRAN STATEMENT	72
C		EMISSION OF AN ELECTRON GAS.	
1		READ 101, ZM, ZK, PI, ZH, E	
		TYPE 102	
		TYPE 103	
2		ACCEPT 104, PHI	← MISTAKE
		ZHBAR=ZH/(2.*PI)	
		T=500.	
3		ZJ=ZM*ZK**2*T**2*EXPF(E*PHI/(ZK*T))/(2.*PI**2*ZHBAR**3),	
		TYPE 105, T, ZJ	← MISTAKE
		T=T+100	
		GO TO 3	
101		FORMAT(1E10.0,,E11.0,,F9.0,,E10.0,,E11.0)	
102		FORMAT(1/28HRATE OF EMISSION OF ELECTRONS.//)	← MISTAKE
103		FORMAT(18HbbbbbbbbbbbbbbbbJ//)	
104		FORMAT(F5.0)	
105		FORMAT(F8.4,,E14.8/)	
		END	

Fig. 55.   Electron gas problem, with errors.

means that A and B are added, and the result is stored in memory at the address X.

We remind you, at this point, that some keypunches do not have FORTRAN symbols. On a business keypunch, the following symbols are equivalent to FORTRAN symbols:

Business	FORTRAN
%	(
☐	)
&	+
#	=
@	— (dash)

23.3   ARITHMETIC IN FORTRAN

We shall distinguish between an *expression* (an indicated arithmetic operation with no equals sign), and an *equation* (which has an equals sign but which, in FORTRAN, may not really be an equation).

The arithmetic operations are *addition*, indicated by $+$; *subtraction*, indicated by the minus $(-)$ sign on the skipkey of the IBM 026; *multiplication*, indicated by $*$; *division* indicated by a slash $(/)$; and *exponentiation* indicated by $**$. In the absence of other instructions, operations are performed from left to right and in the following order of precedence: (*i*) exponentiation, (*ii*) multiplication and division in the order in which they are written, and (*iii*) addition and subtraction in the order in which they are written. If there are parentheses, these take precedence over all other instructions.

ILLUSTRATIVE PROBLEM I

Translate into FORTRAN: $x \cdot \dfrac{(y + z)^2}{w}$.

Solution: $(X * (Y + Z) ** 2)/W$ or $X * (Y + Z) ** 2/W$.

ILLUSTRATIVE PROBLEM II

Translate into algebraic language the FORTRAN statement: $A + B / C * D ** 3$.

Solution: $a + \dfrac{bd^3}{c}$.

ILLUSTRATIVE PROBLEM III

Translate into algebraic language the FORTRAN statement: $A * B ** 2/C/D$.

Solution: $\dfrac{ab^2}{cd}$.

ILLUSTRATIVE PROBLEM IV

Translate into FORTRAN: $\dfrac{(a^2b)^3}{d^4 - f}$.

Solution: (A ** 2 * B) ** 3/(D ** 4−F).

Notice that in algebra, the juxtaposition of two letters, e.g., xy, means that the two variables are to be multiplied. In FORTRAN, however, the symbol XY would simply stand for a single floating-point variable. You need X * Y if you wish to multiply the floating-point variable X by the floating-point variable Y. Note, too, that an expression like A/B/C means that A is divided by B and the result is divided by C. In other words, it is the same as A/(B * C). A/B * C would be equivalent to $\frac{a}{b} \cdot c$.

We warn you, also, that every variable and constant in a FORTRAN expression must be of the same mode, i.e., all floating point, or all fixed point. That is why the tenth card in the sample program (Fig. 55) is incorrect. The right member is an expression in which T is floating point but 100 is fixed point. It will give rise to an error message.

There are three exceptions to the rule against mixed modes: (*i*) all subscripts (to be studied in Sections 25 and 26) *must* be in fixed point regardless of the remainder of the expression, (*ii*) exponents may be either all fixed point or all floating point even if the base is floating point, (*iii*) in an *equation*, one member may be floating point and the other member fixed point. However, this is only used for special purposes. For example, if we have in memory X = $\overline{4}567226\overline{6}00$, the effect of writing

$$I = X$$

will be to truncate the number so that I = $\overline{2}266$. It is not inconceivable that you may want to do this, but it is rather unlikely in most mathematics and science programs.

To make sure that your constants are floating point, place a decimal point in the proper place. For example, 2 * P is a mixed-mode expression and will cause an error message. To correct it, just write 2. * P with a decimal point after the 2.

To make sure your variables are of the proper mode, you must check the initial letter. 3 + SUM is in mixed mode. To correct it, write 3 + ISUM, for example. INIT + 2.75 is in mixed mode (INIT = initial value). To correct it, write ZINIT + 2.75, for example. Programmers try to make their symbolic names meaningful so that the program may be read and understood. In rereading a program, you may (mentally) skip the initial I's and Z's. (You may use other letters if you prefer.)

EXERCISES

Translate the following into algebraic language:

1 A/B * C

2 (A/B) * C

3 A * B/C

4 A ** (B/C)

5 (A+B)/C*D**(X+2.)

6 A + B/C * D ** 2

Translate the following into FORTRAN language:

7 $\dfrac{a + b^2}{c - d^3}$ **8** $a + \dfrac{b^2}{c - d^3}$

9 $a + \left\{ \dfrac{b}{c - d^3} \right\}$ **10** $a + \dfrac{b^2}{c} - d^{3x - 4}$

11 $\dfrac{a + b^{2(x - 5)}}{c} - 5d$ **12** $\left\{ \dfrac{ja + kb^{2y + m}}{c} - nd^{4(j - 2)} \right\}^3$

23.4 FORTRAN FUNCTIONS

The FORTRAN subroutine deck includes six SPS subroutines with new names, as follows:

SINF ( ) computes the sine of the floating-point expression in the parentheses.

COSF ( ) computes the cosine of the floating-point expression in the parentheses.

EXPF ( ) computes $e^{(\ )}$ where a floating-point expression is in the parentheses.

LOGF ( ) computes ln ( ) $= \log_e$ ( ), where a floating-point expression is in the parentheses.

SQRT ( ) computes the square root of the floating-point expression in the parentheses. For the IBM 7090, write SQRTF.

ATAN ( ) computes the arctangent of the floating-point expression in the parentheses. For the IBM 7090, write ATANF.

The floating-point arguments may be as complicated as

$$\text{SQRT } (D - E * \text{ATAN}(X))$$

Here, the machine computes the arctangent of X, multiplies this by E, subtracts the product from D, and finds the square root—all faster than you can blink an eye.

The restrictions on the subroutines are the same as those for the SPS subroutines (since they are exactly the same):

1. for SINF and COSF, the floating-point argument may have a characteristic in the range $[-8, +8]$. For arguments with characteristics > 03, the accuracy diminishes as the argument increases.
2. for EXPF, the absolute value of the argument must not exceed 227.955924206.
3. for LOGF, the argument must, of course, be positive.
4. We should mention that the computation of A ** B is accomplished by equating this to $e^{B \ln A}$ so that the product of B and ln A must not be greater than the number mentioned in (2).

23.5 UNCONDITIONAL BRANCH: GO TO

This command corresponds to the unconditional B 49 P Q which was used in the parts on machine language and SPS. The command GO TO 573 means, "Branch to the statement numbered 573."

In the (incorrect) sample program in Fig. 55, the effect of the branch is to cause the program to perform a simple loop back to the beginning.

23.6 PRECOMPILER

We mentioned that there is a Precompiler which will "look" at your program and tell you, via error messages, whether you made any of fifty-one very common errors. As an aid in evaluating these errors, they have been grouped into seven categories as follows:

> Arithmetic statements
> Variables in arithmetic statements
> DO loops
> Constants
> Statement numbers
> Transfer statements
> General

When an error is detected, an error code is typed on the console typewriter. This code consists of an alphabetic abbreviation of one of the categories listed above, followed by a number that designates the particular error in the category:

ARITH

1. Unacceptable form to left of = sign.
2. Multiple = signs.
3. This code has been deleted.
4. Successive operation symbols, or a function which is followed by an operation symbol.
5. Missing operation symbol or operand.
6. Right parenthesis encountered before corresponding left parenthesis.
7. Missing right parenthesis.
8. Mixed mode expression (expression contains fixed and floating point).
9. No variable to the left of equal sign.
10. Involution of a fixed-point variable or constant.

VAR

1. Variable name longer than five alphameric characters.
2. Variable appearing in an expression or as a subscript not previously defined in an input statement; as the index of a DO loop; or defined as the left side of another arithmetic statement.
3. Variable written with a subscript has not been previously defined in a DIMEN-SION statement.
4. Variable previously defined in a DIMENSION statement has not been subscripted correctly: subscript is in unacceptable form, number of subscripts does not agree with the number specified in DIMENSION statement, numerical subscript is greater than maximum allowed by DIMENSION statement or is less than one.

DO

1. In the statement DO n i $= m_1, m_2, m_3$, the indices m_1, m_2, and m_3, if given, are not all unsigned fixed-point variables or constants greater than zero. There are more than three indices given.
2. The second index, m_2, is less than m_1, when both are constants.
3. The third index, m_3, is signed, is zero, or is missing when specified as a constant.
4. The statement number n is not in acceptable form or is missing.
5. The variable name has either been omitted, or is incorrectly stated, or the DO statement is incorrect.
6. The statement specified as the end of an outer loop in a nest of DO's has been found before an inner loop is complete.
7. A DO loop terminates with a transfer statement, GO TO, computed GO TO, or IF.

CONST

1. Fixed-point constant longer than four digits.
2. Floating-point constant outside the allowable range.
3. Decimal point omitted from floating-point constant that is written with a decimal exponent.
4. The decimal exponent following the E in a floating-point constant is incorrectly expressed in form or size.
5. The exponent following an E has been omitted.
6. Floating-point number followed by an alphameric character other than E.

STNO

1. Statement number longer than four digits.
2. Statement number has been previously defined.
3. Unnumbered CONTINUE statement. (Should be numbered when used as last statement in a DO loop.)
4. Statement immediately following a transfer statement is not numbered, and is therefore inaccessible to the source program. (If the previous statement is a transfer, the only way the program can process this statement is by a *transfer* to it, and therefore it must always be numbered.)

TRANS

1. Statement numbers in a transfer statement (GO TO, computed GO TO, or IF) are not acceptable fixed-point numbers; there is no comma between statement numbers, or there is not the required number of statement numbers.
2. Comma missing after the right parenthesis in a computed GO TO statement.
3. Index in a computed GO TO statement is not a fixed-point variable, or is missing.
4. Nonnumerical character follows right parenthesis in an IF statement.
5. In an IF statement, a character other than a left parenthesis follows the word IF.
6. No arithmetic statement within the parentheses after the IF. (However, empty parentheses in an arithmetic statement will not be detected.)

GEN

1. Misspelled or unacceptable nonarithmetic statement.
2. Statement contains an unacceptable character.
3. More than 72 characters in statement (not applicable to cards).
4. Symbol table full (occupies more than 2,500 digits in storage).
5. Statement contains decimal point that is not in a floating-point constant.
6. Input-output statement contains no FORMAT number, or is incorrectly stated.
7. First character in an input-output list is not alphabetic, or the final character is not a letter or a digit.
8. In a DIMENSION statement, a nonalphabetic character precedes the first variable name or a dimension, or three dimensions have been specified (only two-dimensional arrays are permitted).
9. A specified dimension is incorrect; a parenthesis has been omitted, a floating-point constant or an unacceptable fixed-point constant has been used, etc.
10. Unnumbered FORMAT statement.
11. Incomplete FORMAT statement: invalid or incorrect specification, missing parentheses, character after right parenthesis, etc.
12. In an input-output statement, comma is missing after the FORMAT statement number, or the list is missing or invalid.
13. The toal record width specified in a FORMAT statement exceeds 87.
14. A variable appearing in a DIMENSION statement has been previously defined.
15. H or X missing in alphameric FORMAT specification or the width of alphameric specification is greater than 49.

To precompile a program, the following steps are taken:

1. Clear the machine with the command 31 00003 00002.
2. Load the Precompiler Deck.
3. Set the switches. There are many possibilities. We suggest SW 2 "off" and all the others "on." This will print your program and your error messages. Ordinarily, you can see what is wrong with the command when it is called to your attention. If SW 2 is left "on," the machine will punch out a corrected deck when you type in the corrected command, but there are some complications which make this less useful than it sounds. In any case, the O'FLOW switch must be "off."
   For your convenience, we offer the complete list of switch settings for the Precompiler Deck:

Input	Print On Typewriter	Punch Edited Source Program	SW 1	SW 2	SW 4
Cards/Tape		Yes	On	On	On
Cards/Tape			On	Off	On
Cards/Tape	No	Yes	On	On	Off
Cards/Tape	No	No	On	Off	Off
Typewriter	No	Yes	Off	On	On/Off
Typewriter	No	No	Off	Off	On/Off

Switch 3 has the following function:

On — Error correction routines are bypassed.

Off — Error correction routines are not bypassed.

NOTE: Switch 4 is normally turned off. When you make an error in typing either an original or a corrected source statement, turn this switch on, press the release and start keys, and return the switch to its normal off position. You must then retype the entire statement.

4. Read in your source program (by pushing START, then READER START).

5. After the errors for individual commands, there is a summary. The summary includes information about possible sources of error not detectable in individual source statements, and is in the form of four alphabetic messages together with related lists, as follows:

UNDEFINED STATEMENT NUMBERS

$$\bar{n} \, n \, n \, n$$

$$\bar{n} \, n \, n \, n \ldots$$

The numbers listed are those which have not been used for statement identification but have been referenced by transfer or DO statements.

UNREFERENCED STATEMENT NUMBERS

$$\bar{n} \, n \, n \, n$$

$$\bar{n} \, n \, n \, n \ldots$$

The numbers listed are those which have been used for statement identification but have not been referenced by transfer or DO statements. These numbers are not necessary to the compilation of the source program and may be eliminated.

RELOCATABLE SUBROUTINES CALLED

LOG

SIN . . .

The names listed are those of the functional subroutines used in the source program.

OBJECT PROGRAM DATA TABLE

XXXXX STORAGE POSITIONS

The number of storage positions given includes those used for variables, constants, and statement numbers, but not the total number of storage positions that will be required in the FORTRAN object program, since this depends upon the number of machine instructions produced when the source program is compiled.

Premature typing of the summary indicates that the END statement appears earlier than anticipated in the source program. Conversely, if the END statement has been omitted, the summary will not be typed.

If statement number 999 is used it will cause errors in the final program summary. However, no damage will be done to the precompiler. If there are no undefined or unreferenced statement members, the first two summary statements will be omitted. If there are no relocatable subroutines used, e.g., SINF, this will be omitted.

6. After the final summary, the message, "PROCESSING COMPLETE" is typed. If the START key is pressed, the precompiler will now process another program. *Every FORTRAN program should be precompiled to save time and cards.*

23.7   BACK TO THE SAMPLE PROGRAM

Having said this, we now proceed to precompile the sample program (from Fig. 55). The horrifying result is shown below. It seems that, among other things, the programmer was a little absent-minded. Some of the errors are omissions, others are correctly typed from the written program, but were incorrectly written.

EXERCISES

From the list of error messages at the beginning of this subsection, interpret the precompiler listing below. Can you correct the commands? Can you correct statement 3?

```
ENTER SOURCE PROGRAM
THEN PUSH START
C  EMISSION OF AN ELECTRON GAS
GEN 12

        READ 101 ZM
        TYPE 102
GEN 06·

        TYPE, 103
VAR 02

        ZHBAR = ZH/-2+*PI
2       ACCEPT 104,PHI
        T = 500.
GEN 01

3
VAR 02

3       ZJ=ZM*ZK**2*T**2*EXPF(E*PHI/(ZK*T))/(2.*PI**2*ZHBAR**3)
        TYPE 105, T, ZJ
ARITH 08

        T = T + 100
TRANS 01

        GO TO, 3
GEN 11

101     FORMAT(E10.0)
GEN 11

102     FORMAT(/28HRATE OF EMISSION OF ELECTRONS.//)
103     FORMAT(18H    Γ            J//)
104     FORMAT(F5.0)
105     FORMAT(F8.4,E14.8/)
106     FORMAT(E14.8)
        END
```

```
UNREFERENCED STATEMENT NUMBERS
0002
0003
0103
0106

OBJECT PROGRAM DATA TABLE
00260 STORAGE POSITIONS

PROCESSING COMPLETE
```

23.8   REVIEW OF FORTRAN PROCEDURE

For reference, let us make a single list of all the steps which you should take in making a FORTRAN program.

1. Make a flow chart for the program. Using actual (simple) values, "walk" through the program to make sure that it does what you command. Remember that the computer is a perfect slave. It won't do what you *want*; it will, however, do what you *command*, provided this is possible, of course.

2. Using a desk calculator, if possible, choose a set of values of approximately the same magnitude as the ones you will use in your program, and go through the entire calculation in the same order that you think the machine will. *Make a careful record of your intermediate results.* You will need them for debugging.

3. Now you are ready to write your instructions. You will find this a relatively easy job, because all the housekeeping is done for you. Write them carefully, making sure that if you call upon subroutines such as SINF, COSF, and EXPF, or if you have anything of the form A ** B, that the limitations mentioned in Subsection 23.7 are adhered to.

4. Punch the cards carefully. The cover card should be a *Comment* card with a C in cc 1 and two blank spaces following. FORTRAN programs are so short, compared to machine language or SPS, that you can well afford to take your time and get the cards exactly as you wish them. Even a missing or surplus comma or parenthesis may cause you hours of labor, wasted cards, and wasted machine time.

5. List your cards on the IBM 407 or equivalent. Check very carefully at this point for commas and parentheses, and for mixed mode. These are the most common errors for the beginner.

6. *Precompile your program.* If you have listed them already, you won't need another listing and you may leave Switch 1 "off." The error message will type anyhow.

7. Make your corrections. Now you are ready to compile the program.

8. Clear the machine. Place a full load of fresh cards in the left hopper of the IBM 1622 (Read-Punch unit). (It is well to non-process run-out a card before starting to assemble the program. This is to make sure that there is nothing wrong with the punch unit, such as a card stuck in it.)

9. Set your switches. For compilation, all switches may be "off" but, before a program is debugged, always set Swith 2 "on" in order to include a *tracer*

in your compiled program. If Switch 1 is "on," the statements will list. However, you already have a listing from step 5 (or 6) and you can save a great deal of time by not relisting. In a FORTRAN program, it does not help very much to know the location of the steps. You may compromise by listing just the first instruction (to see where the program begins), then turn Switch 1 "off" to save time.

10. Load the FORTRAN compiler deck. If the first card read is not card 1, the machine will stop with an operation code of 00 in the OP register. If cards 2 through 24 are not read in proper sequence, the message CARDxx will be typed and the machine will stop. The cards must be removed and the deck arranged properly, then reloaded. Beginning with card 25, if *any* card is out of sequence, the typewriter will print "CARD $\overline{0}$xxxx OUT OF SEQUENCE" and the machine will halt. Remove the cards from the reader and put the proper card in place of the one out of sequence. Depress READER START, then START.

11. Shortly after the compiler deck is loaded, the PUNCH NO FEED light will go on. Depress PUNCH START. The cards should start punching. If at any time there is a malfunction of the punch, remove the cards from the punch hopper, remove the bottom few, straighten the remainder, non-process run-out whatever is in the machine, replace the straightened deck, depress PUNCH START and hope for the best. Before allowing the compiler to proceed, check the numbers of the cards just before and after the stoppage. They are numbered in the last few card columns. If they are not in sequence, you might just as well throw them all away and start over again. (It is best to make sure the cards in the punch hopper are properly inserted to begin with.)

12. After the compiler deck is loaded, the typewriter will display "ENTER SOURCE PROGRAM. PUSH START." Place your source program in the read hopper and push START on the reader and on the console. At this time, if there are any more errors in language in your program, an error message will type, as follows:

1. Incorrectly formed statement.

2. Subscripted variable for which no DIMENSION statement has previously appeared in the program, dimensioned variable used without subscripts, variable in DIMENSION statement has already appeared in the source program.

3. Floating-point number not in allowable range of values, or fixed-point number contains more than four digits.

4. Symbol table full.

5. Mixed mode expression.

6. Variable name in an expression contains more than five characters.

7. Switch number has been omitted in an IF (SENSE SWITCH n) statement, or there is a comma after IF.

8. A comma follows the statement number in a DO statement.

9. A DIMENSION statement ends with a comma, or more than two dimen-

sions have been specified in a DIMENSION statement.

10. Unnumbered FORMAT statement.

11. Incorrect FORMAT statement: *(i)* special character in numerical field specification, *(ii)* alphabetic character other than E,F,I in a numerical field specification, *(iii)* decimal point missing, *(iv)* the number of positions not given, *(v)* a record mark in the numerical field specification or an alphanumeric field, and *(vi)* left parenthesis missing or misplaced.

12. The total record width specified in a FORMAT statement is greater than 87 characters.

13. A FORMAT statement number has been omitted in an I-O statement.

However, if you have followed instructions with reference to precompiling, it is unlikely that this will happen.

There is one other kind of error, however, that may appear at this time. If the program is too long, the message OVERLAP will appear on the typewriter, with an indication of how much excess there is. If this misfortune takes place, you can either purchase a supplementary module or two (20,000 positions per module) or segment your program. An example of this will be given in Section 26.

13. If all is well, the program will compile and the following message will appear on the typewriter:

SW1 ON FOR SYMBOL TABLE. PUSH START.

Ordinarily, there is no point in finding the addresses of the various designated areas. Unless there is, turn Switch 1 "off" at this point, then push CONSOLE START. Now another message appears:

SW1 OFF TO IGNORE SUBROUTINES, PUSH START.

It is a great convenience to have the subroutines compiled with your program, and you are advised to turn Switch 1 "on" at this point, then depress START. The machine will then select from the FORTRAN SUBROUTINES deck which you read in all the subroutines which you actually need in your program.

To review: we advise that you turn Switch 1 "off," depress START, then turn Switch 1 "on," then depress START, then read in the SUBROUTINES deck. To do this, you must depress CONSOLE START and READER START.

14. At the end, the typewriter displays "PROCESSING COMPLETE." Run out your last card from the punch hopper. Now carefully write (in ink) the name of the program on the first card and on the back of the last card. (They all look the same when they are compiled.) The input source deck may have only a few cards, perhaps a dozen—and the output object deck may have hundreds of cards. You are now ready to run your program.

15. Clear the machine. (Strictly speaking, this is not necessary, but it does no harm. The processor deck cannot be used for another source deck anyhow.)

16. Load your object deck. We assume that you have prepared data cards (if data cards are needed) and that you know all the correct answers, including the intermediate result.

17. Run your program with Switch 4 "off." If your answer is correct, you're done—except that you may wish to reprocess your source deck with Switch 2 "off" (to eliminate the tracer). However, this is unlikely, even if you are brilliant, patient, and experienced. The chances are that you made a mistake. If you get an answer, but the wrong one, recheck your data. These may be wrong. If the data are correct, check your *hand* calculations. They may be wrong. If not, you must go back to your program and run it with Switch 4 "on." This will trace the program for all arithmetic calculations. You take the type-out to a quiet corner and figure out where the error(s) is (are). This is not fun, but it's very nice when you have the debugged program.

From time to time, the error will be in a subroutine. If there are certain types of errors, the typewriter will display messages while your object deck is running. The subroutine error messages are as follows:

E1 Overflow in addition or subtraction.

E2 Underflow in addition or subtraction.

E3 Overflow in multiplication.

E4 Underflow in multiplication.

E5 Overflow in division.

E6 Underflow in division.

E7 Zero divisor in floating division.

E8 Zero divisor in fixed division.

F1 Loss of all significance in sine or cosine.

F2 Logarithm of zero.

F3 Logarithm of a negative number.

F4 Overflow in exponentiation.

F5 Underflow in exponentiation.

F6 Exponentiation with a negative base, e.g., $(-7)^x$, or the square root of a negative number.

F7 Input data is in incorrect form, or outside allowable range.

F8 Output data is in incorrect form, or outside allowable range.

F9 The record is longer than 72 characters, or there is an unspecified number in output or input.

To *summarize* FORTRAN operations at the console:

1. Clear the machine with 310000300002.
2. *Load* the Precompiler.
3. *Read in* your source program. We suggest that Switches 1, 3, and 4 be "on" and Switch 2 be "off."
4. After correcting your errors, *load* the compiler.

5. *Read in* your source deck. We suggest that only Switch 2 be "on" (with Switches 1, 3, and 4 "off"). This will compile a *tracer* with your program.
6. Do *not* type the symbol table (Switch 1 "off").
7. *Do* compile the subroutines: turn Switch 1 "on" and *read in* the subroutine deck.
8. Load the resulting compilation (the object deck) with Switch 4 "off" unless you wish a trace to be typed.

For your general information, here are the other switch settings for the FORTRAN compiler:

1. *Switch 1.* If this is "on," the source statements are typed on the console typewriter as they are processed. The first five-digit field is the machine address of the *first* instruction compiled for the symbolic instruction.
2. *Switch 2.* If this is "on," the trace instructions are compiled.
3. *Switch 3.* This must be "on" if input is via the typewriter. It is "off" for input via card reader or paper tape reader.
4. *Switch 4.* This switch is used in conjunction with Switch 3 when Switch 3 is "on." It provides the ability to restart the typing of a statement if you have made an error. Switch 4 is normally "off." When a typing error is made in a source statement and it is to be corrected, this switch is turned "on," the R-S key is depressed, and then Switch 4 is turned "off." The statement can now be typed.

23.9   RETURN TO THE SAMPLE PROGRAM

In accordance with the information gained from the precompiler, let us assume that we have corrected the errors in *language* for the sample program. We now precompile it once more to make sure that there are no other errors introduced by the corrections.

The result is shown below. There are no errors. Statements 1 and 2 were not used, but that makes no difference in this program. (The time required to place these in the symbol table, and the few spaces needed are not significant here—they are significant if we are crowded for time or space.) We have also taken the opportunity to change the order of the statements a bit. They didn't make much sense the other way. (Compare the original with this one, and see what the differences are.)

At the bottom of the sample program are shown the remarks made when this program was compiled. It compiled without difficulty.

```
ENTER SOURCE PROGRAM
THEN PUSH START
C   EMISSION OF AN ELECTRON GAS
        READ 101, ZM, ZK, PI, ZH, E
1       TYPE 102
2       ACCEPT 104, PHI
        TYPE 103
        ZHBAR = ZH/(2.*PI)
        T = 500.
```

```
3        ZJ=ZM*ZK**2*T**2*EXPF(E*PHI/(ZK*T))/(2.*PI**2*ZHBAR**3)
         TYPE 105, T, ZJ
         T = T + 100.
         GO TO 3
101      FORMAT(E10.0,E11.0,F9.0,E10.0,E11.0)
102      FORMAT(/30HRATE OF EMISSION OF ELECTRONS.//)
103      FORMAT(18H     T                    J//)
104      FORMAT(F5.0)
105      FORMAT(F8.4,E14.8/)
         END

UNREFERENCED STATEMENT NUMBERS
0001
0002

RELOCATABLE SUBROUTINES CALLED
EXP

OBJECT PROGRAM DATA TABLE
00340 STORAGE POSITIONS

PROCESSING COMPLETE
```

Unfortunately, we are not "out of the woods" yet. We were careless. We did not make an arithmetic check of the expected results—the program looked so very easy!

The program would not run. Why not? A look at the "logic" seemed to show that all was well. Upon reinserting the deck and turning on Switch 4, the following data were obtained:

```
RATE OF EMISSION OF ELECTRONS.

4.685IIS

      T                 J

+.10544333E-26
+.50000000E+03
ERROR F4
ERROR E5
+.99999999E+99
ERROR F8 +.50000000E+03
         +.99999999E+99

+.60000000E+03
ERROR F4
ERROR E5
+.99999999E+99
ERROR F8 +.60000000E+03
         +.99999999E+99

+.70000000E+03
ERROR F4
ERROR E5
+.99999999E+99
ERROR F8 +.70000000E+03
         +.99999999E+99

+.80000000E+03
ERROR F4
ERROR E5
+.99999999E+99
ERROR F8 +.80000000E+03
         +.99999999E+99
```

23.10   ARITHMETIC DEBUGGING

Having wasted about 400 cards and innumerable hours, we return to do something we should have done *first*. We shall make a calculation of the expected result for 500° Absolute. The formula was:

$$j = \frac{m\ k^2\ T^2}{2\pi^2\ h^3}\ e^{-\epsilon\ \phi/kT}$$

Substituting the constants (given in Subsection 23.1) and T = 500°:

$$j = \frac{9.1085\ *\ 10^{-28}\ *\ (1.38042\ *\ 10^{-16})^2\ *\ (500)^2}{2\ *\ (3.1415927)^2\ *\ \left(\dfrac{6.6252\ *\ 10^{-27}}{2\ *\ (3.1415927)}\right)^3}\ *$$

$$e^{\dfrac{-4.80288\ *\ 10^{-10}\ *\ 4.685}{1.38042\ *\ 10^{-16}\ *\ 500}}$$

To evaluate the exponential part of the right member, let

$$x\ =\ e^{-\epsilon\ \phi/kT}$$

Then

$$\log x\ =\ -\ \frac{\epsilon\ \phi}{k\ T}\ \log\ e$$

Using a desk calculator, $\epsilon\ \phi\ /\ k\ T = 3.26009\ *\ 10^4$ and (from a handbook) $\log e = 0.4342944819$.

$$\therefore\ \ \log x\ =\ -14158.4$$
$$x\ =\ 10^{-14158.4}$$

We can convert this to base e by using

$$x\ =\ e^{-14158.4\ \ln\ 10}\ =\ e^{-32600.8}$$

In any case, it should be quite clear that the exponent is far too high in absolute value for the EXPF subroutine. We were warned that the exponent of e must not be as small as −228 or as large as +228. The exponent we calculated is too *low* (below −228). As soon as the machine attempts to perform this exponentiation, it should type error F5, "underflow in exponentiation."

Looking back at the trace, we find, to our surprise, that the error is F4, "overflow in exponentiation!" This shows that there is another error. Sure enough, we forgot the minus sign in the exponent. (If we had written the minus sign, we would have received the F5 error message and the program would not have run anyhow.) It should be clear that the machine has no intention of performing these instructions, with or without the minus sign.

Before continuing, let us finish the arithmetic and see what the answer should be, for T = 500°. Using a desk calculator, we find that

$$\frac{m\ k^2\ T^2}{2\ \pi^2\ h^3}\ =\ 1.88\ *\ 10^{26}$$

This means that the answer (for T = 500°) is in the neighborhood of 1.88 * 10^{26} * $10^{-14158.4}$, or approximately 7 * 10^{-14133} electrons per square centimeter.

Now we must search for a more sensible plan of action. In the first place, we shall simplify the formula by replacing $\hbar$ by its equal, $h/(2\pi)$. The result is

$$j = (4\ \pi\ m\ k^2\ T^2)\ e^{-\epsilon\ \phi/kT}\ /\ h^3$$

This is a shorter formula, but does not, of course, remove the underflow condition. We need to avoid the exponentiation. Of course! We shall use logarithms:

$$\ln\ j = \ln\ (4\pi mk^2T^2)\ -\ \frac{\epsilon\phi}{kT}\ -\ \ln\ (h^3)$$

So long as $\ln$ j is in $(10^{-99}, 10^{+99})$, we are perfectly safe. After calculating $\ln$ j, we can find $\log$ j by using the conversion formula

$$\log\ j = 0.43429448\ \ln\ j$$

We know (from our preliminary calculation) that $\log$ j will turn out to be approximately -14132 when T = 500° Absolute. The natural thing to do would be to try to convert $\log$ j to j by using the relationship

$$j = 10^{\log\ j}$$

However, this would obviously cause an underflow, again.

For the present, we shall content ourselves with the calculation of $\log$ j. In Subsection 24.5, when we have more commands, we shall demonstrate a subroutine which will "trick" the machine into giving us the results in terms of j instead of $\log$ j.

In the following sample program, the simplified computation is shown. Following the program is a table of values for T and $\log$ j, with the temperature incremented by 10,000° in each loop (in order to shorten the output). Notice that at 230,500° Absolute, the metal theoretically emits $10^{0.8804}$ (almost·8) electrons per square centimeter of surface.

```
ENTER SOURCE PROGRAM
THEN PUSH START
C   EMISSION OF AN ELECTRON GAS @ SIMPLIFIED
        READ 100,ZM,ZK,PI,ZH,E
        TYPE 101
        ACCEPT 102, PHI
        TYPE 103
        TYPE 104
        T=500.
1       ZLNJ=LOGF(4.*PI*ZM*ZK**2*T**2)-(E*PHI/(ZK*T))-LOGF(ZH**3)
        ZLOGJ=0.43429448*ZLNJ
        TYPE 105,T,ZLOGJ
        T = T + 10000.
        GO TO 1
100     FORMAT(E10.0,E11.0,F9.0,E10.0,E11.0)
101     FORMAT(18HTYPE VALUE OF PHI.)
102     FORMAT(F5.0)
103     FORMAT(/30HRATE OF EMISSION OF ELECTRONS./)
104     FORMAT(3X,1HT,15X,5HLOG J)
105     FORMAT(F9.0,6X,F12.5)
        END

RELOCATABLE SUBROUTINES CALLED
LOG
```

```
OBJECT PROGRAM DATA TABLE
00340 STORAGE POSITIONS

PROCESSING COMPLETE
```

Although FORTRAN (and all floating-point) computations are much slower than machine language, the following table was produced *at the speed of the typewriter*, i.e., the computations were performed while the carriage of the typewriter returned!

```
TYPE VALUE OF PHI.
4.685RS

RATE OF EMISSION OF ELECTRONS.

     T              LOG J
   +500.       -14132.13400
 +10500.         -645.29237
 +20500.         -315.82841
 +30500.         -202.26135
 +40500.         -144.70515
 +50500.         -109.90058
 +60500.          -86.57303
 +70500.          -69.84277
 +80500.          -57.25374
 +90500.          -47.43485
+100500.          -39.56041
+110500.          -33.10338
+120500.          -27.71151
+130500.          -23.14046
+140500.          -19.21535
+150500.          -15.80774
+160500.          -12.82115
+170500.          -10.18172
+180500.           -7.83192
+190500.           -5.72629
+200500.           -3.82843
+210500.           -2.10882
+220500.            -.54332
+230500.           +.88804
+240500.          +2.20195
+250500.          +3.41240
+260500.          +4.53125
+270500.          +5.56861
+280500.          +6.53315
+290500.          +7.43235
+300500.          +8.27269
```

EXERCISES

Write programs for the following:

1 Make a table for $Y = 3.778146 X^5 + 2.158114 X^3$ starting at $X = -5$ and incrementing by 0.1. The table is to be headed "X" and "Y."

2 Make a table for the sum of the first n cubes, punching the results in cc 1-20 and cc 30-40.

3 Kepler's Third Law, slightly improved, states that the period, T, of rotation, in seconds, of a planet about the Sun is given by

$$T = \frac{2 \pi a^{3/2}}{\sqrt{G (m_1 + m_2)}}$$

where a is the semi-major axis of the orbit (in centimeters), G is the universal constant of gravitation = $6.670 * 10^{-8}$ gm^{-1} cm^3 sec^{-2}, m_1 is the mass of the Sun (in grams), and m_2 is the mass of the planet (in grams). The masses and periods of various planets can be found in handbooks. Write a program to calculate the semi-major axis of the orbit for each planet, with the answer in miles. The program will also work for the Earth and the artificial satellites, of course. (Write a PAUSE and a branch to the beginning to accept a new m_2 from the typewriter or read it from a card.)

4 The Ostwald Dilution Law is

$$K = \frac{\alpha^2}{(1 - \alpha)\ v}$$

where K is the dissociation constant, v is the volume (in liters), and α is the degree of dissociation. Write a program to calculate α for various volumes, starting from $v = 1$ and proceeding to $v = 1000$, multiplying v by 10 in each loop. (For acetic acid at $25°$, the dissociation constant is $1.753 * 10^{-5}$. Other values can be found in Handbooks.)

PROJECTS

Prepare the cards and run one of these programs.

Section 24. Iterative Programs In FORTRAN

24.1 SOLVING AN EQUATION

We have already solved an equation by the use of SPS. We shall now illustrate how a similar equation is solved in FORTRAN language. Our problem is to solve

$$x^2 + k \sin x = 0$$

where k is a constant accepted into memory via the console typewriter, and x_0, the starting value for x, determined by some approximate method (such as a graph), is also accepted via the console typewriter. In this case, we shall take $k = 4$. If we now graph $z = x^2$ (a parabola) and $z = 4 \sin x$ (a sine wave with amplitude $= 4$) on the same pair of x,z axes, we find that one solution is in $(-2,-1)$. Therefore, our starting value of x can be $x_0 = -2$. In the sample problem to be shown later, we actually started with $x_0 = -3$ in order to show the trace.

Our general plan is to set

$$y = x^2 + k \sin x$$

calculate successive values of y, and terminate when the error in x is satisfactorily small.

For many reasons, we would prefer to calculate the error in x as demonstrated in Subsection 9.4 for another equation. However, it was shown there that the simple Taylor Series method for calculating error will not apply to this particular equation in the neighborhood of the root desired. This is most unfortunate. However, we can proceed a different way. (Many people prefer this method, anyhow.)

Our strategy is to increment x by smaller and smaller amounts until we reach one-tenth of the precision desired, then to stop when y changes sign. The flow chart in Fig. 56 shows how this operates. This iterative procedure is uniquely suited to computing machines, as are all trial-and-error methods. The limitations are those of the *compiler*, not of the machine. In basic FORTRAN, we are entitled to *eight* significant figures so that in this case, we may expect an answer of the form x.xxxxxx, the eighth one being lost by half-adjustment as programmed. In newer forms of FORTRAN with larger machines, this limitation is much reduced. (In SPS with this machine, 45 significant figures could be obtained in the answer.)

If we have a series of values for k, we may either insert these values into the

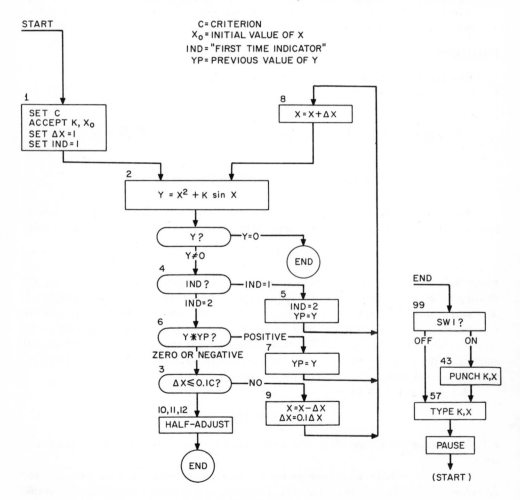

Fig. 56.   Flow chart: $X^2 + K \sin X = 0$.

original program and reset k, or else we may end each determination of x with a PAUSE, then branch back to the beginning when the START key is depressed. In the flow chart for the illustrative problem, we have adopted the latter scheme.

In order to explain the flow chart, we shall have to describe three more methods of branching in FORTRAN.

24.2   THREE MORE BRANCHING INSTRUCTIONS

The first of the three branches is

$$\text{IF (expression) } s_1, s_2, s_3$$

where s_1, s_2 and s_3 are statement numbers. The command

$$\text{IF}(X*Y-2.*Z)\ \ 23,47,59$$

does the following:

1. It evaluates the expression in the parentheses.
2. If this expression is *negative*, the program branches to statement number 23.
3. If this expression is *zero*, the program branches to statement number 47.
4. If this expression is *positive*, the program branches to statement number 59.

This single FORTRAN statement therefore replaces the set of SPS commands such as BNN, BH, and so on.

The punctuation in this FORTRAN command, as in all FORTRAN commands, is mandatory.

In the sample problem, we shall use

$$\text{IF DELTA } -0.1*C)\ \ 10,10,9$$

to determine whether $\triangle x \leqslant 0.1C$. If $(\triangle x - 0.1C)$. is *negative* or *zero*, we branch to statement 10, where a further decision is made. If $(\triangle x - 0.1C)$ is *positive*, meaning that $\triangle x > 0.1C$, we branch to statement 9, where the incrementing is continued. Notice that all three statement numbers are must be given.

The second of our new branching commands is

$$\text{IF(SENSE SWITCH n) } s_1, s_2$$

where n is the number of the switch, and the s_1 and s_2 are statement numbers.

The command

$$\text{IF(SENSE SWITCH 1) } 35,987$$

means that

1. If Program Switch 1 is "on," the program will branch to statement number 35.
2. If Program Switch 1 is "off," the program will branch to statement number 987.

Switches 1-4 and 9 may be addressed. The numbers are as in ordinary machine language:

Sense Switch Number   *Function*

1 to 4   (Console Switches)

9   Last Card Indicator

The IF(SENSE SWITCH 9) s_1,s_2 command is equivalent to *Branch on Last Card*.

In the sample program, sense switch (Program Switch) 1 is used to tell the machine whether or not to punch a card for output. The portion of a flow chart in Fig. 57 is sometimes called *Christmas tree programming*. It enables the programmer by a single program to set switches for *sixteen* different requirements. A series of such Christmas trees can be used for even further variety.

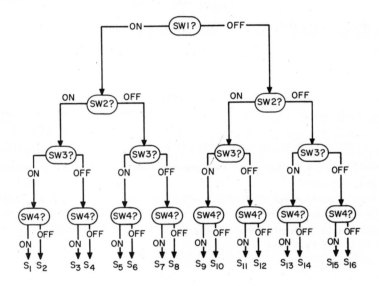

Fig. 57.   Christmas tree switch arrangement.

The third of our new branching command is called the *computed GO TO*:

$$GO\ TO\ (s_1,\ s_2,\ s_3,\ .\ .\ .)\text{,}i$$

where the s_1, s_2 . . . are statement numbers, and i is any fixed-point variable. The command

$$GO\ TO\ (23,57,987,4)\text{,}JOBNO$$

does the following:

1. The machine "looks" at the value of JOBNO which must be 1, 2, 3 or 4 (since only four statement numbers are given).
2. If JOBNO is 1, then the program branches to the *first* of the statement numbers, i.e., 23.
3. If JOBNO is 2, then the program branches to the *second* of the statement numbers, i.e., 57, and so on.

In the sample program, the computed GO TO will be used as a "first time indi-cator." As in many iterative programs, you wish to do one thing the first time around, and something else after that. In the sample program, we wish to calculate y_0 the first time, but every other time we wish to compare the *new* value of y with the previous value of y (to see whether the sign has changed). If the sign has changed, we know that we have passed over the root of the equation and we must back-track, change x to its previous value, y to its previous value, and change Δx to one-tenth of its previous value. The decision is left to a computed GO TO. At the beginning of the program, a fixed-point variable called IND (for "indicator") is set at IND = 1. After the very first computation, we reset IND = 2. Then, the instruction

$$GO\ TO\ (5,6),\ IND$$

branches the program to statement number 5 the first time and statement number 6 thereafter.

24.3   TRACE OUTPUT

While FORTRAN is very easy to write, it is very difficult to debug. This under-lines the great importance of being very careful in preparing the flow chart, in making the preliminary analysis, and in calculating some approximate intermediate results. Occasionally, there will be programming errors which will be shown in precompiling or, as E or F messages, while running the actual program. However, if the errors are in *logic*, the computer will not be able to tell you about them.

We have already mentioned that a *trace* is compiled together with your program when the switches are set as recommended in this book. Then, when Switch 4 is turned "on," the machine types every arithmetic result.

The program and its trace output follow.

```
ENTER SOURCE PROGRAM, PUSH START
08000 C    X**2 + K SIN X = 0 TO THE NEAREST MILLIONTH
08000           C = 10.**(-6)
08048 1        TYPE 101
08072          ACCEPT 102, ZK
08096          TYPE 103
08120          ACCEPT 102, X
08144          DELTA = 1.
08180          IND = 1
08216 2        Y = X ** 2 + ZK * SINF(X)
08312          IF (Y) 4,99,4
08368 4        GO TO (5,6), IND
08444 5        IND = 2
08480 7        YP = Y
08516          GO TO 8
08524 6        IF(Y*YP)3,3,7
08592 3        IF (DELTA - 0.1 * C) 10,10,9
08684 9        X = X - DELTA
08732          DELTA = 0.1 * DELTA
08780 8        X = X + DELTA
08828          GO TO 2
08836 99       IF (SENSE SWITCH 1) 43,57
08856 43       PUNCH 105, ZK, X
08892 57       TYPE 106, ZK, X
08928          PAUSE
08940          GO TO 1
08948 10       IF(X)11,99,12
09004 11       X=X-5.*10.**(-7)
09088          GO TO 99
09096 12       X=X+5.*10.**(-7)
09168          GO TO 99
09176 101      FORMAT(/17HTYPE K IN F MODE.2X)
09250 102      FORMAT(F10.0)
```

```
09272 103    FORMAT(36HTYPE STARTING POINT FOR X IN F MODE.2X)
09380 105    FORMAT(F15.8,10XF14.6)
09434 106    FORMAT(/2HK=F15.8,10X2HX=F14.6)
09516        END

PROG SW 1 ONFOR SYMBOL TABLE, PUSH START
SW 1 OFF TO IGNORE SUBROUTINES, PUSH START
1620 FORTRAN SUBR. AUTO DIV  9/30/61
PROCESSING COMPLETE
```

THE FOLLOWING IS A TRACE OUTPUT (SWITCH 4 ON) AND THE FINAL
    ANSWER: WHEN K=4, X=−1.933754, CORRECT TO THE
    SPECIFIED PRECISION.

```
TYPE K IN F MODE.
4.ORS
TYPE STARTING POINT FOR X IN F MODE.
-3.ORS
+.84355200E+01
   +2                       +.22504400E-01
+.84355200E+01              +.22504400E-01              +.32900000E-04
-.20000000E+01              -.19370000E+01              -.19337500E+01
+.36281030E-00             +.17195200E-01              -.19900000E-04
+.36281030E-00             +.17195200E-01
-.10000000E+01             -.19360000E+01              -.19337600E+01
-.23658839E+01             +.11891800E-01              +.10000000E-05
-.20000000E+01             +.11891800E-01              -.19337590E+01
+.10000000E-00             -.19350000E+01              +.27700000E-04
-.19000000E+01             +.65941000E-02              +.27700000E-04
-.17520040E-00             +.65941000E-02              -.19337580E+01
-.20000000E+01             -.19340000E+01              +.22400000E-04
+.10000000E-01             +.13022000E-02              +.22400000E-04
-.19900000E+01             +.13022000E-02              -.19337570E+01
+.30644660E-00             -.19330000E+01              +.17100000E-04
+.30644660E-00             -.39840000E-02              +.17100000E-04
-.19800000E+01             -.19340000E+01              -.19337560E+01
+.25064820E-00             +.10000000E-03              +.11800000E-04
+.25064820E-00             -.19339000E+01              +.11800000E-04
-.19700000E+01             +.77330000E-03              -.19337550E+01
+.19541680E-00             +.77330000E-03              +.65000000E-05
+.19541680E-00             -.19338000E+01              +.65000000E-05
-.19600000E+01             +.24440000E-03              -.19337540E+01
+.14075390E-00             +.24440000E-03              +.12000000E-05
+.14075390E-00             -.19337000E+01              +.12000000E-05
-.19500000E+01             -.28430000E-03              -.19337530E+01
+.86661100E-01             -.19338000E+01              -.40000000E-05
+.86661100E-01             +.10000000E-04              -.19337540E+01
-.19400000E+01             -.19337900E+01              +.10000000E-06
+.33139900E-01             +.19160000E-03              -.19337539E+01
+.33139900E-01             +.19160000E-03              +.70000000E-06
-.19300000E+01             -.19337800E+01              +.70000000E-06
-.19808200E-01             +.13870000E-03              -.19337538E+01
-.19400000E+01             +.13870000E-03              +.20000000E-06
+.10000000E-02             -.19337700E+01              +.20000000E-06
-.19390000E+01             +.85800000E-04              -.19337537E+01
+.27819300E-01             +.85800000E-04              -.30000000E-06
+.27819300E-01             -.19337600E+01              -.19337542E+01
-.19380000E+01             +.32900000E-04
```

```
        K=    +4.00000000        X=    -1.933754
```

In the trace output, the switch was turned "on" a split second after the START button was pushed. By this time, the computer had already zipped through the beginning of the flow chart. The first number shown in the trace output is a fixed-point number, +2, which is the value of IND. The successive values shown in the table are those of YP, X, Y, and so on. It is most instructive to follow the entire trace to understand what is happening. In the case of logical trouble, the trace allows you to exert your detective powers to determine what the machine is actually doing.

In this way, you can find your logical error. We had occasion to remark, before, that this is not fun; but it is such a relief when the error is found. In this trace output, see whether you can find how the value of x finally becomes −1.9337537 and is half-adjusted to −1.933754.

We are sometimes asked whether a person has to be a mathematician to do programming. The answer is that anyone can do programming (especially in FORTRAN) who can memorize a dozen rules and exercise reasonable care with parentheses and commas. However, it requires a mathematician to debug a difficult program. We will admit that the illustrative programs were especially chosen to point out the necessity of preliminary analysis and that the overwhelming majority of programs cause no difficulty of any kind. Nevertheless, the best use of a computer depends upon a thorough understanding of what is going on, mathematically.

The other question we are sometimes asked is whether the machine makes mistakes. The reason for this question is always that the programmer cannot find the error in his program. *The machine does not make mistakes.* It follows your instructions.

24.4   ITERATIVE PROBLEMS INVOLVING SERIES

Suppose we are given the expansion:

$$y = \arcsin x = x + \frac{1}{2} \times \frac{x^3}{3} + \frac{1}{2} \times \frac{3}{4} \times \frac{x^5}{5} + \frac{1}{2} \times \frac{3}{4} \times \frac{5}{6} \times \frac{x^7}{7}$$
$$+ \frac{1}{2} \times \frac{3}{4} \times \frac{5}{6} \times \frac{7}{8} \times \frac{x^9}{9} + \ldots$$

and we wish to compute y for various values of x.

Since the series is infinite, we must make up our minds how to tell the machine when to terminate. In other words, we must set up a criterion, as in any program terminating on precision.

We shall go through the planning very carefully and slowly, in order to make clear how this common type of problem is solved.

First, let us settle the most obvious problem: how to do the actual computation. If we call u_n the nth term, S_n the sum to n terms, u_{n+1} the $(n + 1)^{st}$ term, and S_{n+1} the sum to $(n + 1)$ terms, then it is obvious that

$$S_{n+1} = S_n + u_{n+1}$$

If we know S_n and u_{n+1}, we can easily find S_n, in other words. But how shall we find u_{n+1} without a great deal of trouble?

This is not too difficult. We examine the successive terms in the expansion and with a little manipulation find that

$$u_{n+1} = \frac{(2n-1)^2 \, x^2}{(2n+1)(2n)} \times u_n$$

This is called a *recursion formula*. It tells you how to find any term, provided the preceding term is known. Note that it is not in the proper form for FORTRAN, partly because it is in mixed mode. The corresponding FORTRAN statement would be

$$U = (2.*ZN-1.)**2*X**2*U/((2.*ZN+1.)*2*ZN)$$

where ZN has been written for n, and decimal points have been written where necessary.

To use a recursion formula, one must start with the first value. In this case, $u_1 = x$ (from the formula), so that the sequence of commands

$$
\begin{array}{lll}
& S & = & X \\
& U & = & X \\
& ZN & = & 1. \\
1 & U & = & 2.*ZN-1.)**2*X**2*U/((2.*ZN+1.)*2.*ZN) \\
& S & = & S + U \\
& ZN & = & ZN + 1. \\
& \text{GO TO 1} &
\end{array}
$$

will start with S_1 and keep on computing S_2, S_3, forever, or until the limit of capacity (from 10^{-99} to 10^{99}) is reached.

Our second problem is more difficult and is probably the place where most mistakes are made. How do we terminate the computation? One way which is sometimes used is to have the machine type or punch out S_1, S_2, S_3, . . . until the operator notices that the successive partial sums differ by less than some predetermined quantity. This is not very satisfactory to a mathematician, but seems to be all right for certain types of problems in mathematical physics. A far more satisfactory way is to compare the last term computed to some predetermined constant, C, as was done in the sample program of this section. When the absolute value of $U_{n+1} \leqslant C$, we have the machine punch or type the required sum.

If the series is *convergent* and *alternating*, then the error of neglecting all the terms after u_n is less than the first term neglected and, of course, less than the absolute value of u_{n+1}. Therefore, if the series is convergent and alternating, a satisfactory criterion is the comparison of the absolute value of u_{n+1} and C, exactly as was done in the sample program. To make this perfectly clear, we note that $|u_{n+1}| \leqslant c$ is equivalent to $U^2 \leqslant C^2$, which is, in turn, equivalent to $(U^2 - C^2) \leqslant 0$, or $(C^2 - U^2) \geqslant 0$, either of which can be used in conjunction with an IF command to accomplish our desired purpose. (The usual precautions must be taken to see that the criterion can actually be satisfied within the limits of precision of the sub-routines used.)

If the series is not alternating, this method is not satisfactory even if successive terms are diminishing. An example will show why this is so. Consider the *harmonic series*:

$$S = 1 + \frac{1}{2} + \frac{1}{3} + \frac{1}{4} + \dots$$

In spite of the fact that the terms obviously diminish ($u_n = \dfrac{1}{n}$, which approaches 0 as n $\rightarrow \infty$), *this series is not even convergent.* No matter how many terms are taken, and no matter how small u_{n+1} is, the error will always be infinite!

The only satisfactory safe and sound method for a convergent but nonalternating series is to calculate the error term mathematically, e.g., by investigating the Maclaurin Series with Remainder (if this is how the series was obtained), then using a convenient form of the remainder of the series.*

24.5 COMPLETING THE PROBLEM IN ATOMIC PHYSICS

You remember that in Subsection 23.10 we were left in the rather humiliating position of presenting a partial solution to the problem. Perhaps we can be clever enough to persuade the machine to give us a nice clean table, with j (instead of log j) and T.

Let us see. What is the precise difficulty? In the table of values following the program, the logarithms ranged from -14132.13400 (for T = 500° Absolute) to $+8.27269$ (for T = 300500° Absolute). If we were continuing "by hand," we would compute:

1. $\qquad \log j = -14132.13400 = 0.86600 - 14133$

    $\qquad\qquad j = 7.345 * 10^{-14133}$

2. $\qquad \log j = 8.27269$

    $\qquad\qquad j = 1.874 * 10^{8}$

There are at least two interesting facets of this problem. *First,* notice that we have no difficulty with the characteristic (the machine does!), but we do not wish to look up the mantissas (the machine does this beautifully!). *Second,* notice that *positive* and *negative* logarithms must be handled differently.

The flow chart in Fig. 58 shows how the machine was "persuaded" to yield the answer in a desirable form. In the table, ABS $\equiv$ | log j |, DELTA is a parameter which starts at 10^4 and is "stepped" to 10^3, 10^2, 10^1 and 10^0, INDEX is an executive control cell, and COEF and POWER refer to the two portions for the answer (j) in scientific notation.

In order to understand the flow chart, consider two situations:

1. $\qquad \log j = \quad 10132.7500, \ j = 10^{0.7500}10^{10132}$

2. $\qquad \log j = -10132.7500, \ j = 10^{0.2500}10^{-10133}$

The following changes take place as the program proceeds.

---

*We refer you to Dodes and Greitzer, *op. cit.,* for some discussion of this matter, and to books on the Calculus for a full discussion. Look up *Taylor Series with Remainder* and see how many forms of the Remainder terms there are, and which one is most satisfactory for your problem.

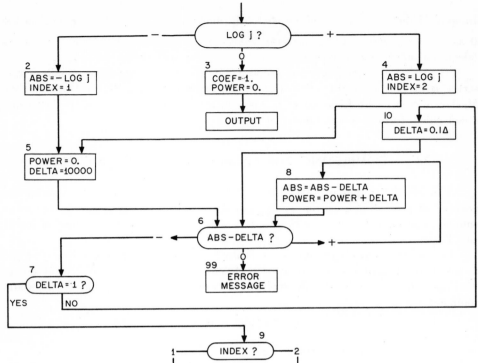

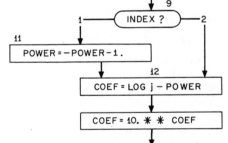

Fig. 58.   Detail flow chart to find antilog.

ZLOGJ	10132.7500	−10132.7500
ABS	10132.7500	10132.7500
INDEX	2	1
POWER	0	0
DELTA	10000	10000
ABS	132.7500	132.7500
POWER	10000	10000
DELTA	1000	1000
DELTA	100	100
ABS	32.7500	32.7500
POWER	10100	10100

DELTA	10	10
ABS	22.7500	22.7500
POWER	10110	10110
ABS	12.7500	12.7500
POWER	10120	10120
ABS	2.7500	2.7500
POWER	10130	10130
DELTA	1	1
ABS	1.7500	1.7500
POWER	10131	10131
ABS	0.7500	0.7500
POWER	10132	10132
POWER	10132	$-10133 \; (= -10132 - 1)$
COEF	0.7500	0.2500
COEF	5.624...	1.778...

The complete program follows:

```
ENTER SOURCE PROGRAM
THEN PUSH START
C   EMISSION OF AN ELECTRON GAS
        READ 100,ZM,ZK,PI,ZH,E
16      TYPE 101
        ACCEPT 102, PHI
        TYPE 103
        TYPE 106
        T = 500.
1       ZLNJ=LOGF(4.*PI*ZM*ZK**2*T**2)-(E*PHI/(ZK*T))-LOGF(ZH**3)
        ZLOGJ=0.43429448*ZLNJ
        IF(ZLOGJ)2,3,4
2       ABS=-ZLOGJ
        INDEX=1
        GO TO 5
4       ABS=ZLOGJ
        INDEX=2
5       POWER=0.
        DELTA=10.**4
6       IF(ABS-DELTA)7,99,8
7       IF(DELTA-1.)99,9,10
99      TYPE 107
        IF(DELTA-1.)99,9,10
8       ABS=ABS-DELTA
        POWER=POWER+DELTA
        GO TO 6
9       GO TO(11,12),INDEX
10      DELTA=0.1*DELTA
        GO TO 6
11      POWER=(-POWER)-1.
12      COEF=ZLOGJ-POWER
        COEF=10.**COEF
        GO TO 13
3       COEF=1.
        POWER=0.
13      TYPE 108,T,COEF,POWER
        IF(250000.-T) 15,14,14
14      T = T + 10000.
        GO TO 1
15      PAUSE
        GO TO 16
100     FORMAT(E10.0,E11.0,F9.0,E10.0,E11.0)
101     FORMAT(18HTYPE VALUE OF PHI.)
102     FORMAT(F5.0)
103     FORMAT(/30HRATE OF EMISSION OF ELECTRONS./)
```

```
106    FORMAT(3X,1HT,23X,1HJ)
107    FORMAT(14HPROGRAM ERROR.)
108    FORMAT(F9.0,4X,F5.2,23H TIMES 10 TO THE POWER  ,F7.0)
       END

RELOCATABLE SUBROUTINES CALLED
LOG
OBJECT PROGRAM DATA TABLE
00630 STORAGE POSITIONS

PROCESSING COMPLETE
```

When the program was compiled, it was compiled with a *trace*. Upon running the program, the trace output was used for the first computed value ($T = 500°$). Then Switch 4 was turned "off" so that the remainder of the table was printed without the trace.

It is very instructive to follow the trace, along with the actual program. Notice that each *arithmetic result* is typed when there is a trace. Notice, also, that the final result in the trace is $7.3451380 * 10^{-14133}$; and that the result, as typed, is $7.34 * 10^{-14133}$. In other words, FORTRAN output is *truncated*, not half-adjusted. (Can you see how the result could have been half-adjusted in one additional step?)

```
THE FOLLOWING SHOWS A TRACE OUTPUT FOR THE FIRST CALCULATION
    (WITH SWITCH 4 ON) FOLLOWED BY OUTPUT WITHOUT A TRACE
    (SWITCH 4 OFF).

TYPE VALUE OF PHI.
4.685RS

RATE OF EMISSION OF ELECTRONS.

     T
+.50000000E+03
-.32540441E+05
-.14132134E+05
+.14132134E+05
     +1
+.00000000E-99
+.10000000E+05
+.41321340E+04
+.10000000E+05
+.10000000E+04
+.31321340E+04
+.11000000E+05
+.21321340E+04
+.12000000E+05
+.11321340E+04
+.13000000E+05
+.13213400E+03
+.14000000E+05
+.10000000E+03
+.32134000E+02
+.14100000E+05
+.10000000E+02
+.22134000E+02
+.14110000E+05
+.12134000E+02
+.14120000E+05
+.21340000E+01
+.14130000E+05
+.10000000E+01
+.11340000E+01
+.14131000E+05
+.13400000E-00
+.14132000E+05
-.14133000E+05
+.86600000E-00
+.73451380E+01
     +500.    +7.34 TIMES 10 TO THE POWER -14133.
   +10500.    +5.10 TIMES 10 TO THE POWER  -646.
   +20500.    +1.48 TIMES 10 TO THE POWER  -316.
   +30500.    +5.47 TIMES 10 TO THE POWER  -203.
   +40500.    +1.97 TIMES 10 TO THE POWER  -145.
```

```
+50500.    +1.25 TIMES 10 TO THE POWER   -110.
+60500.    +2.67 TIMES 10 TO THE POWER    -87.
+70500.    +1.43 TIMES 10 TO THE POWER    -70.
+80500.    +5.57 TIMES 10 TO THE POWER    -58.
+90500.    +3.67 TIMES 10 TO THE POWER    -48.
+100500.   +2.75 TIMES 10 TO THE POWER    -40.
+110500.   +7.88 TIMES 10 TO THE POWER    -34.
+120500.   +1.94 TIMES 10 TO THE POWER    -28.
+130500.   +7.23 TIMES 10 TO THE POWER    -24.
```

We should remark, at this point, that typewritten output wastes a lot of time. If we didn't desire an output suitable for a textbook, it would have been faster and more convenient to change the TYPE instruction to a PUNCH instruction and obtain these results via the IBM 407. In addition, the card output is useful for further input (to continue the problem) whereas the typewriter output is not.

EXERCISES

1 Complete the program for $y = \arcsin x$, using $C = 10^{-7}$ and a suitable remainder term. Remember that arcsin x make sense in the real domain only when $|x| \leqslant 1$. Therefore, part of your program must include an instruction to the machine to examine x. If x is satisfactory, it should compute and print or punch. If x is unsatisfactory, it should not.

2 Write a program to find arctan x. Two different formulas are involved, one when $|x| < 1$, and when $|x| > 1$. (Do not use the built-in subroutine, of course.)

3 Solve $x^x + Ax^2 + B \sin x = 0$ to a satisfactory degree of precision.

4 Solve $\theta + A \sinh \theta + B \ln \theta = 0$ to a satisfactory degree of precision, where sinh is the hyperbolic sine of θ.

5 Solve the simultaneous equations

$$\begin{cases} \sin x = Ay + By^2 \\ \cos y = Cx + D \end{cases}$$

to a satisfactory degree of precision.

6 Write a program to find the four real roots of $x^4 - 56 x^3 + 490 x^2 + 11112 x - 117495 = 0$. The correct answers are approximately 36.9, 22.3, −13.7 and 10.4.

7 Write a program to evaluate

$$\int_0^a \frac{x^3}{e^x - 1}$$

by Simpson's Rule. (When $a = 1.5$, the correct answer is approximately 0.6155.) Simpson's Rule is not the best method for numerical integration by computer.

8 Using the Method of Euler, write a program to solve

$$\frac{dy}{dx} = e^{-x} - y$$

with initial conditions $x_0 = y_0 = 0$.

PROJECTS

Prepare your program for one of the above and run it on the machine.

Section 25. One-Dimensional Arrays

25.1 VECTOR SUBSCRIPTS

A single row, single column, or a vector may be represented by (a_1, a_2, a_3 . . . a_n) in algebraic language. The subscripts are always integers (fixed-point numbers). In FORTRAN language, this same set of numbers is represented by A(1), A(2), . . . or the entire set may be represented by A( ) where any fixed-point variable may be in the parentheses, e.g., SUM(JOB), where JOB takes on various values.

In a program, every subscripted variable must be preceded by a specification statement such as

DIMENSION A(12), X(20), SUM(40),K(7), INIT (30)

which informs the processor that there are 12 * 10 spaces to be set aside for a_i, 20 * 10 spaces to be set aside for x_j, and 40 * 10 spaces to be set aside for S_k. The multiplication by 10 takes place because each floating-point number occupies ten spaces in memory in basic FORTRAN. Fixed-point numbers are each allotted four spaces in memory.

Notice that a single DIMENSION statement can be used to reserve as many spaces as you need (up to cc 72 of the input instruction card). If more space must be reserved, another DIMENSION statement may be used.

The subscripts in the body of the program may be constants or variables (fixed point in both cases), or may be computed. They may be as complicated as

ROW(K*I+JOBNO−58)

but they *must* be actual fixed-point *constants* in the DIMENSION specification statement. Also, all subscripts are positive.

EXERCISES

Which of the following are correct?

1	A(112)	2	FLOW(MAX)
3	TORQ(MIN)	4	SUM(I+3.)
5	SUM(J*KSINX)	6	SUM(J*3(K+2))
7	X(−34)	8	J(I)

25.2 DO LOOP

One of the most amazingly compact commands in FORTRAN language is the *DO command.* The instruction

DO s N = n_1, n_2, n_3

does the following:

1. It sets the fixed-point variable N equal to n_1.

2. It then accomplishes the following instruction steps up to and including the one with statement number s.

3. The program returns to the DO command and increments n_1 by the quantity n_3.

4. The following instructions up to and including statement number s are accomplished.

5. The program returns to the DO command and repeats the entire sequence of instructions up to and including statement number s until n_2 is reached or exceeded.

There are two things to be noted:

6. If n_3 is omitted, the processor assumes that $n_3 = 1$.

7. The last statement in the *range* of the DO loop should not be READ, PRINT, TYPE, PUNCH, IF or GO TO. In these cases, a dummy command, CONTINUE, is used as the last command. (It is actually a *No Operation* command.) *

This single command takes care of setting and stepping wherever fixed-point subscripts are involved. Four examples are given below. (In these examples, the FORMAT specification statements have been omitted.)

25.3   EXAMPLES OF SUBSCRIPTING AND THE DO LOOP

1
> DIMENSION A(5), B(5), C(5)
> DO 3 I = 1,5
> 3 C(I) = A(I) * B(I)
> .
> .

This will cause the machine to execute and store results as follows:

$$C(1) = A(1) * B(1)$$
$$C(2) = A(2) * B(2)$$
$$C(3) = A(3) * B(3)$$
$$C(4) = A(4) * B(4)$$
$$C(5) = A(5) * B(5)$$

after which the program continues to the instruction following statement number 3.

2   This is the same as the above, except that we wish to have each value of c_i punched on a card in some specified format.

> DIMENSION A(5), B(5), C(5)
> DO 3 I = 1,5
> C(I) = A(I) * B(I)
> PUNCH 556, C(I)

---

*The IBM manual does not forbid READ, PRINT, TYPE, PUNCH, but experience has shown that, under certain conditions, the computer will "hang up" on the commands at the end of a DO loop.

         3 CONTINUE

Notice that a CONTINUE statement was provided because a DO loop cannot end with a PUNCH command.

3   A series of 200 scores exists on 100 cards. We wish to read the cards into memory, then find their averages and type these.

         DIMENSION A(100),B(100),C(100)

         DO 11 I = 1,100

         READ 101, A(I), B(I)

         C(I) = (A(I)+B(I))/2.

         TYPE 102, A(I), B(I), C(I)

    11 CONTINUE

4   A series of scores exists on cards as A(1), A(2), . . . A(100), B(1), B(2), . . . B(100). We wish to find A(1) + B(1), A(2) − B(2), A(3) * B(3), A(4) / B(4), then repeat with A(5) + B(5), and so on.

The program is as follows:

    8   DIMENSION A(100), B(100), C(100)

        DO 101, I = 1,100

        READ 753, A(I)

  101   CONTINUE

        DO 2 I = 1,100

        READ 754, B(I)

    2   CONTINUE

        DO 3 I = 1, 100, 4

    3   C(I) =A(I) + B(I)

        DO 4 I = 2, 100, 4

    4   C(I) = A(I) − B(I)

        DO 5 I = 3, 100, 4

    5   C(I) = A(I) * B(I)

        DO 6 I = 4, 100, 4

    6   C(I) = A(I) / B(I)

        DO 7 I = 1, 100

        TYPE 755, A(I), B(I), C(I)

    7   CONTINUE

        PAUSE

        GO TO 8

        (FORMAT specifications 753, 754, 755)

        END

EXERCISES

1 Using Table I, write a program to read into memory the first column as COL1(I) and the second column as COL2(J). Using DO loops, compute the mean and σ of each column, and the Pearson coefficient of correlation, r, between the columns.

2 Write a program to read two vectors, A(I) and B(I), into memory, each one having up to 100 components, and compute $\Sigma(A(I)*B(I))$.

PROJECTS

Prepare one of the above programs and run it on the machine.

Section 26. Two-Dimensional Arrays

26.1 MATRIX NOTATION

We remind you that much of the work done by a scientist has to do with tables of values, such as Table I which we have used throughout this book. This table, like most tables, has *rows* from left to right, and *columns* from top to bottom. This particular table has thirteen rows and eight columns. It is mathematically one example of a *matrix*. Any entry can be found by a double subscript. For example, X_{28} is the entry in the *second* row and *eighth* column. *Notice that the row subscript is first and the column subscript is second.* In FORTRAN language, X(2,8) would be an entry in a matrix of values.

26.2 DOUBLY-SUBSCRIPTED QUANTITIES

The rules for doubly-subscripted quantities are entirely analogous to those for singly-subscripted quantities. The command

DIMENSION X(45,37), A(75)

causes the machine to reserve 45 * 37 * 10 spaces for X-matrix and 75 * 10 spaces for the A-vector.

This represents a total of 17,400 memory cells. Since a FORTRAN program *begins* at 08000, it is evident that this particular program will not fit into the basic machine even if it has only one instruction.

26.3 DO LOOPS WITH DOUBLY-SUBSCRIPTED QUANTITIES

DO loops with matrices work precisely like those with vectors. The variables have two subscripts and the *second* one must be read in first. DO loops may be nested within each other, *but must not overlap*. This rule is illustrated in Fig. 59. (Brackets are used to illustrate the range of a DO.)

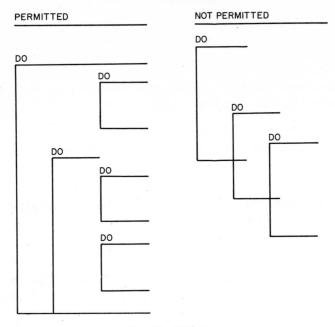

Fig. 59. DO loops.

26.4   MATRIX MULTIPLICATION

If you read the matrix multiplication problem in SPS carefully, you saw that much of the real work involved came about because there was a problem in finding the correct addresses for stepping the addresses for variable instructions. The problem of matrix multiplication is childishly simple in FORTRAN. All the work of addressing is removed since any quantity can be found by reference to the proper subscript. All the work of setting and stepping is removed by DO loops.

In reading the following program, remember that the rule for matrix multiplication is that

$$c_{ik} = \sum_j a_{ij}b_{jk}$$

which means that we multiply the members of the ith row of the first matrix by the members of the kth column in the second matrix, sum them, and store the result as c_{ik}. The actual machine process is, for the entry c_{32}, to compute as follows:

Partial result $= a_{31} * b_{12}$

Partial result $= a_{32} * b_{22} +$ previous result

Partial result $= a_{33} * b_{32} +$ previous result

Partial result $= a_{34} * b_{42} +$ previous result

.

.

continuing until the last value of j is reached. The FORTRAN command for the computation is, therefore,

$$C(I,K) = C(I,K) + A(I,J)*B(J,K)$$

and, as in every iterative process, we must find a first value for $C(I,K)$. This is obviously 0 before the first multiplication. The series of multiplications and additions terminates when J reaches its terminal value which is the number of columns of A or its equal, the number of rows of B. In the program, NRA = number of rows in A, NCA = number of columns in A, and NRB and NCB are similar designations for the B matrix. These are read in on cards.

```
    DIMENSION A(75,75), B(75,75), C(75,75)
  6 READ 101, NRA, NCA
    DO 1 J = 1, NCA
    DO 1 I = 1, NRA
    READ 102, A(I,J)
  1 CONTINUE
    READ 101, NRB, NCB
    DO 2 K = 1, NCB
    DO 2 J = 1, NRB
    READ 102, B(J,K)
  2 CONTINUE
    DO 4 I = 1, NRA
    DO 4 K = 1, NCB
    C(I,K) = 0.0
    DO 4 J = 1,NCA
    C(I,K)=C(I,K)+A(I,J)*B(J,K)
    IF (NCA − J) 5,3,4
  3 TYPE 103, C(I,K)
  4 CONTINUE
  5 PAUSE
    GO TO 6
    (FORMAT specifications 101, 102, 103)
    END
```

26.5   PROBLEM IN STATISTICS

We shall consider a problem which was too ambitious for the basic machine with only 20,000 positions and which therefore had to be done in two parts.

The problem was to take the data of Table I, find all the means, standard deviations, standard errors of the standard deviations, standard errors of the means, intercorrelations, partial correlations for sets of three variables, partial sigmas for sets of three variables, least-squares equations for all sets of three variables referred to column 1, and all the multiple correlations and standard errors of estimate for these least-squares equations.

This program was written quickly (it sounds harder than it is), but when it was compiled the machine announced an "OVERLAP" of several hundred spaces.

A little bit of arithmetic showed that the basic machine would be able to handle everything up to the intercorrelations without trouble. A little thought showed that the rest of the program did not need the basic data, but only the intercorrelations, means, and standard deviations.

The flow chart for Phase I is shown in Fig. 60. The program for Phase I, and its

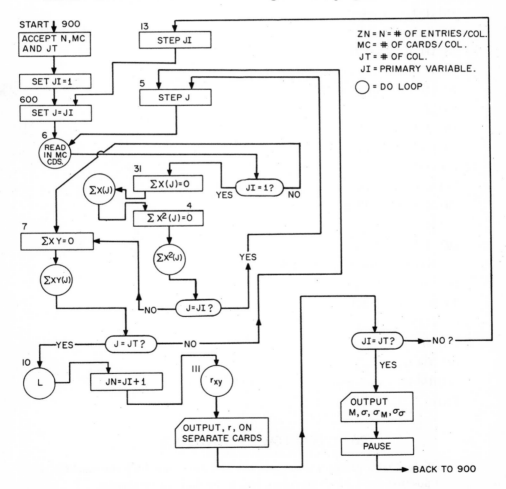

Fig. 60.   Flow chart for phase I of statistics program.

typewritten output, follow.

```
ENTER SOURCE PROGRAM, PUSH START
Ō8000  C STATISTICS PROGRAM, PHASE 1.   I.A. DODES 6/15/62
Ō8000  900     TYPE 50
Ō8024          TYPE 51
Ō8048          ACCEPT 52,N
Ō8072          TYPE 53
Ō8096          ACCEPT 52,MC
Ō8120          TYPE 54
Ō8144          ACCEPT 52,JT
Ō8168          TYPE 56
Ō8192          DIMENSION X(30,8),SUMX(8),SUMXX(8),SUMXY(8),ZL(8)
Ō8192          DIMENSION R(8,7),ZM(8),STERM(8),STERS(8),STDEV(8)
Ō8192          ZN=N
Ō8240          JI=1
Ō8276  600     J=JI
Ō8312  6       I=1
Ō8348          K=1
Ō8384  2       READ 55,X(I,J),X(I+1,J),X(I+2,J),X(I+3,J),X(I+4,J)
Ō8756          IF (MC-K) 1,3,1
Ō8824  1       K=K+1
Ō8872          I=I+5
Ō8920          GO TO 2
Ō8928  3       IF(JI-1) 7,31,7
Ō8996  31      SUMX(J)=0.0
Ō9056          SUMXX(J)=0.0
Ō9116          DO 4 I=1,N
Ō9128          SUMX(J)=SUMX(J)+X(I,J)
Ō9284  4       SUMXX(J)=SUMXX(J)+X(I,J)*X(I,J)
Ō9548          IF (J-JI) 7,5,7
Ō9616  5       J=J+1
Ō9664          GO TO 6
Ō9672  7       SUMXY(J)=0.0
Ō9732          DO 8 I=1,N
Ō9744  8       SUMXY(J)=SUMXY(J)+X(I,JI)*X(I,J)
T0008          IF (JT-J) 5,10,5
T0076  10      DO 11 J=JI,JT
T0088  11      ZL(J)=SQRT(ZN*SUMXX(J)-SUMX(J)**2)
T0316          JN=JI+1
T0364          DO 111 J=JN,JT
T0376  111     R(JI,J)=(ZN*SUMXY(J)-SUMX(J)*SUMX(JI))/(ZL(J)*ZL(JI))
T0748          IF(SENSE SWITCH 1)112,113
T0768  112     DO12J=JN,JT
T0780          TYPE57,JI,J,R(JI,J)
T0888  12      CONTINUE
T0924  113     DO121J=JN,JT
T0936          PUNCH58,R(JI,J),JI,J
T1044  121     CONTINUE
T1080          JP = JT - 1
T1128          IF (JP - JI) 13,14,13
T1196  13      JI=JI+1
T1244          TYPE59
T1268          GO TO 600
T1276  14      TYPE60
T1300          D1=SQRT(ZN-1.0)
T1360          D2=SQRT(2.0*ZN)
T1420          DO 15 J = 1,JT
T1432          ZM(J)=SUMX(J)/ZN
T1528          STDEV(J)=ZL(J)/ZN
T1624          STERM(J)=STDEV(J)/D1
T1720          STERS(J)=STDEV(J)/D2
T1816          TYPE61,J,ZM(J),STDEV(J),STERM(J),STERS(J)
T1984          PUNCH61,J,ZM(J),STDEV(J),STERM(J),STERS(J)
T2152  15      CONTINUE
T2188          PAUSE
T2200          GO TO 900
T2208  50      FORMAT(31HENTRIES,F MODE,CC 1,15,29,43,57)
T2294  51      FORMAT(21HENTRIES/COLUMN AS XXX)
T2360  52      FORMAT(I3)
T2382  53      FORMAT(19HCARDS/COLUMN AS XXX)
T2444  54      FORMAT (23HTOTAL NO. OF COL AS XXX)
T2514  55      FORMAT (F14.8,F14.8,F14.8,F14.8,F14.8)
T2556  56      FORMAT(22HSW1 ON TO TYPE RESULTS)
T2624  57      FORMAT (I4,5X,I4,5X,F15.12)
T2690  58      FORMAT (F15.12,5X,I4,5X,I4)
T2756  59      FORMAT(33HREMOVE TOP COLUMN,RE-INSERT CARDS)
T2846  60      FORMAT (3HVAR9X,4HMEAN13X,7HST.DEV.10X,8HS.E.MEAN9X8HS.E.S.D.)
T3068  61      FORMAT (I3,2X,F15.8,2X,F15.10,2X,F15.10,2X,F15.10)
T3154          END
```

```
PROG SW 1 ONFOR SYMBOL TABLE, PUSH START
SW 1 OFF TO IGNORE SUBROUTINES, PUSH START

PROCESSING COMPLETE
```

THE TYPEWRITER OUTPUT OF PHASE I IS SHOWN IN THE FOLLOWING. THE FIRST
   SET OF TABLES GIVES THE PEARSON CORRELATIONS. THE LAST TABLE GIVES
   THE MEANS, STANDARD DEVIATIONS, STANDARD ERRORS OF THE MEANS, AND
                                                    STANDARD ERRORS OF THE STANDARD
```
ENTRIES,F MODE,CC 1,15,29,43,57               DEVIATIONS.
ENTRIES/COLUMN AS XXX
013RS
CARDS/COLUMN AS XXX
003RS
TOTAL NO. OF COL AS XXX
008RS                     OUTPUT
SW1 ON TO TYPE RESULTS
    +1        +2        +.627229470000
    +1        +3        +.291975720000
    +1        +4        +.417057560000
    +1        +5        +.393728390000
    +1        +6        +.096145398000
    +1        +7        +.177602600000
    +1        +8        -.003254283700
REMOVE TOP COLUMN,RE-INSERT CARDS
    +2        +3        +.463879570000
    +2        +4        +.509950530000
    +2        +5        +.253584730000
    +2        +6        +.006005817600
    +2        +7        +.119034850000
    +2        +8        -.197428590000
REMOVE TOP COLUMN,RE-INSERT CARDS
    +3        +4        -.183932050000
    +3        +5        +.406628670000
    +3        +6        +.227743910000
    +3        +7        +.269836780000
    +3        +8        +.099556431000
REMOVE TOP COLUMN,RE-INSERT CARDS
    +4        +5        +.158792340000
    +4        +6        -.347572630000
    +4        +7        +.107565810000
    +4        +8        -.355891960000
REMOVE TOP COLUMN,RE-INSERT CARDS
    +5        +6        +.321409570000
    +5        +7        +.434869410000
    +5        +8        -.032861461000
REMOVE TOP COLUMN,RE-INSERT CARDS
    +6        +7        +.159245840000
    +6        +8        -.358962930000
REMOVE TOP COLUMN,RE-INSERT CARDS
    +7        +8        -.011867594000
```

VAR	MEAN	ST.DEV.	S.E.MEAN	S.E.S.D.
+1	+548.03923000	+63.0150250000	+18.1908700000	+12.3582630000
+2	+91.84453800	+14.3137900000	+4.1320352000	+2.8071651000
+3	+1680.07690000	+314.2721400000	+90.7225520000	+61.6338370000
+4	+845.15384000	+172.7362300000	+49.8646540000	+33.8763610000
+5	+827.53846000	+114.3212500000	+33.0017020000	+22.4202410000
+6	+1156.92300000	+179.0304200000	+51.6816300000	+35.1107540000
+7	+1137.46150000	+227.5368400000	+65.6842280000	+44.6236450000
+8	-.41284615	+1.2222483000	+.3528326900	+.2397026100

The program was designed to be flexible. Therefore, the first instructions accepted the number of entries per column, the number of cards per column, and the total number of columns.

The output shows the various intercorrelations and the condensed statistics. For example, $r_{12} = 0.62722947$, $M_1 = 548.03923$, $\sigma_1 = 63.015025$, and so on. It was decided to have the output in F-mode because this is so much easier to read.

The punched card output consisted of a set of cards with correlations, and another set of cards with the condensed statistics.

The output of Phase 1 is partly on punched cards. When these cards are read into the computer with the program as shown on the following pages, the output of Phase 2 is (i) partial correlations, (ii) partial sigmas, (iii) regression coefficients, (iv) multiple correlation, and (v) the regression of the first variable on the other two.

The symbols used in the program are as follows:

$P(K)$ = r_{12}, r_{13}, r_{23} where the subscripts refer to the variable sequence as fed in.

$S(K)$ = The standard deviations of the three variables.

$R(K)$ = $r_{23.1}$, $r_{13.2}$, $r_{12.3}$, e.g., $r_{12.3}$ = $\dfrac{r_{12} - r_{13}\, r_{23}}{\sqrt{1 - r^2_{13}}\ \sqrt{1 - r^2_{23}}}$

$$= \frac{P(1) - P(2) * P(3)}{SP(2) * SP(3)}$$

$J(K)$ = The order number of the variable, as fed in.

$SP(1)$ = $\sqrt{1 - r^2_{12}}$ = $\sqrt{1 - P(1)^2}$

$SP(2)$ = $\sqrt{1 - r^2_{13}}$ = $\sqrt{1 - P(2)^2}$

$SP(3)$ = $\sqrt{1 - r^2_{23}}$ = $\sqrt{1 - P(3)^2}$

$PS(1)$ = $\sigma_{1(23)}$ = $\sigma_1\sqrt{1 - r^2_{12.3}}\ \sqrt{1 - r^2_{13.2}}$ = $S(1) * SP(1) * SPP(2)$

$PS(2)$ = $\sigma_{2(13)}$

$PS(3)$ = $\sigma_{3(12)}$

$B(1)$ = $b_{12.3}$ = $r_{12.3} \cdot \sigma_{1.23}/\sigma_{2.13}$ = $R(3) * PS(1)/PS(2)$

$B(2)$ = $b_{13.2}$ = $r_{13.2} \cdot \sigma_{1.23}/\sigma_{3.12}$ = $R(2) * PS(1)/PS(3)$

RM = $R_{1(23)}$ = $\sqrt{1 - \dfrac{\sigma^2_{1.23}}{\sigma_1^2}}$ = $\sqrt{1 - \dfrac{[PS(1)]^2}{S(1)^2}}$

$SPP(K)$ = $\sqrt{1 - (\text{partial correlation})^2}$

The program instructions were quite straightforward. They are shown in the following:

```
ENTER SOURCE PROGRAM, PUSH START

08000 C      STATISTICS PROGRAM, PHASE 2. I. A.  DODES  6/15/62
08000 161    TYPE 621
08024 16     TYPE 62
08048        DIMENSION P(3),S(3),J(3),SP(3),L(3),R(3),SPP(2)
08048        DIMENSION PS(3),LL(3),B(2),LLL(3),ZM(3)
08048        DO 17 K = 1,3
08060        READ 63,P(K)
08108 17     CONTINUE
08144        DO 18 K = 1,3
08156        READ 64,J(K),ZM(K),S(K)
08276 18     CONTINUE
08312        DO 19 K = 1,3
08324 19     SP(K) = SQRT(1.0-P(K)**2)
08492        R(3) =(P(1)-P(2)*P(3))/(SP(2)*SP(3))
08612        R(2)=(P(2)-P(1)*P(3))/(SP(1)*SP(3))
08732        R(1)=(P(3)-P(1)*P(2))/(SP(1)*SP(2))
08852        L(3) = J(1)*100 + J(2) * 10 + J(3)
08960        L(2) = J(1) * 100 + J(3) * 10 + J(2)
09068        L(1) = J(2) * 100 + J(3) * 10 + J(1)
09176        TYPE 65
09200        DO 20 K = 1,3
09212        TYPE 66, L(K),R(K)
09296 20     CONTINUE
09332        SPP(1) = SQRT (1.0 - R(1)**2)
09416        SPP(2) = SQRT(1.0 -  R(2)**2)
09500        PS(1) = S(1) * SP(1) * SPP(2)
09560        PS(2) = S(2) * SP(1) * SPP(1)
09620        PS(3) = S(3) * SP(2) * SPP(1)
09680        TYPE 67
09704         LL(1) = L(3)
09740        LL(2) = J(2) * 100 + J(1) * 10 + J(3)
09848        LL(3) = J(3) * 100 + J(1) * 10 + J(2)
09956        DO 21 K = 1,3
09968        TYPE 68, LL(K), PS(K)
10052 21     CONTINUE
```

```
T0088          TYPE 69
T0112          B(1) = R(3) * PS(1) / PS(2)
T0172          B(2) = R(2) * PS(1) / PS(3)
T0232          LLL(1) = L(3)
T0268          LLL(2) = L(2)
T0304          DO 22 K = 1,2
T0316          TYPE 70,LLL(K),B(K)
T0400  22      CONTINUE
T0436          RM = SQRT(1.0 - PS(1)**2/S(1)**2)
T0568          TYPE 71
T0592          TYPE 72, L(3),RM
T0628          C=ZM(1)-B(1)*ZM(2)-B(2)*ZM(3)
T0748          TYPE 73
T0772          TYPE 74,J(1)
T0796          TYPE 75,B(1),J(2),B(2),J(3),C
T0868          PAUSE
T0880          GO TO 16
T0888  62      FORMAT(//37HREAD IN R,THEN SIGMAS FOR 3 VARIABLES)
T0996  621     FORMAT(44HR(I,II),R(I,III),R(II,III),S(I),S(II),S(III))
T1108  63      FORMAT(F15.12)
T1130  64       FORMAT(I3,2X,F15.8,2X,F15.10)
T1184  65      FORMAT(20HPARTIAL CORRELATIONS)
T1248  66      FORMAT(1HR,1X,I4,1H=,1X,E14.8)
T1312  67      FORMAT(14HPARTIAL SIGMAS)
T1364  68      FORMAT(5HSIGMA,1X,I4,1H=,1X,E14.8)
T1436  69      FORMAT(23HREGRESSION COEFFICIENTS)
T1506  70      FORMAT(1HB,1X,I4,1H=,1X,E14.8)
T1570  71      FORMAT(20HMULTIPLE CORRELATION)
T1634  72      FORMAT(1HR,1X,I4,1H=,1X,E14.8)
T1698  73      FORMAT(19HREGRESSION EQUATION)
T1760  74      FORMAT (12HPREDICTED X(I3,2H)=)
T1824  75  FORMAT(10X,1H(E14.8,3H)X(I3,3H)+(E14.8,3H)X(I3,3H)+(E14.8,1H))
T1964          END
```

```
PROG SW 1 ONFOR SYMBOL TABLE, PUSH START
SW 1 OFF TO IGNORE SUBROUTINES, PUSH START

PROCESSING COMPLETE
```

THE RESULT OF THE PROGRAM IS SHOWN IN THE FOLLOWING.

```
LOAD DATA
 OUTPUT
R(I,II),R(I,III),R(II,III),S(I),S(II),S(III)

READ IN R,THEN SIGMAS FOR 3 VARIABLES

PARTIAL CORRELATIONS
R  +231= +.37688922E-00
R  +132= +.14736621E-02
R  +123= +.58042046E-00
PARTIAL SIGMAS
SIGMA +123= +.49078224E+02
SIGMA +213= +.10325997E+02
SIGMA +312= +.27841285E+03
REGRESSION COEFFICIENTS
B  +123= +.27586687E+01
B  +132= +.25977507E-03
MULTIPLE CORRELATION
R  +123= +.62723049E-00
REGRESSION EQUATION
PREDICTED X( +1)=
        (+.27586687E+01)X( +2)+(+.25977507E-03)X( +3)+(+.29423414E+03)
```

The first output is shown above. First, it gives the partial correlations, e.g., $r_{23.1}$, then the partial sigmas, e.g., $\sigma_{1.23}$, then the regression coefficients of the least-squares equation, e.g., $b_{12.3}$, then the multiple correlation $R_{(1)23}$, and finally the least-squares regression equation which, rounded off, is

$$\tilde{X}_1 = 2.759 \ X_2 + 0.0002598 \ X_3 + 294.234$$

The *standard error of estimate* is the same as $\sigma_{1.23}$.

Upon inserting the cards for other sets of variables, all the predictive data can be

obtained. The speed of this program (as well as the ease with which it was programmed) is truly impressive. By the time the cards are read in, the machine is
typing or punching the answers!

You will find that the basic machine will easily accomplish even long programs
if they are intelligently split into segments with intermediate output on punched
cards.

26.6   WRITING STATISTICAL TABLES

We have not given much attention to *data processing,* the problem of dealing
with large amounts of input data, by the use of FORTRAN. The difficulty, with the
basic machine limitation on space, is that almost half the machine is taken up with
the FORTRAN instructions, leaving rather little room for data. In a scientific or
industrial installation, the use of supplementary modules removes this difficulty for
ordinary work, and the use of larger machines (such as the IBM 7090) increases
tremendously the capacity as well as the capability of the programs.

However, it would be improper to leave you with the impression that the basic
machine (plus some ingenuity) cannot be used for data processing, even when
there are considerable amounts of data.

The problem to be illustrated is an actual one, in which a questionnaire was sent
to approximately 500 heads of departments in New York City. The questionnaire
had twenty-eight questions, each one answerable by checking a box. Some questions
had *two* answers and others had up to *four.* The first question asked about the
respondent's field (there were nine categories). When the questionnaires were
returned, the replies were placed on IBM cards in cc 1-28. The problem now was to
prepare twenty-eight statistical tables in which the entries showed what percent of
the department heads in each category answered the questions in specific ways.

Before showing the solution, we demonstrate two tables of the eventual output,
as shown below.

SURVEY OF LICENSED FIRST ASSISTANTS IN NEW YORK.

```
QUESTION  +1
     PER CENT OF TOTAL RESPONSES IN EACH CATEGORY.

ENGLISH AND SPEECH              +11.60
SOCIAL STUDIES                  +14.91
FOREIGN LANGUAGES                +9.94
MATHEMATICS                     +12.15
PHYSICAL SCIENCE                +17.12
BIOLOGICAL SCIENCE              +10.49
MUSIC AND FINE ARTS              +5.52
BUSINESS AND SECRETARIAL         +4.97
HEALTH ED,HOME EC ET AL.        +13.25
```

```
QUESTION  +5
     PER CENT OF RESPONSES BY ROWS.
CATEGORY                 N.A.        1        2        3        4
ENGLISH AND SPEECH      +66.66   +28.57    +4.76     +.00     +.00
SOCIAL STUDIES          +44.44   +33.33   +11.11    +7.40     +.00
FOREIGN LANGUAGES       +66.66   +33.33     +.00     +.00     +.00
MATHEMATICS             +54.54   +31.81     +.00    +9.09     +.00
```

PHYSICAL SCIENCE	+54.83	+35.48	+3.22	+.00	+.00
BIOLOGICAL SCIENCE	+63.15	+36.84	+.00	+.00	+.00
MUSIC AND FINE ARTS	+40.00	+40.00	+20.00	+.00	+.00
BUSINESS AND SECRETARIAL	+66.66	+22.22	+11.11	+.00	+.00
HEALTH ED.HOME EC ET AL.	+50.00	+37.50	+4.16	+8.33	+.00
TOTALS	+55.80	+33.70	+4.97	+3.31	+.00

First, it was desired to show what percent of the total responses were in each category. In Table 1 it is shown that 11.11 percent of the total responses were from people who were heads of departments in English and speech.

Tables 2, 3 . . . 28 consisted of 10 x 5 matrices in which the first column (N.A.) gave the percent in each row who did not answer, and the other columns have answers 1, 2, 3, and 4. The last row was the total.

How was this accomplished?

The program is shown below. There are some notable features:

1. Because the basic machine will not (at the present time) accept a variable FORMAT instruction, it was necessary to make a separate FORMAT instruction for each of the 28 card columns. Notice that the first card column is read in each time. This was necessary because the first card column contained the information about "category" (from 1 to 9). The X was used to omit unwanted information. On larger machines, the entire set of 500 cards could have been read in to memory *once*, and a variable instruction made to replace these 28 FORMAT commands. (SPS could, of course, have been used since it affords complete control over input and output.) However, we do not wish to exaggerate the difficulty of this procedure. It takes just a few minutes to type twenty-eight easy cards. *The entire running of the program plus programming took less time than it would have taken to calculate one row of one table by desk calculator.*

2. Of special interest is the use of the COMPUTED GO TO following statements numbered 2092 and 2082. *K* was, in each case, the number of the card column, hence the question, being analyzed and we wished to read the cards in a different way for each card column. When K = 1, we had computed Table 1 in the usual fashion, and when K = 2, we wished to go to statement 2. There are several ways this could have been done. For example, the command

$$GO\ TO\ (1,2,3,\ldots 14),K$$

would have accomplished this because (at this point in the program) K cannot equal 1 and no damage would be done. However, we chose to define a new fixed point constant, L = K − 1, which accomplished the same purpose. We could also have used

$$GO\ TO\ (2,3\ldots 14),\ K-1$$

of course. The problem now arose that we couldn't fit all the statement numbers 2 . . . 29 on a single card. In larger machines, cc 6 ("Continuation") can be used, but we had to substitute ingenuity. Notice that statement number 2002 served to branch the program to statement 2092 for K $\leqslant$ 14, and to statement 2082 for K > 14.

3. To save space, the machine was instructed to form a matrix with the total numbers A(MC,J) in each cell of the matrix, then use the very same spaces for the calculated percents. "MC" stands for "category." (Why couldn't we use "C"?) Notice that in statement number 2003, the machine updates the total in each cell of the matrix, then—after all the input cards are entered—computes the totals by rows (statement 2006), the total percents (2007), and finally converts each cell into a percent (2008).

4. Lastly, it is of interest to note the type-out instructions, TYPE 9015, etc. In larger machines, it is possible to have subscripted variables in these instructions. The spacing was accomplished by allowing extra spaces in the FORMAT statements (see 9015, for example). It could also have been done by using nX commands in the FORMAT command.

```
     ENTER SOURCE PROGRAM
     THEN PUSH START
C    PROGRAM TO FORM A STATISTICAL MATRIX
             ACCEPT 9000, NT
1        TYPE 9001
         DIMENSION A(9,5),T(9),P(9),Q(5)
         K=1
         DO 1001 MC = 1,9
1001     T(MC) = 0.
         N = 0
1002     READ 66, MC
         N = N + 1
         T(MC) = T(MC) + 1.0
         IF (N - NT) 1002,1003,1003
1003     ZT = 0.0
         DO 1004 MC = 1,9
1004     ZT = ZT + T(MC)
         DO 1005 MC = 1,9
1005     P(MC) = T(MC) * 100.0/ZT
         TYPE 9002, K
         TYPE 9003
         TYPE 9004, P(1)
         TYPE 9005, P(2)
         TYPE 9006, P(3)
         TYPE 9007, P(4)
         TYPE 9008, P(5)
         TYPE 9009, P(6)
         TYPE 9010, P(7)
         TYPE 9011, P(8)
         TYPE 9012, P(9)
         K = 2
2000     DO 2001 J = 1,5
         DO 2001 MC = 1,9
2001     A(MC,J) = 0.0
         N = 0
2002     IF (K-14) 2092,2092,2082
2092     L = K - 1
         GO TO (2,3,4,5,6,7,8,9,10,11,12,13,14),L
2082     L = K - 14
         GO TO (15,16,17,18,19,20,21,22,23,24,25,26,27,28,29),L
2003     A(MC,J) = A(MC,J) + 1.0
         N = N + 1
         IF (N - NT) 2002,2004,2004
2004     DO 2005 J = 1,5
2005     Q(J) = 0.0
         DO 2006 J = 1,5
         DO 2006 MC = 1,9
2006     Q(J) = Q(J) + A(MC,J)
         DO 2007 J = 1,5
2007     Q(J) = Q(J) * 100.0 /ZT
         DO 2008 J = 1,5
         DO 2008 MC = 1,9
2008     A(MC,J) = A(MC,J) * 100.0 / T(MC)
         TYPE 9002, K
         TYPE 9013
         TYPE 9014
         TYPE 9015,A(1,1),A(1,2),A(1,3),A(1,4),A(1,5)
         TYPE 9016,A(2,1),A(2,2),A(2,3),A(2,4),A(2,5)
         TYPE 9017,A(3,1),A(3,2),A(3,3),A(3,4),A(3,5)
```

```
          TYPE 9018,A(4,1),A(4,2),A(4,3),A(4,4),A(4,5)
          TYPE 9019,A(5,1),A(5,2),A(5,3),A(5,4),A(5,5)
          TYPE 9020,A(6,1),A(6,2),A(6,3),A(6,4),A(6,5)
          TYPE 9021,A(7,1),A(7,2),A(7,3),A(7,4),A(7,5)
          TYPE 9022,A(8,1),A(8,2),A(8,3),A(8,4),A(8,5)
          TYPE 9023, A(9,1),A(9,2),A(9,3),A(9,4),A(9,5)
          TYPE 9024,Q(1),Q(2),Q(3),Q(4),Q(5)
          K = K + 1
          GO TO 2000
2         READ 2111, MC, J
          GO TO 2003
3         READ 31, MC, J
          GO TO 2003
4         READ 41, MC, J
          GO TO 2003
5         READ 51, MC, J
          GO TO 2003
6         READ 61, MC, J
          GO TO 2003
7         READ 71, MC, J
          GO TO 2003
8         READ 81, MC, J
          GO TO 2003
9         READ 91, MC, J
          GO TO 2003
10        READ 101, MC, J
          GO TO 2003
11        READ 111, MC, J
          GO TO 2003
12        READ 121, MC, J
          GO TO 2003
13        READ 131, MC, J
          GO TO 2003

14        READ 141, MC, J
          GO TO 2003
15        READ 151, MC, J
          GO TO 2003
16        READ 161, MC, J
          GO TO 2003
17        READ 171, MC, J
          GO TO 2003
18        READ 181, MC, J
          GO TO 2003
19        READ 191, MC, J
          GO TO 2003
20        READ 201, MC, J
          GO TO 2003
21        READ 211, MC, J
          GO TO 2003
22        READ 221, MC, J
          GO TO 2003
23        READ 231, MC, J
          GO TO 2003
24        READ 241, MC, J
          GO TO 2003
25        READ 251, MC, J
          GO TO 2003
26        READ 261, MC, J
          GO TO 2003
27        READ 271, MC, J
          GO TO 2003
28        READ 281, MC, J
          GO TO 2003
29        PAUSE
          GO TO 1
9000          FORMAT (13)
9001      FORMAT(48HSURVEY OF LICENSED FIRST ASSISTANTS IN NEW YORK.)
66        FORMAT(11)
2111      FORMAT(11,11)
31        FORMAT(11,1X,11)
41        FORMAT(11,2X,11)
51        FORMAT(11,3X,11)
61        FORMAT(11,4X,11)
71        FORMAT(11,5X,11)
81        FORMAT(1X,6X,11)
91        FORMAT(11,7X,11)
101       FORMAT(11,8X,11)
111       FORMAT(11,9X,11)
121       FORMAT(11,10X,11)
131       FORMAT(11,11X,11)
141       FORMAT(11,12X,11)
151       FORMAT(11,13X,11)
161       FORMAT(11,14X,11)
171       FORMAT(11,15X,11)
181       FORMAT(11,16X,11)
191       FORMAT(11,17X,11)
201       FORMAT(11,18X,11)
211       FORMAT(11,19X,11)
221       FORMAT(11,20X,11)
```

```
231     FORMAT(I1,21X,I1)
241     FORMAT(I1,22X,I1)
251     FORMAT(I1,23X,I1)
261     FORMAT(I1,24X,I1)
271     FORMAT(I1,25X,I1)
281     FORMAT(I1,26X,I1)
9002    FORMAT(/9HQUESTION 13)
9003    FORMAT(5X,45HPER CENT OF TOTAL RESPONSES IN EACH CATEGORY./)
9004    FORMAT(18HENGLISH AND SPEECH,11X,F6.2)
9005    FORMAT(14HSOCIAL STUDIES,15X,F6.2)
9006    FORMAT(17HFOREIGN LANGUAGES,12X,F6.2)
9007    FORMAT(11HMATHEMATICS,18X,F6.2)
9008    FORMAT(16HPHYSICAL SCIENCE,13X,F6.2)
9009    FORMAT(18HBIOLOGICAL SCIENCE,11X,F6.2)
9010    FORMAT(19HMUSIC AND FINE ARTS,10X,F6.2)
9011    FORMAT(24HBUSINESS AND SECRETARIAL,5X,F6.2)
9012    FORMAT(24HHEALTH ED,HOME EC ET AL.,5X,F6.2)
9013    FORMAT(5X,30HPER CENT OF RESPONSES BY ROWS.)
9014    FORMAT(8HCATEGORY,25X,4HN.A.,6X,1H1,7X,1H2,7X,1H3,7X,1H4)
9015    FORMAT(18HENGLISH AND SPEECH,11X,F8.2,F8.2,F8.2,F8.2,F8.2)
9016    FORMAT(14HSOCIAL STUDIES,15X,F8.2,F8.2,F8.2,F8.2,F8.2)
9017    FORMAT(17HFOREIGN LANGUAGES,12X,F8.2,F8.2,F8.2,F8.2,F8.2)
9018    FORMAT(11HMATHEMATICS,18X,F8.2,F8.2,F8.2,F8.2,F8.2)
9019    FORMAT(16HPHYSICAL SCIENCE,13X,F8.2,F8.2,F8.2,F8.2,F8.2)
9020    FORMAT(18HBIOLOGICAL SCIENCE,11X,F8.2,F8.2,F8.2,F8.2,F8.2)
9021    FORMAT(19HMUSIC AND FINE ARTS,10X,F8.2,F8.2,F8.2,F8.2,F8.2)
9022    FORMAT(24HBUSINESS AND SECRETARIAL,5X,F8.2,F8.2,F8.2,F8.2,F8.2)
9023    FORMAT(24HHEALTH ED,HOME EC ET AL.,5X,F8.2,F8.2,F8.2,F8.2,F8.2)
9024    FORMAT(/6HTOTALS,23X,F8.2,F8.2,F8.2,F8.2,F8.2)
        END
```

```
OBJECT PROGRAM DATA TABLE
01940 STORAGE POSITIONS
```

PROCESSING COMPLETE

EXERCISES

1 Write a program to add two conformable matrices.

2 Write a program to multiply a vector by a matrix.

3 Write a program to evaluate a determinant.

4 Write a program to solve ten simultaneous equations by means of the Gauss-Jordan method.

5 Write a program to invert a matrix.

6 Write a program to compute $B^{-1}AB$, where A and B are square matrices, and B^{-1} is the inverse of B.

7 Write a program to compute χ^2 for a matrix of data, using some suitable hypothesis.

8 Write a program to find the eigenvalues of a matrix. (You may read about eigenvalues in books on mathematical physics.)

9 Write a program to solve a problem in *linear programming.**

10 Write a program to solve a problem in the *Theory of Games.**

11 Write a program to solve a problem in astronomy, e.g., satellite problems.*

12 Read some of the literature on the *Monte Carlo Method,* and use this to invert a matrix or solve a system of equations.

PROJECTS

Prepare the cards for one of the above programs and run them on the IBM 1620.

---

*Refer to Dodes, I. A. and Greitzer, S. L., *op. cit.,* in performing exercises 9-11.

ANSWERS TO SELECTED EXERCISES IN PART I

A few of the answers for Part I are offered to assist in Review. Answers to the exercises for Parts II, III and IV should be checked on the machine: by dumping in Part II, and by listings (with error messages) in Parts III and IV.

SECTION 1.4

1 [2.85, 2.95)   2 (−3.675, −3.665]
3 −32.4655, −32.4645]   4 [156.22285, 156.22295)
5 35.4   6 127.52
7 −98.2   8 −30.10

SECTION 2.5

1 $1.59 * 10^6$ 2 $2.44 * 10^5$
4 $7.84 * 10^5$

SECTION 5.2

3 −14.101   4 $3.18569 * 10^{-5}$
5 52,354.64   6 −52,483.9

SECTION 6.6

Answers to statistical problems will be found in section 26.5

SECTION 7.5

1 $\tilde{Y} = -28.677\ X^2 + 47.028\ X + 151.502$ (parabola)
2 $\tilde{Y} = 468.6 * 10 ** (-0.3763\ X)$ (exponential decline)
3 $\tilde{Y} = 6.114 * X ** (-0.6278)$
4 $\tilde{Y} = -8.593\ X - 10.056$ (straight line)
5 Standard error of the Mean: 13.5836, 22.8102
6 t = 1.57, apparently not significant
7 t = 2.18, statistically significant

SECTION 9.5

Check in handbooks.

Appendix

Appendix 1. Bronx High School of Science Load Program

LOAD AND LIST PROGRAM (13 CARDS)

The following program will load a program in the normal manner when Switch 1 is "off," and will load and list a program when Switch 1 is "on." As written, the program will start in location 01000, but the beginning of the program can be relocated to any permissible address by inserting the (even) number in cc 51-55 of card 3 and cc 51-55 of card 12. It will list record marks correctly only if they are at the end of instructions, e.g., 15 18107 0000$\ddagger$. If, however, the record mark is packed in the middle of an instruction, e.g., 30 0$\ddagger$567 89102, the listing will be incorrect, i.e., it will list 34 0$\ddagger$000 00000.

In ordinary circumstances, it is better to list cards on the IBM 407.

Card 1:

(Spaces are left to facilitate reading.)

(00000)	36	00782	00500
(00012)	36	00854	00500
(00024)	36	00926	00500
(00036)	49	00782	

Beginning with card column 44:
05759564759415400535641444544$\ddagger$

Card 2:

(00782)	36	00100	00500
(00794)	36	00172	00500

    (00806)   36   00244   00500
    (00818)   36   00316   00500
    (00830)   36   00388   00500
    (00842)   36   00462   00500

Card 3:

    (00854)   36   00534   00500
    (00866)   36   00606   00500
    (00878)   36   00701   00500
    (00890)   25   00781   00400
    (00902)   36 $\overline{0}$1000   0$\pm$500
    (00914)   46   00402   00100

Card 4:

    (00926)   46   00962   00900
    (00938)   11   00908 $\overline{0}$0012
    (00950)   49   00902   00000
    (00962)   34   000$\pm$0   00102
    (00974)   39   00045   00100
    (00986)   49   00642 $\overline{0}$0012

Cards 5-8:

(These cards contain the arithmetic tables.)

Card 9:

(Card columns 1-14 contain the remainder of the arithmetic tables. The following begins in cc 15.)

    (00402)   16   00997 $\overline{0}$0012
    (00414)   21   00997   00908
    (00426)   26   00444   00997
    (00438)   15 $\overline{0}$1012   0000$\pm$
    (00450)   26   00473   00908

Card 10:

    (00462)   31   19998 $\overline{0}$1000
    (00474)   34   00000   00102
    (00486)   38   00904   00100
    (00498)   39   00965   00100
    (00510)   35   19998   00100

    (00522)   39   00965   00100

Card 11:

    (00534)   26   00557   00473

    (00546)   31   19993 $\bar{0}$1000

    (00558)   35   19995   00100

    (00570)   39   00965   00100

    (00582)   26   00605   00473

    (00594)   31   19988 $\bar{0}$1000

Card 12:

    (00606)   35   19995   00100

    (00618)   26   19999   00682

    (00630)   49   00926   00000

    (00642)   48   00000   00000

    (00654)   49   01$\bar{0}$00   00000

The remainder of card 12 is blank, except for a $\neq$ in cc 78. (Cards 1-12 should be numbered in cc 79-80.)

Card 13:

This card has 80 card columns of numeric blanks (8,4).

ARITHMETIC CARDS

Card 5:

00000000000010203040002040608000306090210040802161005001510200602181420000000005

Card 6:

70411282008061422300908172630000000000050607080900121416181518112427202420000000006

Card 7:

822363520353045403632484455324946536048465462754453627180123456789123456000000007

Card 8:

789$\bar{0}$234567890$\bar{1}$3456789$\bar{0}$$\bar{1}2456789\bar{0}$$\bar{1}2\bar{3}56789\bar{0}$$\bar{1}2\bar{3}46789\bar{0}$$\bar{1}2\bar{3}4\bar{5}7890\bar{1}2\bar{3}4\bar{5}689\bar{0}$$\bar{1}2\bar{3}4\bar{5}$00000008

Card 9:

$\bar{6}$$\bar{7}9\bar{0}$$\bar{1}2\bar{3}4\bar{5}6\bar{7}8\neq$01600997$\bar{0}$001221009970090826004440099715$\bar{0}$10120000$\neq$260047300908000009

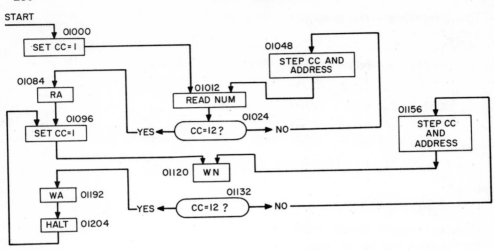

Fig. A1.1 Flow chart for duplicating load cards.

The preceding program locates numeric blanks in locations 00701 to 00780. There is a record mark in 00781. There are zeros in 00658 to 00682 with a record mark in 00683 and a flag on 00658. There is also a flagged zero at 19975. At the end of the loading, 00100-00401 are filled with arithmetic tables and some of the spaces from 0042-00999 are filled with expendable instructions. These spaces may be used for *numeric* work. (They may be cleaned for alphameric work by transmitting zeros.) The rest of the machine is clean except for the spaces used by your instructions.

PROGRAM FOR DUPLICATING SETS OF LOAD CARDS

The following program should be loaded with the preceding load program. (The flow chart is shown in Fig. A1.1.) Then the load program cards are read in as data. Every time the START button on the console is pushed, a set of 13 load cards will be produced by the IBM 1622.

The instructions in this program should be punched in cc 1-12 without spaces, in the usual fashion.

This program was written to illustrate the use of a count cell and also to illustrate the consecutive printing or punching of alphameric material. It is an interesting project to rewrite the program using the terminal address method.

Appendix 2. Summary of Procedure for Machine Language

(See Subsection 10.5.)

1. Clear the computer (use 26 00002 00003).
2. Set the check switches to "stop."
3. Clear the Read-Punch unit.
4. Load the program.
5. Depress CONSOLE START.
6. Prepare for punched card output.

Appendix 3. Summary of Procedure for SPS, Including Error Messages

(See Subsection 17.16 for Procedure and Subsection 20.6 for Error Messages.)

1. Clear the computer (use 31 $\overline{0}0003$ 00002).
2. Switches 1 and 2 "on", Switches 3 and 4 "off."
3. Load SPS II Processor.
4. Read in your source program. At this time the following error messages may appear:

ER 1 A record mark is in the label or opcode field.

ER 2 For address adjustment, a product greater than 10 digits has resulted from a multiplication.

ER 3 An invalid operation code has been used.

ER 4 A dollar sign which is being used as a HEAD indicator is incorrectly positioned in an operand.

ER 5 (i) The symbolic address contains more than six characters. (ii) The actual address contains more than five digits. (iii) An undefined symbolic address or an invalid special character such as) or (is used in the operand.

ER 6   A DSA statement has more than ten operands.

ER 7   A DSB statement has the second operand missing.

ER 8   (*i*) A DC, DSC, DAC or DNB has a specified length more than 50. (*ii*) A DC, DSC or DAC statement has no constant specified. (*iii*) A DC or DSC has a specified length which is less than the number of digits in the constant itself. (*iv*) A DAC statement has a specified length not equal to the number of characters in the constant itself.

ER 9   The symbol table is full.

ER 10   A label is defined more than once.

ER 11   An assembled address is greater than five digits.

ER 12   An invalid special character is used as a head character in a HEAD statement.

ER 13   A HEAD statement operand contains more than one character.

ER 14   An invalid special character is used in a label. The eight invalid special characters are: blank ( ) + $ * —,. An all-numerical label is also invalid.

5. After PASS I is completed, set switches for IBM 407 listing as follows: SW 2 "on," all others "off."

6. Read in your corrected source program for PASS II.

7. Load Subroutines if necessary.

During the run of the program, the following floating-point subroutine error messages may appear:

01   FA or FS, exponent overflow. (This means that the result is $\geqslant 10^{99}$.)

02   FA or FS, exponent underflow. (This means that the result $< 10^{-99}$.)

03   FM, exponent overflow.

04   FM, exponent underflow.

05   FD, exponent overflow.

06   FD, exponent underflow.

07   FD, division by zero.

08   FSQR, square root of a negative number.

09   FSIN or FCOS, input argument too great.

10   FSIN or FCOS, input argument too small.

11   FEX or FEXT, exponent overflow.

12   FEX or FEXT, exponent underflow.

13   FLN or FLOG, input argument is zero.

14   FLN or FLOG, input argument is negative.

The message is typed in the form RRRRROOEC, where RRRRR is the *return address to the main program* and EC is the error code.

Appendix 4. Summary of Procedure for FORTRAN, Including Error Messages

(See Subsection 23.6 for Precompiler Procedure, and Subsection 23.8 for FORTRAN Procedure and Error Messages.)

1. Precompile your program with SW 2 "off," all others "on."
2. Clear the machine (31 00003 00002).
3. Set switches: SW 1 and 2 "on," SW 3 and 4 "off."
4. *Load* the FORTRAN compiler deck.
5. *Read in* your source program with SW 2 "on," SW 1, 3, and 4 "off." The following *error* messages may appear:

    1. Incorrectly formed statement.

    2. Subscripted variable for which no DIMENSION statement has previously appeared in the program, dimensioned variable used without subscripts, variable in DIMENSION statement has already appeared in the source program.

    3. Floating-point number not in allowable range of values, or fixed-point number contains more than four digits.

    4. Symbol table full.

    5. Mixed mode expression.

    6. Variable name in an expression contains more than five characters.

    7. Switch number has been omitted in an IF (SENSE SWITCH n) statement, or there is a comma after IF.

    8. A comma follows the statement number in a DO statement.

    9. A dimension statement ends with a comma, or more than two dimensions have been specified in a DIMENSION statement.

    10. Unnumbered FORMAT statement.

    11. Incorrect FORMAT statement: (*i*) special character in numerical field specification; (*ii*) alphabetic character other than E, F, or I in a numerical field specification; (*iii*) demical point missing; (*iv*) number of positions not given; (*v*) record mark in the numerical field specification or an alphanumeric field; (*vi*) left parenthesis missing or misplaced.

    12. The total record width specified in a FORMAT statement is greater than 87 characters.

    13. A FORMAT statement number has been omitted in an I-O statement.

6. Do *not* type the symbol table (turn SW 1 "off"); *do* compile the subroutines (SW 1 "on").
7. In testing your program, if SW 4 is "off" the trace will not operate. However, if you need a trace, turn SW 4 "on." The *subroutine error messages* are as follows:

E1   Overflow in addition or subtraction.

E2   Underflow in addition or subtraction.

E3   Overflow in multiplication.

E4   Underflow in multiplication.

E5   Overflow in division.

E6   Underflow in division.

E7   Zero divisor in floating division.

E8   Zero divisor in fixed division.

F1   Loss of all significance in sine or cosine.

F2   Logarithm of zero.

F3   Logarithm of a negative number.

F4   Overflow in exponentiation.

F5   Underflow in exponentiation.

F6   Exponentiation with a negative base, e.g., $(-7)^x$; or the square root of a negative number.

F7   Input data is in incorrect form, or outside allowable range.

F8   Output data is in incorrect form, or outside allowable range.

F9   The record is longer than 72 characters, or there is an unspecified number in output or input.

Appendix 5. Summary of Limitations on Subroutines

1. In the sine and cosine subroutines, the absolute value of the argument (for angles, the number of radians) may be as large as 10^8. For arguments above 10^3 in absolute value, the accuracy diminishes as the argument increases in absolute value.

2. In the exponential subroutines, the exponent of e must not exceed 227.95592406 in absolute value. It should be remembered that expressions of the form A ** B are internally converted to

$$e^{B \ \ln \ A}$$

so that the restriction applies to B ln A, where ln means $\log_e$.

3. For logarithms, the argument must be positive.

These restriction apply to the SPS subroutines: FSQR, FSIN, FCOS, FATN, FEX, FEXT, FLN, and FLOG; and to the FORTRAN subroutines: SINF, COSF, EXPF, LOGF, SQRT, and ATAN. Note that FEX = EXPF, and FLN = LOGF.

Appendix 6. Switch Numbers (Q_8Q_9) for the IBM 1620

01 Program Switch 1

02 Program Switch 2

03 Program Switch 3

04 Program Switch 4

06 Read Check Indicator

07 Write Check Indicator

09 Last Card Indicator

11 High-Positive Indicator

12 Equal-Zero Indicator

13 High-Positive or Equal-Zero Indicator

14 Overflow Check Indicator

16 MBR-Even Check Indicator

17 MBR-Odd Check Indicator

19 Any Data Check

Appendix 7. Time and Space Requirements for the 1962 Model of the IBM 1620

1 Table A7.1 gives the time required for various instructions in machine language, including SPS, for the basic machine (1962 model), and the formulas for computing execution times of instructions. All times are in microseconds (1 microsecond = 1/1,000,000 second). The symbols used in the formulas are defined as follows:

D_P = Number of digits, including high-order zeros, in the field at P.

D_Q = Number of digits, including high-order zeros, in the field at Q or in the record at Q.

D_Q = Number of digits, including high-order zeros, in the Q-part of the instruction.

D_Z = Number of positions compared prior to detection of digits other than zero.

D_N = Number of digits in dividend.

D_V = Number of digits in divisor.

Q_T = Number of digits in quotient.

Table A7.1   TIME AND SPACE REQUIREMENTS

INSTRUCTION	FORMULA	REMARKS
Add (21 A)	$160 + 80D_P$ $80 (D_P + 1)$	Basic Time Recomplement Time
Add (Immediate) (11—AM)	$160 + 80D_P$ $80 (D_P + 1$	Basic Time Recomplement Time
Branch (49—B)	200	Constant Time
Branch And Transmit (27—BT)	$200 + 40D_Q$	
Branch And Transmit (Immediate) (17—BTM)	$200 + 40D_Q$	
Branch Back (42—BB)	200	Constant Time
Branch Indicator (46—BI)	160 200	If No Branch Occurs If Branch Occurs
Branch No Flag (44—BNF)	200 240	If No Branch Occurs If Branch Occurs
Branch No Indicator (47—BNI)	160 200	If No Branch Occurs If Branch Occurs
Branch No Record Mark (45—BNR)	200 240	If No Branch Occurs If Branch Occurs
Branch On Digit (43—BD)	200 240	If No Branch Occurs If Branch Occurs
Clear Flag (33—CF)	200	Constant Time
Compare (24—C)	$200 + 80D_Z$ $160 + 80D_P$	Unlike Signs Like Signs
Compare (Immediate) (14—CM)	$200 + 80D_Z$ $160 + 80D_P$	Unlike Signs Like Signs
Control (34—K)	—	Depends upon control function and speed of I-O device selected.
Load Dividend (28—LD) *	$400 + 40D_N$	
Load Dividend (Immediate) (18—LDM) *	$400 + 40D_N$	
Dump Numerically (35—DN)	—	Depends upon speed of output device and number of characters being written.
Halt (48—H)	160	Constant Time
Divide (29—D) *	$160 + 520D_V Q_T$ $+ 740Q_T$	
Divide Immediate (19—D) *	$160 + 520D_V Q_T$ $+ 740Q_T$	
Multiply (23—M)	$560 + 40D_Q +$ $(168D_Q \times D_P)$	
Multiply (Immediate) (13—MM)	$560 + 40D_Q' +$ $(168 D_Q' \times D_P)$	
No Operation (41—NOP)	160	Constant Time

Table A7.1   TIME AND SPACE REQUIREMENTS (Cont'd)

Read Alphamerically (37—RA)	—	Depends upon speed of input device and number of characters being read (Card I-O-3.4ms)
Read Numerically (36—RN)	—	Depends upon speed of input device and number of characters being read (Card I-O-3.4ms)
Set Flag (32—SF)	200	Constant Time
Subtract (22—S)	$160 \times 80D_P$ $80(D_P + 1)$	Basic Time Recomplement Time
Subtract (Immediate) (12—SM)	$160 \times 80D_P$ $80(D_P + 1)$	Basic Time Recomplement Time
Transmit Digit (25—TD)	200	Constant Time
Transmit Digit (Immediate) (15—TDM)	200	Constant Time
Transmit Field (26—TF)	$160 + 40D_Q$	
Transmit Field (Immediate) (16—TFM)	$160 + 40D_Q'$	
Transmit Record (31—TR)	$160 + 40D_Q$	
Write Alphamerically (39—WA)	—	Depends upon speed of output device and number of characters being written (Card I-O-3.4ms)
Write Numerically (38—WN)	—	Depends upon speed of output device and number of characters being written (Card I-O-3.4ms)

*Special Feature

2   The following formula gives the allowable number of symbols in an SPS program:

$$K = \left\{ \sum_{e=1}^{e=5} L_e (8 + 2e) \right\} + 18 L_6$$

where K = 19980 (for the basic machine) minus 17517 = 2463, e = number of characters in label, L_e = number of labels of length e, and L_6 = number of six-character labels. For supplementary modules, K is increased by 20,000 for each module.

3   The following gives the time required for various SPS subroutines: T is in microseconds unless otherwise indicated. The time for PICK must be added to each subroutine since it is a part of each subroutine.

PICK: T = 100 L + 7600. L = length of mantissa.

FA: T = 9 ms (ms = milliseconds)

FS: T = 10.5 ms

FM: T = $168 L^2 + 240 L + 7400$

FD: $T = 520 L^2 + 1500 L + 7890$ (machine with automatic divide)

DIV (= fixed point divide) : T (in ms) $= 980 + 0.040$ LDVD $+ (0.520$ DLVR $+ 0.740) (100 - B1)$ where LDVD is the length of the dividend, LDVR is the length of the divisor, and B1 is the value specified in the macro-instruction.

TFLS: $T = 400 + 40 L$

BTFS: $T = 2280 + 40 L$

FSQR: $T = 620 L^2 + 9776 L + 5328$

FSIN: $T = 168 L^3 + 3792 L^2 + 13340 L + 4708$

FCOS: $T = 168 L^3 + 3792 L^2 + 13340 L + 5228$

FATN: $T = 168 L^3 + 2996 L^2 + 7792 L + 7260$

FEX: $T = 168 L^3 + 35824 L^2 + 15890 L + 26418$ (positive exponent)

FEXT: $T = 168 L^3 + 3656 L^2 + 15414 L + 24538$ (positive exponent)

FLN: $T = 168 L^3 + 3440 L^2 + 10530 L + 12180$

FLOG: $T = 168 L^3 + 3608 L^2 + 11610 L + 15108$

Appendix 8. Input-Output Speeds (Basic Machine)

Typewriter: 10 characters per second
Card Punch: 125 cards per minute
Card Reader: 250 cards per minute

Appendix 9. Summary of FORTRAN Commands

Command	Example
ACCEPT	ACCEPT 23, X
	This statement causes the machine to read information from the console typewriter according to FORMAT statement 23. The information read in is designated as X.
CONTINUE	CONTINUE
	This statement corresponds to a "No Operation." It is used as the last statement in the range of a DO loop when there is a transfer of command.

DIMENSION

DIMENSION X(100), N(25), SUM(20,20)

This statement allocates storage for elements to be designated as X(1), X(2), . . . X(100), N(1), N(2), . . . N(25), SUM(1,1), SUM(1,2), . . . SUM (1,20), SUM(2,1), . . . SUM (20,20).

DO

DO 3 J=1,10,3

See the discussion in the text. In brief, the effect of this statement is to *set* J = 1, then accomplish all the steps up to and including statement number 3, then *step* J to J + 3, then accomplish all the steps up to and including statement number 3 until J = 10. The looping is continued until J reaches the highest value which does not exceed J = 10. If the third constant is omitted, e.g., J = 1,10, the statement is treated as though it had been written J = 1,10,1.

END

END

This is the last statement in the source program.

FORMAT

FORMAT(6HRESULT,F14.8,E14.7,I3,10X)

See text for description of FORMAT statements.

GO TO

GO TO 5

This is an unconditional branch to the statement numbered 5.

Computed GO TO

GO TO (5,1,7),K

When K = 1, the program branches to statement 5;
when K = 2, the program branches to statement 1;
when K = 3, the program branches to statement 7.

IF

IF (Y*Y—10.**2) 23,56,71

When $y^2 - 100 < 0$, the program branches to statement number 23; when $y^2 - 100 = 0$, the program branches to statement number 56; when $y^2 - 100 > 0$, the program branches to statement number 71.

IF (SENSE SWITCH)

IF (SENSE SWITCH 1) 100,37

If Switch 1 is "on," the program branches to statement number 100; if Switch 1 is "off," the program branches to statement number 37.

PAUSE

PAUSE

This causes the program to stop. Pressing console START causes the program to continue from the very next step.

PUNCH

PUNCH 57, X, N, P(I), P(I+1)

See text for a full description. Each PUNCH causes one card to be punched in accordance with FORMAT statement 57. If the current value of I is 7, the card will contain X, N, P(7), and P(8).

READ

READ 23, X, N, Q(8)

Each READ command causes one card to be read in accordance with FORMAT statement 23.

TYPE

TYPE   57, X, N, P(I), P(I+1)

PRINT

PRINT 57, X, N, P(I), P(I+1)

Either of these commands causes the console typewriter to type in accordance with FORMAT statement 57.

STOP

STOP

This statement causes the computer to halt, return the carriage, and type the word "STOP."

Index